A2-Level
Chemistry
for OCR A

CGP

The Complete Course for OCR A

Contents

Unit 5

How to use this book

Learning Objectives
- These tell you exactly what you need to learn, or be able to do, for the exam.
- There's a specification reference at the bottom that links to the OCR specification.

Tips
These are here to help you understand the theory.

Exam Tips
There are tips throughout the book to help with all sorts of things to do with answering exam questions.

(Sample page reproduced at right:)

Learning Objectives:
- Be able to explain that the acid dissociation constant, K_a, shows the extent of acid dissociation.
- Be able to deduce expressions for K_a and pK_a for weak acids.
- Be able to calculate pH from $[H^+_{(aq)}]$ and $[H^+_{(aq)}]$ from the pH of weak monobasic acids.
- Be able to calculate K_a for a weak acid, given appropriate data.

Specification Reference 5.1.3

Tip: K_a is a type of equilibrium constant, so the formula for K_a is based on the one for K_c.

Figure 1: Lemon juice contains citric acid. It turns this universal indicator paper orange, which shows that it's a weak acid.

Exam Tip
It's really important to show all the steps of your working when you're answering an exam question — that way the examiner can give you some marks for your method even if your final answer is wrong.

11. The Acid Dissociation Constant
You've already seen how to calculate the pH of strong acids and strong bases. Now get ready for part three: calculating the pH of weak acids.

What is the acid dissociation constant?
Weak acids don't ionise fully in solution, so the $[H^+]$ isn't the same as the acid concentration. This makes it a bit trickier to find their pH. You have to use yet another equilibrium constant — the **acid dissociation constant**, K_a. The units of K_a are mol dm^{-3} and the equation for K_a is derived as follows:

For a weak aqueous acid, HA, you get the equilibrium $HA_{(aq)} \rightleftharpoons H^+_{(aq)} + A^-_{(aq)}$. As only a tiny amount of HA dissociates, you can assume that [HA] at the start of the reaction is the same as [HA] at equilibrium. So if you apply the equilibrium law, you get:

$$K_a = \frac{[H^+][A^-]}{[HA]}$$

When dealing with weak acids, you can assume that all the H^+ ions come from the acid, so $[H^+] = [A^-]$. So the formula for K_a can be simplified to:

$$K_a = \frac{[H^+]^2}{[HA]}$$

Finding the pH of weak acids
You can use K_a to find the pH of a weak acid. Just follow these steps.
Step 1: Write an expression for K_a for the weak acid. (You can write out the equilibrium equation first if it helps you write this expression.)
Step 2: Rearrange the equation and substitute in the values for K_a and [HA] to find $[H^+]^2$.
Step 3: Take the square root of the number to find $[H^+]$.
Step 4: Substitute $[H^+]$ into the pH equation to find the pH.

Example
Find the pH of a 0.020 mol dm^{-3} solution of propanoic acid (CH_3CH_2COOH) at 298K. K_a for propanoic acid at this temperature is 1.30×10^{-5} mol dm^{-3}.

1. First write an expression for K_a for the weak acid.
Propanoic acid equilibrium: $CH_3CH_2COOH \rightleftharpoons H^+ + CH_3CH_2COO^-$

So, $K_a = \frac{[H^+][CH_3CH_2COO^-]}{[CH_3CH_2COOH]} = \frac{[H^+]^2}{[CH_3CH_2COOH]}$

2. Rearrange the equation to find $[H^+]^2$:
$[H^+]^2 = K_a[CH_3CH_2COOH]$
$= (1.30 \times 10^{-5}) \times 0.020 = 2.60 \times 10^{-7}$

3. Take the square root of this number to find $[H^+]$:
$[H^+] = \sqrt{2.60 \times 10^{-7}}$
$= 5.10 \times 10^{-4}$ mol dm^{-3}

4. Use $[H^+]$ to find the pH of the acid:
$pH = -\log_{10}[H^+]$
$= -\log_{10} 5.10 \times 10^{-4} = 3.29$

(Sample page reproduced at lower left:)

Each peak on a chromatogram corresponds to a substance with a particular **retention time** (see Figure 3). Retention times are measured from zero to the centre of each peak, and can be looked up in a database, or reference table, to identify the substances present.

The area under each peak tells you the relative amount of each component that's present in the mixture (see Figure 3). For example, if a peak has three times the area of another peak, it tells you that there is three times as much of the first substance in the mixture (compared to the second substance).

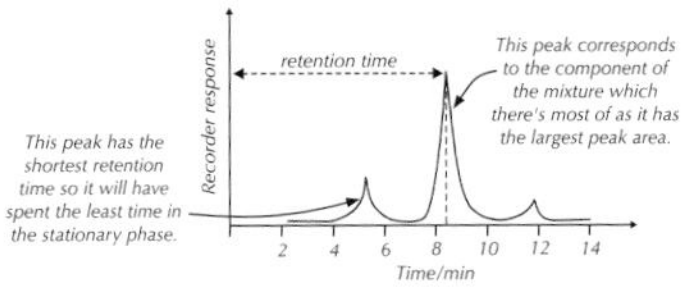

Tip: If you ever need to estimate the area of a peak, you can treat it as a triangle and find the area of that.

Tip: If you're looking at the amount of each compound present, it's the area of the peaks (not the height) that's important — the tallest peak won't always represent the most abundant substance.

Figure 3: A chromatogram showing the separation of three components in a mixture.

You can use the retention times to identify the components of the mixture.

Example
If you wanted to know if a mixture contained octane, you could run a sample of the mixture through the system, then look up the retention time for octane run under those conditions and see if they're the same.

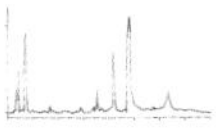

If you're looking up retention times in a reference table, you must make sure that the sample was run under the same conditions (e.g. at the same temperature and using the same stationary phase). Changing the conditions will alter the retention time.

Figure 4: Gas chromatogram. The horizontal axis shows the retention time of each component in the mixture.

The limitations of gas chromatography
Although a very useful and widely used technique, GC does have limitations when it comes to identifying chemicals.

Compounds which are similar often have very similar retention times, so they're difficult to identify accurately. A mixture of two similar substances may only produce one peak, so you won't be able to identify the substances. This also means that you can't tell how much of each one there is.

Tip: Handily, you can combine GC with mass spectrometry to make a much more powerful identification tool — there's more on this on page 83.

Example
On the right is a gas chromatogram for a mixture of alcohols.

Peak 2 is a bit wobbly. It looks like it's one big peak made up of smaller peaks that overlap. The mixture must contain some alcohols with very similar retention times.

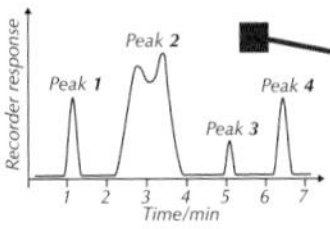

Tip: Sometimes you can separate the peaks out by changing the conditions and running the experiment again.

Exam Help
There's a section at the back of the book stuffed full of things to help with your exams.

How Science Works
- For A2 Chemistry you need to know about How Science Works. There's a section on it at the front of the book.
- How Science Works is also covered throughout the book wherever you see this symbol.

Examples
These are here to help you understand the theory.

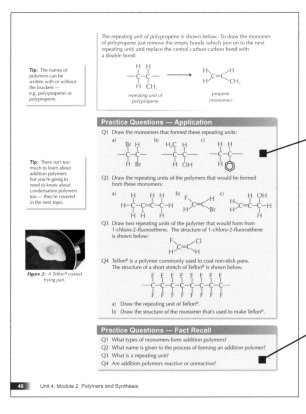

Practice Questions — Application

- Annoyingly, the examiners expect you to be able to apply your knowledge to new situations — these questions are here to give you plenty of practice at doing this.

- All the answers are in the back of the book (including any calculation workings).

Practice Questions — Fact Recall

- There are a lot of facts to learn for A2 Chemistry — these questions are here to test that you know them.

- All the answers are in the back of the book.

Glossary

There's a glossary at the back of the book full of all the definitions you need to know for the exam, plus loads of other useful words.

Exam-style Questions

- Practising exam-style questions is really important — you'll find some at the end of each section.

- They're the same style as the ones you'll get in the real exams — some will test your knowledge and understanding and some will test that you can apply your knowledge.

- All the answers are in the back of the book, along with a mark scheme to show you how you get the marks.

Practical Skills in Chemistry

- For A2 Chemistry you'll have to complete Unit F326 — Practical Skills in Chemistry 2.

- There's a section at the back of the book with loads of stuff to help you plan, analyse and evaluate experiments.

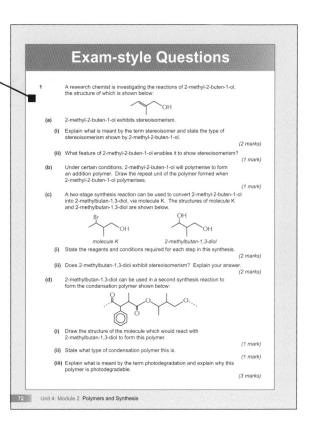

Published by CGP

Editors:
Katie Braid, Mary Falkner, Helen Ronan, Megan Tyler.

Contributors:
Robert Clarke, Ian Davis, John Duffy, Lucy Muncaster, Paul Warren.

ISBN: 978 1 84762 794 0

With thanks to Katherine Craig, Chris Elliss, Chetna Gohil and Jamie Sinclair for the proofreading.
With thanks to Anna Lupton for the copyright research.

OCR Specification reference points are reproduced by permission of OCR.

Data used to compile the spectra on pages 87-106 taken from SDBSWeb: http://riodb01.ibase.aist.go.jp/sdbs/
(National Institute of Advanced Industrial Science and Technology, date of access: 04/05/12).

Groovy website: www.cgpbooks.co.uk

Printed by Elanders Ltd, Newcastle upon Tyne.
Jolly bits of clipart from CorelDRAW®

The Scientific Process

Science tries to explain how and why things happen. It's all about seeking and gaining knowledge about the world around us. Scientists do this by asking questions, suggesting answers and then testing them to see if they're correct — this is the scientific process.

Developing and testing theories

A **theory** is a possible explanation for something. Theories usually come about when scientists observe something and wonder why or how it happens. (Scientists also sometimes form a **model** too — a simplified picture or representation of a real physical situation.) Scientific theories and models are developed and tested in the following way:

- Ask a question — make an observation and ask why or how whatever you've observed happens.

- Suggest an answer, or part of an answer, by forming a theory or a model (a possible explanation of the observations or a description of what you think is actually happening).

- Make a prediction or **hypothesis** — a specific testable statement, based on the theory, about what will happen in a test situation.

- Carry out tests — to provide evidence that will support the prediction or refute it.

> **Tip:** A theory is only scientific if it can be tested.

Examples

Question: Why does sodium chloride dissolve in water?

Theory: Sodium chloride is made up of charged particles which are pulled apart by the polar water molecules.

Hypothesis: Sodium chloride will dissolve in polar solvents but not in non-polar solvents.

Test: Add sodium chloride to polar solvents such as water and to non-polar solvents such as toluene. If it dissolves in the polar solvents but not in the non-polar solvents then the evidence would support the hypothesis.

Figure 1: Sodium chloride dissolving in water.

Question: How do substances change during a redox reaction?

Theory: During a redox reaction electrons move from one substance to another.

Hypothesis: When electrons move, a current flows. So a current will flow between the electrodes of an electrochemical cell when an oxidation reaction takes place at one electrode and a reduction reaction at the other.

Test: Set up an electrochemical cell using substances with different electrode potentials. Put an ammeter in the circuit and observe whether a current is flowing. If a current is flowing then this evidence supports the hypothesis.

> **Tip:** The results of one test can't prove that a theory is true — they can only suggest that it's true. They can however disprove a theory — show that it's wrong.

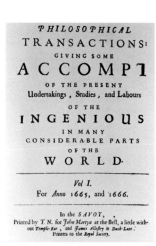

Figure 2: *The first scientific journal, 'Philosophical Transactions of the Royal Society', published in 1665.*

Tip: Scientific research is often funded by companies who have a vested interest in its outcomes. Scientists are ethically obliged to make sure that this does not bias their results.

Tip: Once an experimental method is found to give good evidence it becomes a protocol — an accepted method to test that particular thing that all scientists can use.

Figure 3: *A representation of the delocalised electron model of benzene.*

Communicating results

The results of testing a scientific theory are published — scientists need to let others know about their work. Scientists publish their results in scientific journals (see Figure 2). These are just like normal magazines, only they contain scientific reports (called papers) instead of the latest celebrity gossip.

Scientists use standard terminology when writing their reports. This way they know that other scientists will understand them. For instance, there are internationally agreed rules for naming organic compounds, so that scientists across the world will know exactly what substance is being referred to.

Scientific reports are similar to the lab write-ups you do in school. And just as a lab write-up is reviewed (marked) by your teacher, reports in scientific journals undergo **peer review** before they're published. The report is sent out to peers — other scientists who are experts in the same area. They go through it bit by bit, examining the methods and data, and checking it's all clear and logical. Thorough evaluation allows decisions to be made about what makes a good methodology or experimental technique. Individual scientists may have their own ethical codes (based on their personal moral or religious beliefs), but having their work scrutinised by other scientists helps to reduce the effect of personal bias on the conclusions drawn from the results.

When the report is approved, it's published. This makes sure that work published in scientific journals is of a good standard. But peer review can't guarantee the science is correct — other scientists still need to reproduce it. Sometimes mistakes are made and bad work is published. Peer review isn't perfect but it's probably the best way for scientists to self-regulate their work and to publish quality reports.

Validating theories

Other scientists read the published theories and results, and try to test the theory themselves. This involves repeating the exact same experiments, using the theory to make new predictions, and then testing them with new experiments. This is known as **validation**. If all the experiments in the world provide evidence to back it up, the theory is thought of as scientific 'fact' (for now). If new evidence comes to light that conflicts with the current evidence the theory is questioned all over again. More rounds of testing will be carried out to try to find out where the theory falls down. This is how the scientific process works — evidence supports a theory, loads of other scientists read it and test it for themselves, eventually all the scientists in the world agree with it and then bingo, you get to learn it.

┌─ **Example** ─────────────────────────────

The structure of benzene

Benzene is an organic molecule with the formula C_6H_6. It was first purified in 1825, but nobody knew back then what its structure was like.

In 1865 Kekulé suggested a possible structure for the benzene molecule. His idea was a ring of six carbon atoms with alternate double and single bonds between them, with one hydrogen atom bonded to each carbon.

But in the 20th century, data from X-ray diffraction studies and enthalpy experiments suggested that the Kekulé model was wrong. So scientists came up with a new model (the delocalised electron model — see Figure 3) that fitted the new data better. (There's lots more about this on pages 5 and 6). This is the model of the benzene molecule that we use today.

How do theories evolve?

Our currently accepted theories have survived this 'trial by evidence'. They've been tested over and over again and each time the results have backed them up. But they never become totally indisputable fact. Scientific breakthroughs or advances could provide new ways to question and test the theory, which could lead to changes and challenges to it. Then the testing starts all over again. This is the tentative nature of scientific knowledge — it's always changing and evolving.

Tip: Sometimes data from one experiment can be the starting point for developing a new theory.

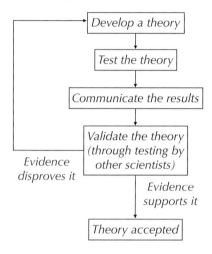

Figure 4: *Flow diagram summarising the scientific process.*

Example

CFCs and the ozone layer

When CFCs were first used in fridges in the 1930s, scientists thought they were problem-free — well, why not? There was no evidence to say otherwise. It was decades before anyone found out that CFCs were actually making a whopping great hole in the ozone layer.

A couple of scientists developed a theory that CFCs were destroying ozone in the stratosphere, and this was tested, shared and validated by other scientists worldwide. The rigour of the scientific process meant that there was strong enough evidence against CFCs that governments could impose bans and restrictions in order to protect the ozone layer.

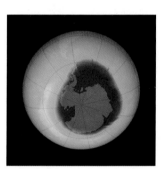

Figure 5: *The Antarctic ozone hole.*

Collecting evidence

1. Evidence from lab experiments

Results from controlled experiments in laboratories are great. A lab is the easiest place to control **variables** so that they're all kept constant (except for the one you're investigating). This means you can draw meaningful conclusions.

Tip: There's more on controlling variables and drawing conclusions from lab experiments on pages 225 and 228 in the Practical Skills in Chemistry section.

Example

Reaction rates

If you're investigating how temperature affects the rate of a reaction you need to keep everything but the temperature constant. This means controlling things like the pH of the solution, the concentration of the solution, etc. Otherwise there's no way of knowing if it's the change in temperature that's affecting the rate, or some other changing variable.

2. Investigations outside the lab

There are things you can't study in a lab. And outside the lab controlling the variables is tricky, if not impossible.

Examples

Are increasing CO_2 emissions causing climate change?

There are other variables which may have an effect, such as changes in solar activity. You can't easily rule out every possibility. Also, climate change is a very gradual process, so it's really tricky for scientists to work out if their predictions are correct over a short space of time (like a few years).

Does eating food containing trans fatty acids increase the risk of heart disease and strokes?

There are always differences between groups of people. The best you can do is to have a well-designed study using matched groups — choose two groups of people (those who eat a lot of trans fats and those who don't) which are as similar as possible (same mix of ages, same mix of diets etc.). But you still can't rule out every possibility. Taking newborn identical twins and treating them identically, except for making one consume a lot of trans fats and the other none at all, might be a fairer test, but it would present huge ethical problems.

Figure 6: *A selection of fatty foods.*

Tip: See pages 32 and 34 for loads more on trans fats.

Tip: Don't get mixed up — it's not the scientists who make the decisions, it's society. Scientists just produce evidence to help society make the decisions.

Science and decision-making

Lots of scientific work eventually leads to important discoveries that could benefit humankind and improve everyone's quality of life. But there are often risks attached (and almost always financial costs). Society (that's you, me and everyone else) must weigh up the information in order to make decisions — about the way we live, what we eat, what we drive, and so on. Information can also be used by politicians to devise policies and laws. However, there is not always enough information available for society and politicians to be certain about the decisions made. The scientific evidence we do have can also be overshadowed by other influences such as personal bias and beliefs, public opinion, and the media. Decisions are also affected by social, ethical and economic factors.

Examples

Fuel cells

Hydrogen-oxygen fuel cells are an alternative to traditional fuel cells (see page 191). They're better for the environment than batteries, because their only waste product is water. But energy is used to produce the hydrogen and oxygen. And hydrogen is flammable, so it's tricky to store safely.

Developing drugs

Pharmaceutical drugs are expensive to develop and drug companies want to make money. So they put lots of effort into developing drugs that they can sell for a good price. Society has to consider the cost of buying drugs — the NHS can't afford the most expensive drugs without sacrificing other things.

Disposal of plastics

Synthetic polymers are very useful — they're cheap to produce and very durable. But they're hard to dispose of (they don't break down easily). So we need to make choices about how we can best dispose of plastics and whether we should try to reduce the amount that we use, or work to develop more biodegradable plastics (see page 54).

Figure 7: *Waste plastic on a landfill site.*

1. Benzene

Benzene is one of the most important molecules in organic chemistry. Loads of exciting organic molecules contain benzene rings, like aspirin, morphine, dopamine and styrene (to name just a few).

What is benzene?

Benzene has the formula C_6H_6. It has a cyclic structure, as its six carbon atoms are joined together in a ring. The ring itself is planar (flat) and the hydrogens all stick out in the same plane. There are two main models to explain the structure of the benzene ring — the Kekulé model and the delocalised model.

The Kekulé model

This was proposed by German chemist Friedrich August Kekulé in 1865. He came up with the idea of a ring of C atoms with alternating single and double bonds between them (see Figure 1).

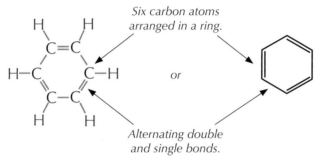

Six carbon atoms arranged in a ring.

or

Alternating double and single bonds.

Figure 1: *The structure of benzene according to Kekulé.*

He later adapted the model to say that the benzene molecule was constantly flipping between two forms (isomers) by switching over the double and single bonds (see Figure 2).

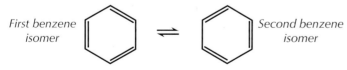

First benzene isomer ⇌ *Second benzene isomer*

Figure 2: *Benzene flipping between two forms in the adapted Kekulé model.*

If the Kekulé model was correct, you'd expect there to always be three bonds with the length of a C–C bond (147 pm) and three bonds with the length of a C=C bond (135 pm). However X-ray diffraction studies have shown that all the carbon-carbon bonds in benzene have the same length (140 pm) — they're between the length of a single bond and a double bond. So the Kekulé structure can't be quite right, but it's still used today as it's useful for drawing reaction mechanisms.

HOW SCIENCE WORKS

Learning Objectives:

- Be able to compare the Kekulé and delocalised models for benzene in terms of p-orbital overlap forming π bonds.
- Be able to review the evidence for a delocalised model of benzene in terms of bond lengths and enthalpy change of hydrogenation.

Specification Reference 4.1.1

Tip: In skeletal structures like this one...

...there is a carbon atom at each corner and you work out the positions of the hydrogens by looking at the number of bonds coming from each carbon. There should be four — if there aren't, add one or more hydrogens.

Tip: pm stands for picometre. A picometre is 1×10^{-12} metres — that's very small indeed.

The delocalised model

The bond-length observations are explained by the **delocalised** model. In this model, the p-orbitals of all six carbon atoms overlap to create π bonds. This creates two ring-shaped clouds of electrons — one above and one below the plane of the six carbon atoms (see Figure 3).

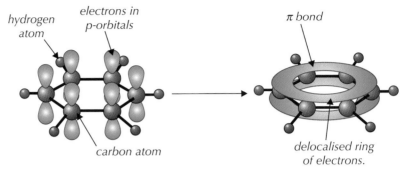

Figure 3: The formation of π bonds in benzene.

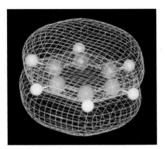

Figure 4: A computer graphic showing the structure of benzene.

All the carbon-carbon bonds in the ring are the same length because all the bonds are the same. The electrons in the rings are said to be delocalised because they don't belong to a specific carbon atom. They are represented as a circle in the ring of carbons rather than as double or single bonds (see Figure 5).

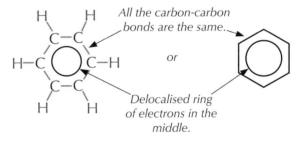

Figure 5: The structure of benzene according to the delocalised model.

Evidence for delocalisation

All the carbon-carbon bonds in benzene are the same length (see previous page). This is good evidence for the delocalised model (see above), but even more evidence for this model comes from enthalpy change data.

Cyclohexene has one double bond. When it's hydrogenated, the enthalpy change is -120 kJ mol^{-1}. If benzene had three double bonds (as in the Kekulé structure), you'd expect it to have an enthalpy of hydrogenation of -360 kJ mol^{-1}. But the experimental enthalpy of hydrogenation of benzene is -208 kJ mol^{-1} — far less exothermic than expected (see Figure 6).

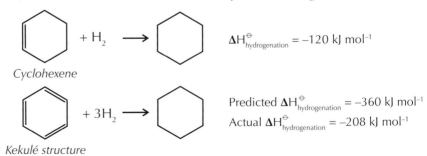

Figure 6: Enthalpies of hydrogenation for cyclohexene and benzene.

Energy is put in to break bonds and released when bonds are made. So more energy must have been put in to break the bonds in benzene than would be needed to break the bonds in the Kekulé structure. This difference indicates that benzene is more stable than the Kekulé structure would be. This is thought to be due to the delocalised ring of electrons. In a delocalised ring the electron density is shared over more atoms, which means that the molecule is more stable.

Naming aromatic compounds

Compounds containing a benzene ring are called arenes or '**aromatic compounds**'. Aromatic compounds all contain a benzene ring. Naming them can be a bit tricky. They're named in two ways:

1. In some cases, the benzene ring is the main functional group and the molecule is named as a substituted benzene ring — the suffix is -benzene and there are prefixes to represent any other functional groups.

┌─ Examples ─────────────────────────────────────

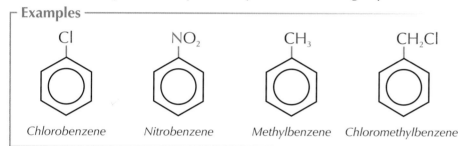

Chlorobenzene   Nitrobenzene   Methylbenzene   Chloromethylbenzene

2. In other cases, the benzene ring is not the main functional group and the molecule is named as having a phenyl group (C_6H_5) attached. Phenyl- is used as a prefix to show the molecule has a benzene ring and the suffix comes from other functional groups on the molecule (e.g. -ol if it's an alcohol, -amine if it's an amine).

┌─ Examples ─────────────────────────────────────

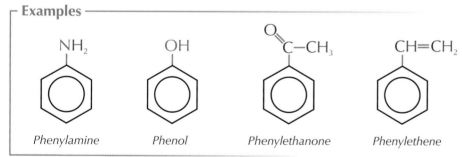

Phenylamine   Phenol   Phenylethanone   Phenylethene

Figure 7: A molecular model of phenol.

Unfortunately there's no simple rule to help you remember which molecules should be something –benzene and which molecules should be phenyl–something. You just have to learn these examples.

Numbering the benzene ring

If there is more than one functional group attached to the benzene ring you have to number the carbons to show where the groups are. If all the functional groups are the same, pick any group to start from and count round either clockwise or anticlockwise — whichever way gives the smallest numbers. If the functional groups are different, start from whichever functional group gives the molecule its suffix (e.g. the –OH group for a phenol) and continue counting round whichever way gives the smallest numbers.

Exam Tip
For the exam you need to know three pieces of evidence for the delocalised model of benzene — bond length data (page 5), enthalpy change data (page 6) and the fact that benzene is relatively unreactive (there's more about this coming up on page 9).

Tip: Non-aromatic molecules are called aliphatic molecules — don't get the terms aromatic and aliphatic mixed up.

Tip: If there is only one functional group you don't have to number the carbons because all the positions around the carbon ring are the same.

Exam Tip
You're unlikely to be asked to name anything too complicated in the exam. If you need to give the product of a reaction, don't try and name it unless they specifically ask for the name — giving the structure should be enough to get the marks.

Examples

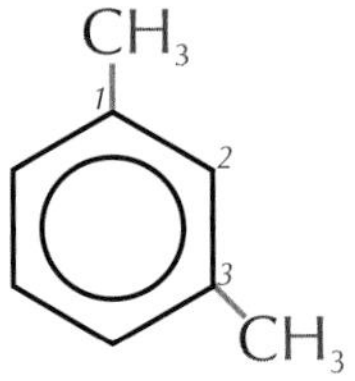

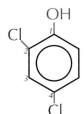

This benzene ring only has methyl groups attached so it will be named as a substituted benzene ring.

Starting from the methyl group at the top and counting clockwise there is another methyl group on carbon-3.

So this is 1,3-dimethylbenzene.

This benzene ring has an OH group attached so the stem is phenol.

Starting from the OH group (the group which gives the molecule its name) and counting anticlockwise there are chlorines on carbon-2 and carbon-4.

So this is 2,4-dichlorophenol.

Practice Questions — Application

Q1 Name these aromatic compounds:

a)

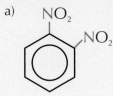

b)

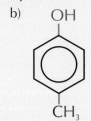

c)

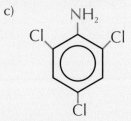

Q2 The graph below shows the enthalpies of hydrogenation of cyclohexene and benzene.

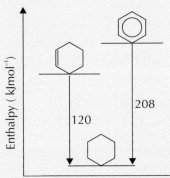

a) Describe Kekulé's model for the structure of benzene.

b) Use the information in the graph to explain why Kekulé's model for the structure of benzene was incorrect.

Practice Questions — Fact Recall

Q1 Describe the structure of benzene according to the delocalised model.

Q2 Explain how information on the bond lengths in benzene provides support for the delocalisation model.

Q3 What are aromatic compounds?

2. Reactions of Benzene

Learning Objectives:

- Be able to review the evidence for a delocalised model of benzene in terms of its resistance to reaction.
- Know how to explain the relative resistance to bromination of benzene, compared to alkenes, in terms of the delocalised electron density of the π bonds in benzene compared with the localised electron density of the C=C bond in alkenes.
- Be able to outline the mechanism of electrophilic substitution in arenes, using the mononitration and monohalogenation of benzene as examples.
- Be able to describe the electrophilic substitution of arenes with a halogen in the presence of a halogen carrier.
- Be able to describe the electrophilic substitution of arenes with concentrated nitric acid in the presence of concentrated sulfuric acid.

Specification Reference 4.1.1

There are quite a few reactions that chemists can use to add different functional groups to benzene — that's what makes it so good as a starting point for making other compounds. The ones that you need to know about are in this topic...

Alkenes, benzene and addition reactions

Alkenes react easily with bromine water at room temperature. The reaction is the basis of the test for a double bond, as the orange colour of the bromine water is lost. It's an addition reaction — bromine atoms are added to the alkene.

--- Example ---

Ethene will react with bromine water in an addition reaction.

| ethene | bromine | 1,2-dibromoethane |

This reaction occurs because the alkene C=C bond is a localised area of high electron density — it attracts an electrophile which adds to the double bond.

If the Kekulé structure (see page 5) was correct, you'd expect a similar reaction between benzene and bromine. In fact, to make it happen you need hot benzene and ultraviolet light — and it's still a real struggle.

This difference between benzene and other alkenes is explained by the delocalised electron rings above and below the plane of carbon atoms (see page 6). They make the benzene ring very stable, and spread out the negative charge. So benzene is very unwilling to undergo addition reactions which would destroy the stable ring.

So, in alkenes, addition reactions occur across C=C bonds as electrophiles react with them to form stable alkanes. In benzene, this reaction isn't as favourable because the benzene ring is so stable. So benzene prefers to react by **electrophilic substitution**.

Electrophilic substitution

The benzene ring is a region of high electron density, so it attracts **electrophiles**. Electrophiles are electron pair acceptors — they are usually electron deficient (short of electrons) so are attracted to areas of high electron density. Common electrophiles include positively charged ions (e.g. H^+ or NO_2^+), and polar molecules (e.g. carbonyl compounds), which have a partial positive charge.

As the benzene ring's so stable, it tends to undergo electrophilic substitution reactions, which preserve the delocalised ring. The general mechanism for electrophilic substitution on a benzene ring is shown below:

Tip: Benzene's stability is further evidence for the delocalised model (see page 6).

Tip: Remember, electrophiles are positively charged ions or polar molecules that are attracted to areas of negative charge.

1. The electron dense region at the centre of the benzene ring attracts an electrophile (EI^+).
2. The electrophile steals a pair of electrons from the centre of the benzene ring and forms a bond with one of the carbons.
3. This partially breaks the delocalised electron ring and gives the molecule a positive charge.
4. To regain the stability of the benzene ring, the carbon which is now bound to the electrophile loses a hydrogen.
5. So you get the substitution of an H^+ with the electrophile.

You need to know two electrophilic substitution mechanisms for benzene — halogenation using a halogen carrier (below) and the nitration reaction (see page 11).

Halogenation using a halogen carrier

A **halogen carrier** can be used to add a halogen atom onto a benzene ring via an electrophilic substitution reaction. Without the halogen carrier, the electrophile doesn't have a strong enough positive charge to attack the stable benzene ring. Here's a bit about how halogen carriers work:

Halogen carriers make the electrophile stronger by accepting a lone pair of electrons from the electrophile. As the lone pair of electrons is pulled away, the polarisation in the electrophile increases and a permanent dipole forms. This makes it a much, much stronger electrophile, and gives it a strong enough charge to react with the benzene ring. Examples of halogen carriers include aluminium halides (e.g. $AlCl_3$), iron halides (e.g. $FeCl_3$) and iron.

> **Example**
>
> Aluminium chloride can combine with a bromine molecule to form a more reactive polarised species.
>
>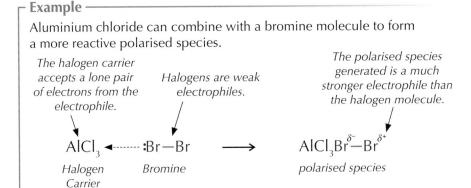
>
> *The halogen carrier accepts a lone pair of electrons from the electrophile.*
>
> *Halogens are weak electrophiles.*
>
> *The polarised species generated is a much stronger electrophile than the halogen molecule.*

Here's the overall equation for a halogenation reaction using a halogen carrier:

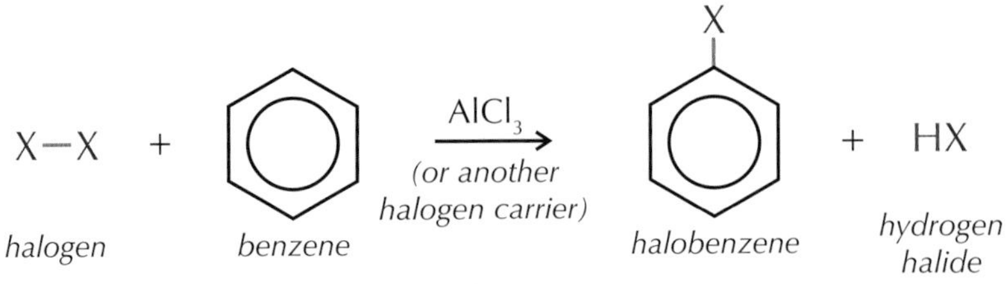

And here's an example of an electrophilic substitution reaction using a halogen carrier:

> **Example**
>
> Benzene will react with bromine, Br–Br, in the presence of aluminium chloride, $AlCl_3$. Br–Br is the electrophile. $AlCl_3$ acts as the halogen carrier. A Br atom is substituted in place of a H atom.

Electrons in the benzene ring are attracted to the partially positively charged bromine atom. Two electrons from the benzene bond with the bromine, the Br–Br bond is broken and a Br^- ion is formed. This partially breaks the delocalised ring and gives it a positive charge.

The negatively charged Br^- ion bonds with the hydrogen. This removes the hydrogen from the ring, forming HBr and bromobenzene.

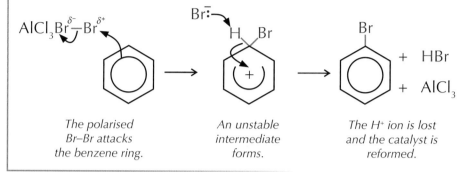

The polarised Br–Br attacks the benzene ring.　　　*An unstable intermediate forms.*　　　*The H^+ ion is lost and the catalyst is reformed.*

Exam Tip
When drawing the intermediates of these reactions, make sure the horseshoe in the middle of the benzene ring comes over half way up:

If you make it any smaller you'll lose marks.

Nitration

When you warm benzene with concentrated nitric acid and concentrated sulfuric acid, you get nitrobenzene. The overall equation for this reaction is:

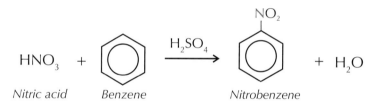

Nitric acid　　　*Benzene*　　　*Nitrobenzene*

Tip: This mechanism works for other arenes too, not just benzene. Take a look at the next page for an example.

Sulfuric acid acts as a catalyst — it helps to make the nitronium ion, NO_2^+, which is the electrophile. The formation of the nitronium ion is the first step of the reaction mechanism. The equation for this reaction is shown below:

$$HNO_3 + H_2SO_4 \rightarrow HSO_4^- + NO_2^+ + H_2O$$

Once the nitronium ion has been formed, it can react with benzene to form nitrobenzene. This is the electrophilic substitution step in the reaction.

Here's the mechanism for the electrophilic substitution part of the reaction:

Exam Tip
In the exam, you might be asked to write out the equation for the formation of the nitronium ion before giving the rest of the mechanism for nitration — so make sure you learn it.

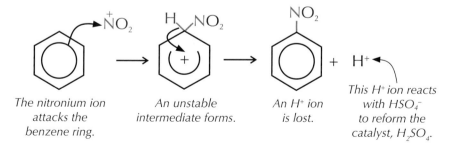

The nitronium ion attacks the benzene ring.　　*An unstable intermediate forms.*　　*An H^+ ion is lost.*　　*This H^+ ion reacts with HSO_4^- to reform the catalyst, H_2SO_4.*

Figure 1: *Blocks of TNT explosives. Substitution of three hydrogen atoms for NO_2 groups on a methylbenzene molecule will produce TNT.*

If you only want one NO_2 group added (mononitration), you need to keep the temperature below 55 °C. Above this temperature you'll get lots of substitutions.

Tip: This reaction will produce some 1-methyl-2-nitrobenzene, some 1-methyl-3-nitrobenzene and some 1-methyl-4-nitrobenzene. But the majority of the product formed will be the 1-methyl-2-nitrobenzene. The reasons for this are quite complicated and you don't need to know them for A2-Level (but if you're interested ask your teacher...).

Example

Warming methylbenzene with concentrated nitric acid and concentrated sulfuric acid at a temperature below 55 °C will produce 1-methyl-2-nitrobenzene.

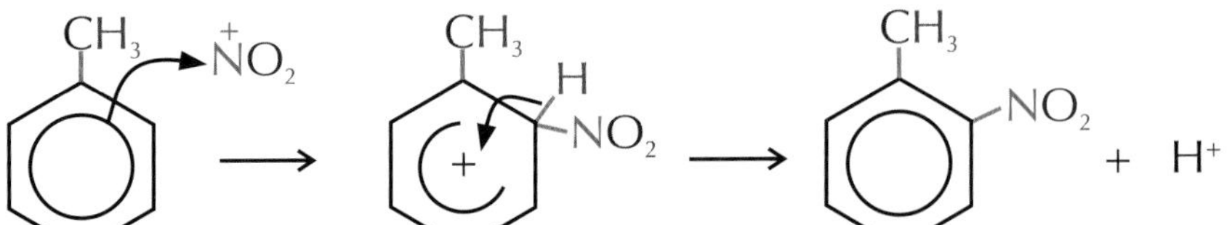

Practice Questions — Application

Q1 The structure of 1-chloro-2,4,6-trimethylbenzene is shown below.

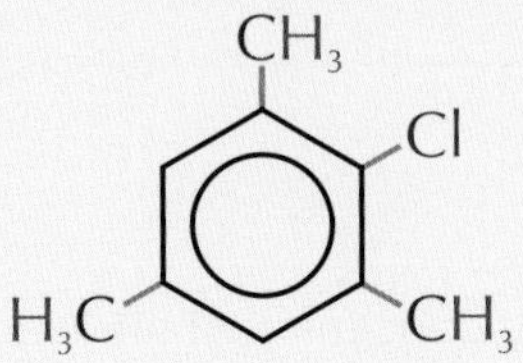

a) Write out the equation for the production of 1-chloro-2,4,6-trimethylbenzene from 1,3,5-trimethylbenzene and chlorine.

b) Suggest a suitable catalyst for this reaction.

c) Outline the mechanism for this reaction.

Q2 a) Draw the mechanism for the formation of nitrobenzene from benzene and concentrated nitric acid.

b) What two conditions are needed for this reaction to occur?

Q3 An evil scientist is trying to create the explosive TNT. The IUPAC name for TNT is 1-methyl-2,4,6-trinitrobenzene.

a) Draw the structure of TNT.

b) The scientist uses a nitration reaction to create TNT. What is important about the temperature that the reaction is carried out at? Explain your answer.

Exam Tip

Examiners can be tricksy and you might have to draw a mechanism for an odd looking molecule in the exam. Don't panic. All electrophilic substitution reaction mechanisms are the <u>same</u> — use the steps shown on the previous pages and make sure your equation is <u>balanced</u> and you'll be fine.

Practice Questions — Fact Recall

Q1 Explain why alkenes will react via addition reactions at room temperature but benzene won't.

Q2 Explain why electrophiles are attracted to aromatic compounds.

Q3 a) Give two examples of halogen carriers.

b) Explain why halogen carriers are needed for benzene to react with Br_2.

Q4 Write an equation to show the formation of a nitronium ion (NO_2^+) from chemical reagents.

Tip: A reagent is a chemical that can be used straight out of a bottle or container (see page 61).

3. Phenols

Phenols are aromatic alcohols. They have an –OH group attached to a benzene ring. This –OH group gives the benzene ring different properties.

Nomenclature of phenols

Phenol has the formula C_6H_5OH. Other phenols have various groups attached to the benzene ring.

Examples

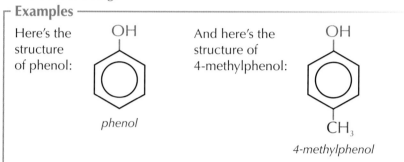

Here's the structure of phenol:

phenol

And here's the structure of 4-methylphenol:

4-methylphenol

Phenols are named in a very similar way to alcohols except you add the suffix -phenol instead of -ol. You have to number the carbon atoms too — the carbon with the –OH group attached is always carbon-1.

Examples

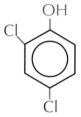

2,4-dichlorophenol

The phenol has two chlorine groups, one on carbon-2 and one on carbon-4.
So this phenol is 2,4-dichlorophenol.

The phenol has a nitro group on carbon-3.
So this phenol is 3-nitrophenol.

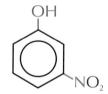

3-nitrophenol

Phenol salts

Phenol is weakly acidic, so will undergo typical acid-base reactions.

$$\text{acid} + \text{base} \rightarrow \text{salt} + \text{water}$$

Phenol reacts with sodium hydroxide solution at room temperature to form sodium phenoxide and water.

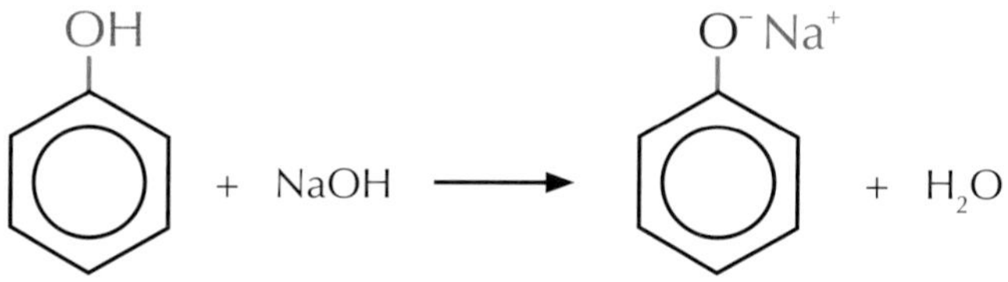

$$\text{OH} + \text{NaOH} \longrightarrow \text{O}^-\text{Na}^+ + H_2O$$

phenol   *sodium phenoxide*

Learning Objectives:

- Be able to describe the reaction of phenol with aqueous alkalis and with sodium to form salts.
- Be able to explain the relative ease of bromination of phenol compared with benzene, in terms of electron-pair donation to the benzene ring from an oxygen p-orbital in phenol.
- Be able to describe the reaction of phenol with bromine to form 2,4,6-tribromophenol.
- Know the uses of phenols in production of plastics, antiseptics, disinfectants and resins for paints.

Specification Reference 4.1.1

Tip: Have a look back at your AS-Level notes if you can't remember how to name alcohols using the IUPAC rules.

Tip: A salt is a species where a hydrogen ion has been replaced by a metal ion or an ammonium (NH_4^+) ion. You learnt all about salts at AS-Level so have a look back at your notes if you're struggling to remember this.

Sodium phenoxide is also formed when sodium metal is added to liquid phenol. Hydrogen gas fizzes off this time.

Tip: If you need to prove that hydrogen is given off during the reaction you can use the squeaky pop test — hurrah.

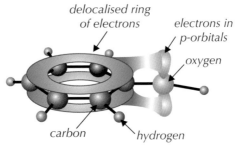

$$2 \quad \text{(phenol, OH)} \quad + \quad 2Na \quad \longrightarrow \quad 2 \quad \text{(sodium phenoxide, } O^-Na^+\text{)} \quad + \quad H_2$$

phenol   *sodium phenoxide*

Phenol doesn't react with sodium carbonate solution though. Sodium carbonate is not a strong enough base and so can't remove the hydrogen ion from the oxygen atom.

Electrophilic substitution

If you shake phenol with orange bromine water, it will undergo an electrophilic substitution reaction — bromine atoms will be added to the phenol ring. Benzene doesn't react with bromine water (see page 9), so phenol's reaction must be to do with the OH group.

During the reaction, one of the lone pairs of electrons in a p-orbital of the oxygen atom overlaps with the delocalised ring of electrons in the benzene ring (see Figure 1) — this pair of electrons is partially delocalised into the ring.

Figure 2: *Bromination of phenol. The reaction of phenol with bromine produces 2,4,6-tribromophenol, a white precipitate.*

delocalised ring of electrons   electrons in p-orbitals

oxygen

carbon   hydrogen

Figure 1: *The orbital overlap during the reaction of phenol with bromine.*

This increases the electron density of the ring, especially at positions 2, 4 and 6. The extra electron density in the ring means that phenol can polarise the bromine molecule making it a better electrophile. The polarised bromine molecule can then react with the phenol molecule in an electrophilic substitution reaction.

The hydrogen atoms at 2, 4 and 6 are substituted by bromine atoms. The product is called 2,4,6-tribromophenol — it's insoluble in water and precipitates out of the mixture to form a white solid (see Figure 2). It smells of antiseptic.

Exam Tip
Don't forget to mention electron density when you're answering exam questions on the reactivity of phenol — it's the increased electron density in the ring that allows the bromine to react with phenol.

$$\text{phenol (OH, positions 2,3,4,5,6)} \quad + \quad 3Br_2 \quad \longrightarrow \quad \text{2,4,6-tribromophenol (OH, Br at 2,4,6)} \quad + \quad 3HBr$$

phenol   *2,4,6-tribromophenol*

The uses of phenol

Phenol is a major chemical product, with more than 8 million tonnes being produced each year. The first major use was as an antiseptic during surgery (see Figure 3). Joseph Lister was the first to use it to clean wounds. It wasn't used like this for long though as it was too damaging to tissue. It's still used today in the production of antiseptics and disinfectants such as TCP™ (see Figure 4).

Another important use is in the production of polymers. Kevlar® (see page 50) and polycarbonate are both produced from substances made from phenol. Bisphenol A (see Figure 5) is used to make polycarbonates, which are used in things like bottles, spectacle lenses and CDs.

Bisphenol A is also used in the manufacture of resins called epoxies. These have a variety of important uses including adhesives and paints. They're also really important in electronic circuits where they're used as electrical insulators.

One of the earliest "plastics" was Bakelite™, a polymer of phenol and formaldehyde (the old name for methanol). It is a resin with good insulating properties and was used to make things like telephones and radio casings. Today, similar compounds are used to make all sorts of objects including saucepan handles, electrical plugs, dominoes, billiard balls and chess pieces.

Figure 3: *A phenol solution being used as an antiseptic during surgery in the 1870s.*

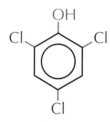

Figure 4:
2,4,6-trichlorophenol (in TCP™)

Practice Questions — Application

Q1 Name the following phenols:

a)

b)

c)
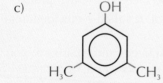

d)
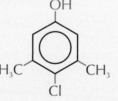

Q2 Write equations for the reaction of each of the phenols in Q1 with $NaOH_{(aq)}$ at room temperature.

Q3 Write equations for the reaction of each of the phenols in Q1 with $Na_{(s)}$ at room temperature.

Q4 Describe what would happen if you reacted 2-methylphenol with sodium carbonate.

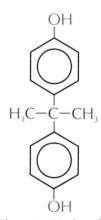

Figure 5: *Bisphenol A (used to make polymers)*

Tip: Remember that when you name molecules you write the prefixes in alphabetical order — for example, ethyl comes before methyl. (You ignore any di- or tri- bits though — for example, ethyl comes before dimethyl.)

Practice Questions — Fact Recall

Q1 What gas is evolved when phenol reacts with sodium metal?

Q2 Draw the structure of the organic product that forms when phenol reacts with bromine water.

Q3 Explain why phenol will react with bromine water but benzene won't.

Q4 Give two uses of phenol and/or phenol derivatives.

- Be able to describe the oxidation of alcohols using $Cr_2O_7^{2-}/H^+$ (i.e. $K_2Cr_2O_7/H_2SO_4$).
- Be able to describe the oxidation of primary alcohols to form aldehydes and carboxylic acids.
- Know how to control the oxidation product of the oxidation of primary alcohols using different reaction conditions.
- Know that you can oxidise aldehydes using $Cr_2O_7^{2-}/H^+$ to form carboxylic acids.
- Be able to describe the oxidation of secondary alcohols to form ketones.

Specification Reference 4.1.2

4. Aldehydes and Ketones

Aldehydes and ketones are compounds that are made by oxidising alcohols. You should remember aldehydes and ketones from AS-level, but just in case you can't here's a quick review...

What are aldehydes and ketones?

Aldehydes and **ketones** are both **carbonyl compounds** as they both contain the carbonyl functional group, C=O. The difference is, they've got their carbonyl groups in different positions. Aldehydes have their carbonyl group at the end of the carbon chain. Ketones have their carbonyl group in the middle of the carbon chain, see Figure 1.

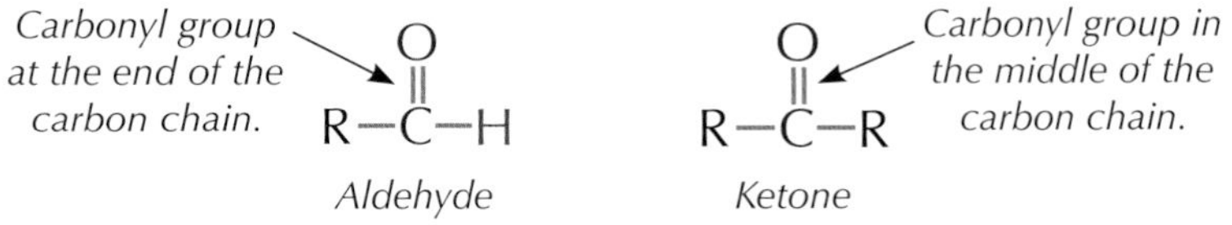

Carbonyl group at the end of the carbon chain.

Carbonyl group in the middle of the carbon chain.

Aldehyde

Ketone

Figure 1: The difference between an aldehyde and a ketone. 'R' represents a carbon chain of any length.

Nomenclature

Aldehydes have the suffix -al. You don't have to say which carbon the functional group is on — it's always on carbon-1. Naming aldehydes follows very similar rules to the naming of alcohols.

Tip: This is all a recap of stuff you learnt at AS-level, so if it doesn't seem familiar, have a look at your AS notes.

Example

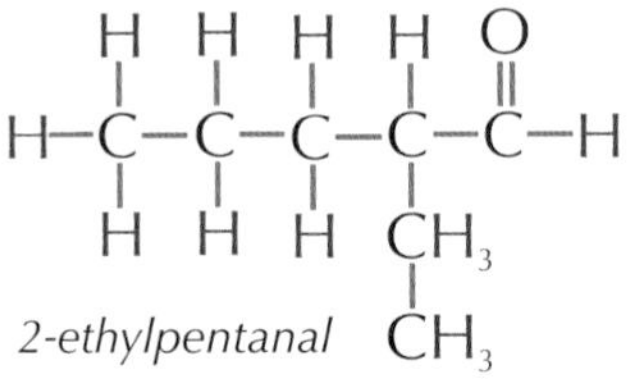

2-ethylpentanal

The longest carbon chain containing the aldehyde functional group is 5 carbon atoms, so the stem is pentane.

There's an ethyl- group attached to the second carbon atom so there's a 2-ethyl- prefix.

So, the aldehyde is called 2-ethylpentanal.

The suffix for ketones is -one. For ketones with five or more carbons, you always have to say which carbon the functional group is on. (If there are other groups attached, such as methyl groups, you have to say it for four-carbon ketones too.)

Example

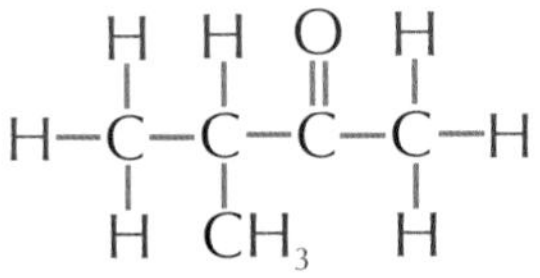

3-methylbutan-2-one

The longest continuous carbon chain is 4 carbon atoms, so the stem is butane.

The carbonyl is found on the second carbon atom and there is a methyl group on the third carbon.

So, the ketone is called 3-methylbutan-2-one.

Tip: When naming ketones, the carbonyl group has the highest priority. So you always number the carbons from the end that means the carbonyl group carbon has the lowest number possible.

Oxidising alcohols

You can use the **oxidising agent** acidified potassium dichromate(VI) ($K_2Cr_2O_7$ / H_2SO_4) to mildly oxidise alcohols. In the reaction, the orange dichromate(VI) ion ($Cr_2O_7^{2-}$) is reduced to the green chromium(III) ion, Cr^{3+}. Primary alcohols are oxidised to aldehydes and then to carboxylic acids. Secondary alcohols are oxidised to ketones only. Tertiary alcohols aren't oxidised.

Oxidation of primary alcohols

A primary alcohol is first oxidised to an aldehyde. This aldehyde can then be oxidised to a carboxylic acid. You can use the notation [O] to represent an oxidising agent — this saves you having to write down 'acidified potassium dichromate(VI)' every time you write out a reaction. This means you can write equations like this:

$$R-CH_2-OH + [O] \longrightarrow R-\overset{\overset{\displaystyle O}{\|}}{C}-H + [O] \xrightarrow{\text{reflux}} R-\overset{\overset{\displaystyle O}{\|}}{C}-OH$$

$$\text{primary alcohol} \qquad \text{aldehyde} \qquad \text{carboxylic acid}$$

$$+ H_2O$$

You can control how far the alcohol is oxidised by controlling the reaction conditions.

Figure 2: *Alcohol oxidation. As the alcohol is oxidised, the potassium dichromate(VI) is reduced to chromium(III) — so the solution turns from orange to green.*

Oxidising primary alcohols to aldehydes

Gently heating propan-1-ol with potassium dichromate(VI) solution and sulfuric acid in a test tube should produce the aldehyde propanal.

$$\underset{\text{propan-1-ol}}{H-\overset{\overset{\displaystyle H}{|}}{\underset{\underset{\displaystyle H}{|}}{C}}-\overset{\overset{\displaystyle H}{|}}{\underset{\underset{\displaystyle H}{|}}{C}}-\overset{\overset{\displaystyle H}{|}}{\underset{\underset{\displaystyle H}{|}}{C}}-OH} + [O] \xrightarrow{\text{distillation}} \underset{\text{propanal}}{H-\overset{\overset{\displaystyle H}{|}}{\underset{\underset{\displaystyle H}{|}}{C}}-\overset{\overset{\displaystyle H}{|}}{\underset{\underset{\displaystyle H}{|}}{C}}-\overset{\overset{\displaystyle O}{\|}}{C}-H} + H_2O$$

However, it's really tricky to control the amount of heat and the aldehyde is usually oxidised to form "vinegar" smelling propanoic acid. To get just the aldehyde, you need to get it out of the solution as soon as it's formed.

You can do this by gently heating excess alcohol with a controlled amount of oxidising agent and acid in distillation apparatus (see Figure 3). The aldehyde, which boils at a lower temperature than the alcohol, is distilled off immediately.

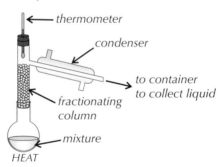

thermometer

condenser

to container
to collect liquid

fractionating
column

mixture

HEAT

Figure 3: *Distillation apparatus.*

Figure 4: *Distillation apparatus.*

Oxidising primary alcohols to carboxylic acids

To produce a carboxylic acid, the alcohol has to be vigorously oxidised.

$$\underset{\text{propan-1-ol}}{H-\overset{\overset{\displaystyle H}{|}}{\underset{\underset{\displaystyle H}{|}}{C}}-\overset{\overset{\displaystyle H}{|}}{\underset{\underset{\displaystyle H}{|}}{C}}-\overset{\overset{\displaystyle H}{|}}{\underset{\underset{\displaystyle H}{|}}{C}}-OH} + 2[O] \xrightarrow{\text{reflux}} \underset{\text{propanoic acid}}{H-\overset{\overset{\displaystyle H}{|}}{\underset{\underset{\displaystyle H}{|}}{C}}-\overset{\overset{\displaystyle H}{|}}{\underset{\underset{\displaystyle H}{|}}{C}}-\overset{\overset{\displaystyle O}{\|}}{C}-OH} + H_2O$$

The alcohol is mixed with excess oxidising agent and heated under reflux (see Figures 5 and 6). Heating under reflux means you can increase the temperature of an organic reaction to boiling without losing volatile solvents, reactants or products. Any vaporised compounds cool, condense and drip back into the reaction mixture. Very handy...

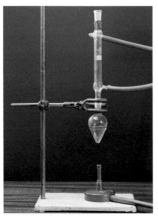

Figure 6: *Refluxing apparatus.*

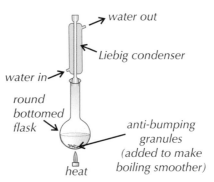

Figure 5: *Refluxing apparatus.*

If you start off with an aldehyde, rather than a primary alcohol, you can oxidise it to a carboxylic acid using the same oxidising agent and apparatus:

$$H-\overset{\overset{\displaystyle H}{|}}{\underset{\underset{\displaystyle H}{|}}{C}}-\overset{\overset{\displaystyle H}{|}}{\underset{\underset{\displaystyle H}{|}}{C}}-\overset{\overset{\displaystyle O}{\|}}{C}-H \ + \ [O] \ \xrightarrow{\text{reflux}} \ H-\overset{\overset{\displaystyle H}{|}}{\underset{\underset{\displaystyle H}{|}}{C}}-\overset{\overset{\displaystyle H}{|}}{\underset{\underset{\displaystyle H}{|}}{C}}-\overset{\overset{\displaystyle O}{\|}}{C}-OH$$

propanal   *propanoic acid*

> **Tip:** You might see primary, secondary and tertiary alcohols written as 1°, 2° and 3° alcohols.

Oxidation of secondary alcohols

Refluxing a secondary alcohol with acidified dichromate(VI) produces a ketone.

$$R_1-\overset{\overset{\displaystyle R_2}{|}}{\underset{\underset{\displaystyle H}{|}}{C}}-OH \ + \ [O] \ \longrightarrow \ R_1-\overset{\overset{\displaystyle O}{\|}}{C}-R_2 \ + \ H_2O$$

secondary alcohol   *ketone*

> **Tip:** Tertiary alcohols don't react with acidified potassium dichromate(VI) at all — the solution stays orange. The only way to oxidise tertiary alcohols is by burning them.

─── **Example** ───────────────────

$$H-\overset{\overset{\displaystyle H}{|}}{\underset{\underset{\displaystyle H}{|}}{C}}-\overset{\overset{\displaystyle OH}{|}}{\underset{\underset{\displaystyle H}{|}}{C}}-\overset{\overset{\displaystyle H}{|}}{\underset{\underset{\displaystyle H}{|}}{C}}-H \ + \ [O] \ \longrightarrow \ H-\overset{\overset{\displaystyle H}{|}}{\underset{\underset{\displaystyle H}{|}}{C}}-\overset{\overset{\displaystyle O}{\|}}{C}-\overset{\overset{\displaystyle H}{|}}{\underset{\underset{\displaystyle H}{|}}{C}}-H \ + \ H_2O$$

propan-2-ol   *propanone*

Ketones can't be oxidised easily, so even prolonged refluxing won't produce anything more.

> **Tip:** Remember, when you're naming molecules, the carbon attached to the group that gives the molecule its name (e.g. the –OH group in an alcohol) must be included in the chain used to find the stem of the name. Even if it's not the longest carbon chain in the molecule.

Practice Questions — Application

Q1 Name these molecules:

a)
$$H-\overset{\overset{\displaystyle H}{|}}{\underset{\underset{\displaystyle H}{|}}{C}}-\overset{\overset{\displaystyle H}{|}}{\underset{\underset{\displaystyle H}{|}}{C}}-\overset{\overset{\displaystyle O}{\|}}{C}-\overset{\overset{\displaystyle H}{|}}{\underset{\underset{\displaystyle H}{|}}{C}}-H$$

b)
$$H-\overset{\overset{\displaystyle H_3C}{|}}{\underset{\underset{\displaystyle H_3C}{|}}{C}}-\overset{\overset{\displaystyle H}{|}}{\underset{\underset{\displaystyle CH_2}{|}}{C}}-\overset{\overset{\displaystyle O}{\|}}{C}-H$$
$$CH_3$$

Q2 Both of the molecules in Q1 can be produced by reacting an alcohol with acidified potassium dichromate(VI). For each molecule, name the alcohol that could be used to produce it and the conditions needed for the reaction.

Q3 The alcohol, heptan-1-ol is heated with acidified potassium dichromate(VI) solution in distillation apparatus.
Name the organic product formed in this reaction.

Q4 Alcohol **A** is reacted with acidified potassium dichromate(VI) solution under reflux. The product of this reaction is 3-ethylpentan-2-one. Draw the structure of alcohol **A**.

Q5 Which of the alcohols (**A-D**) below can be oxidised to carboxylic acids?

A

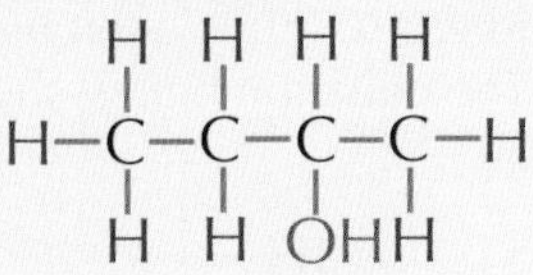

H−C−C−C−C−H with H H H H on top and H H OH H on bottom

B

H−C−C−C−H with H OH H on top and H CH₃ H on bottom

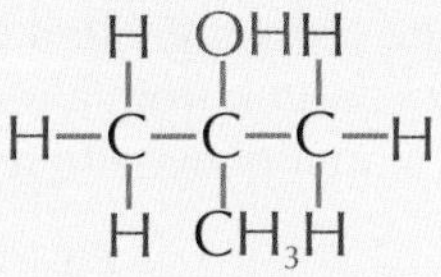

C

HO−C−C−OH with H H on top and H H on bottom

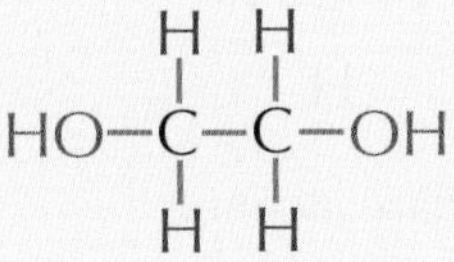

D

H₃C−C−CH₃ with OH, H−C−H above and CH₃ below

> **Tip:** Don't forget — primary alcohols are oxidised to aldehydes or carboxylic acids and secondary alcohols are oxidised to ketones.

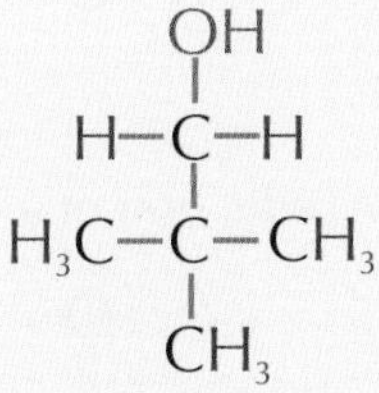

Q6 Write an equation for the oxidation of 2-methylbutan-1-ol to produce 2-methylbutanoic acid.

Q7 Write an equation for the oxidation of ethanal to ethanoic acid.

> **Tip:** You can use [O] to stand for the oxidising agent in questions 6 and 7 (phew...).

Q1 What is the difference between an aldehyde and a ketone?

Q2 Give the molecular formula of the negative ion that is found in potassium dichromate.

Q3 Describe the colour change that would be seen if ethanol was oxidised to ethanal using acidified potassium dichromate(VI).

Q4 What type of compound is produced when an aldehyde is oxidised?

Q5 What apparatus do you need to use to oxidise a primary alcohol to a carboxylic acid?

5. Reducing Carbonyls

Reduction is the opposite of oxidation. So you can reduce aldehydes, ketones and carboxylic acids to alcohols. Read on for a bit more detail...

Reducing aldehydes and ketones

Learning Objectives:

- Be able to describe the reduction of carbonyl compounds using $NaBH_4$ to form alcohols.
- Be able to outline the mechanism for nucleophilic addition reactions of aldehydes and ketones with hydrides, such as $NaBH_4$.

Specification Reference 4.1.2

In the previous topic you saw how primary alcohols can be oxidised to produce aldehydes and carboxylic acids, and how secondary alcohols can be oxidised to make ketones. Using a reducing agent you can reverse these reactions. $NaBH_4$ (sodium tetrahydridoborate(III) or sodium borohydride) is usually the reducing agent used. But in equations, [H] is often used to indicate a hydrogen from a reducing agent. The equation below shows the reduction of an aldehyde to a primary alcohol:

$$R-\underset{\displaystyle \overset{\|}{O}}{C}-H \ + \ 2[H] \longrightarrow R-\underset{\displaystyle \underset{H}{|}}{\overset{\displaystyle \overset{OH}{|}}{C}}-H$$

Exam Tip
When you're writing equations like this in an exam make sure you balance the [H]s as well as the molecules.

And here's the reduction of a ketone to a secondary alcohol:

$$R-\underset{\displaystyle \overset{\|}{O}}{C}-R \ + \ 2[H] \longrightarrow R-\underset{\displaystyle \underset{H}{|}}{\overset{\displaystyle \overset{OH}{|}}{C}}-R$$

Nucleophilic addition reactions

Tip: Remember that a nucleophile is an electron pair donor.

You need to understand the reaction mechanisms for the reduction of aldehydes and ketones back to alcohols. These are **nucleophilic addition** reactions — an H^- ion from the reducing agent acts as a nucleophile and adds on to the δ^+ carbon atom of a carbonyl group. You haven't covered nucleophilic addition reactions before so here's the mechanism...

Exam Tip
You need to be able to draw the mechanism for the reduction of any aldehyde or ketone — so make sure you understand all the steps of these nucleophilic addition reactions.

1. The C=O bond is polar so the $C^{\delta+}$ attracts the negatively charged lone pair of electrons on the H^- ion.
2. The H^- ion attacks the slightly positive carbon atom and donates its lone pair of electrons, forming a dative covalent bond with the carbon.
3. As carbon can only have 4 bonds, the addition of the H^- ion causes one of the carbon-oxygen bonds to break. This forces a lone pair of electrons from the C=O double bond onto the oxygen.
4. The negatively charged oxygen donates its lone pair of electrons to a $H^{\delta+}$ atom on a water molecule and...
5. ...the electrons from the O–H bond are donated to the $O^{\delta-}$ atom.
6. A primary alcohol and an ¯OH ion are produced.

The mechanism for the reduction of a ketone is the same as for an aldehyde — you just get a secondary alcohol at the end instead of a primary alcohol:

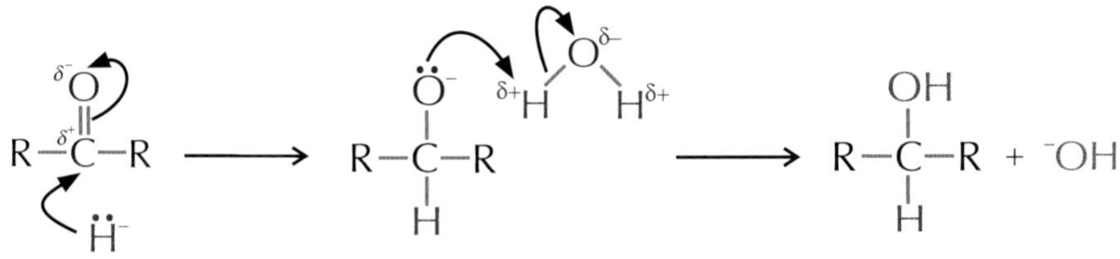

This reaction mechanism can be applied to any aldehyde or ketone.

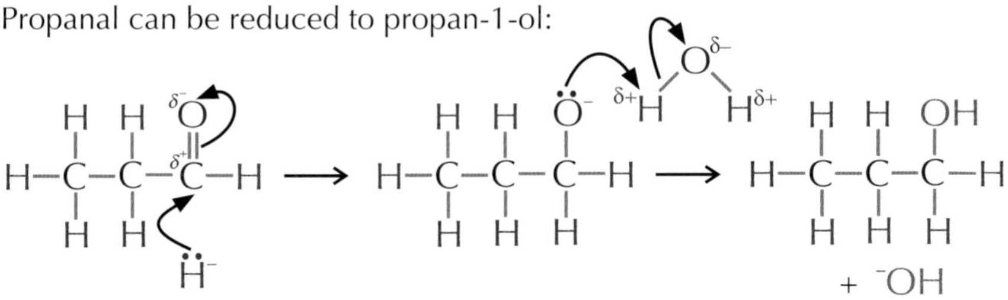

Exam Tip
You <u>must</u> draw the curly arrows coming from the lone pair of electrons. If you don't — you won't get the marks for the mechanism in the exam.

Example

Propanal can be reduced to propan-1-ol:

Practice Questions — Application

Q1 For each molecule below, draw the mechanism for its reduction to an alcohol.

a)

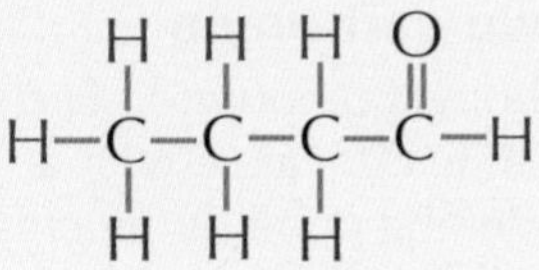

b)

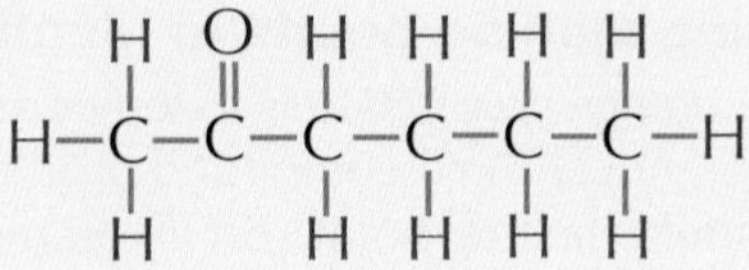

c)

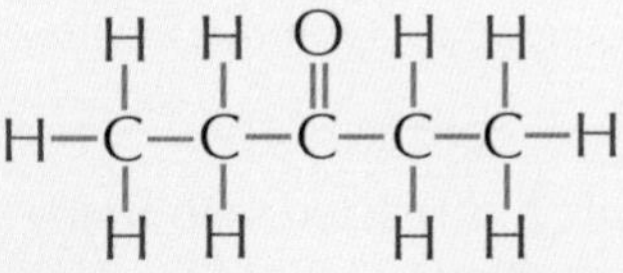

d)

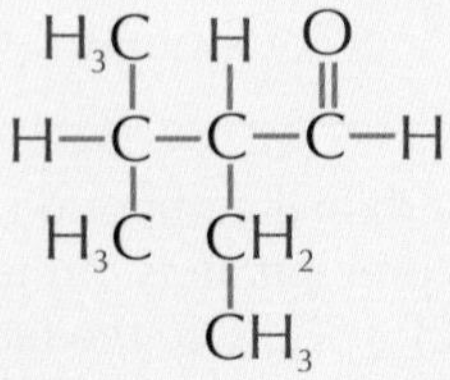

Tip: Don't forget — aldehydes are reduced to primary alcohols and ketones are reduced to secondary alcohols.

Q2 Write an equation for the reduction of pentan-2-one to pentan-2-ol. Use [H] to represent a reducing agent.

Q3 Write an equation for the reduction of 2-methylhexanal to an alcohol. Use [H] to represent a reducing agent.

Q4 Write an equation for the reduction of pentan-2,4-dione to an alcohol. Use [H] to represent a reducing agent.

Q5 The product of reducing molecule **X** is 2-methylbutan-1,3-diol. Write down the structural formula of molecule **X**.

Tip: Remember that <u>all</u> the carbonyl groups in a molecule will be reduced if you add a reducing agent.

Practice Questions — Fact Recall

Q1 Name a reducing agent which could be used to reduce an aldehyde to a primary alcohol.

Q2 Is a secondary alcohol formed by reducing an aldehyde or a ketone?

Q3 Name the reaction mechanism that takes place when ketones are reduced to alcohols.

Figure 2: *Brady's reagent reacting with propanone.*

Tip: A derivative of a compound is a similar compound to the original or one that has been made from it.

6. Tests for Carbonyls

Using tests to identify unknown compounds is an important skill if you want to be a CSI or an MI6 agent. But it's also pretty useful in the lab when you want to know what you've made — here are two tests you've got to know.

Brady's Reagent

Brady's reagent is 2,4-dinitrophenylhydrazine (2,4-DNPH) (see Figure 1) dissolved in methanol and concentrated sulfuric acid.

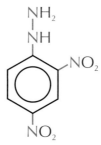

Figure 1: *Brady's reagent (2,4-dinitrophenylhydrazine).*

The 2,4-dinitrophenylhydrazine forms a bright orange precipitate if a carbonyl group is present (see Figure 2). This only happens with $C=O$ groups, not with ones like COOH, so it only tests for aldehydes and ketones.

Using melting points to identify unknown carbonyls

The orange precipitate is a derivative of the carbonyl compound. Each different carbonyl compound produces a crystalline derivative with a different melting point. So if you measure the melting point of the crystals and compare it against the known melting points of the derivatives, you can identify the carbonyl compound.

┌─ **Example** ─────────────────────────────────

An unknown carbonyl compound, molecule **J**, is reacted with Brady's reagent and an orange precipitate is formed. The melting point of the product was found to be 115.3 °C. Use the table below to identify molecule **J**.

Carbonyl compound	Melting point of 2,4-DNPH derivative (°C)
Propanal	156
Methylpropanal	182
Butan-2-one	115
3-methylbutan-2-one	124

Butan-2-one has a 2,4-DNPH derivative with a melting point of 115 °C. So molecule **J** must be butan-2-one.

Tollens' reagent

This test lets you distinguish between an aldehyde and a ketone. It uses the fact that an aldehyde can be easily oxidised to a carboxylic acid, but a ketone can't.

The only way to oxidise a ketone would be to break a carbon-carbon bond so ketones are not easily oxidised.

$$R-\overset{\overset{\displaystyle O}{\|}}{C}-R \ + \ [O] \ \longrightarrow \ \text{Nothing happens}$$

Tip: In these equations [O] is used to represent an oxidising agent.

But aldehydes can be easily oxidised to carboxylic acids because they have a hydrogen attached to the carbonyl group:

$$R-\overset{\overset{\displaystyle O}{\|}}{C}-H \ + \ [O] \ \longrightarrow \ R-\overset{\overset{\displaystyle O}{\|}}{C}-OH$$

As the aldehyde is oxidised, the oxidising agent is reduced — so a reagent is used that changes colour as it's reduced.

Tollens' reagent is a colourless solution of silver nitrate ($AgNO_3$) dissolved in aqueous ammonia. If it's heated in a test tube with an aldehyde, a silver mirror forms after a few minutes (see Figure 3). As the aldehyde is oxidised the silver ions in the Tollens' reagent are reduced, producing a silver mirror:

Tip: Silver nitrate dissolved in aqueous ammonia is sometimes called ammoniacal silver nitrate.

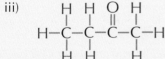

Colourless   *Silver*

$$Ag^+_{(aq)} \ + \ e^- \ \rightarrow \ Ag_{(s)}$$

Silver ions in the Tollens' reagent are reduced.

Electrons come from the oxidation of the aldehyde.

The silver produced forms a silver mirror.

Tip: Aldehydes and ketones are flammable, so they must be heated in a water bath rather than over a flame.

As ketones aren't easily oxidised, they won't react with Tollens' reagent — so there'll be no colour change.

Practice Question — Application

Q1 Describe what you would observe if you reacted each of the compounds below with: a) Brady's reagent,
b) Tollens' reagent.

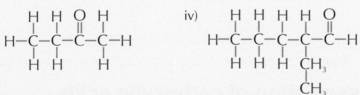

Figure 3: Tollens' reagent. The test-tube on the left shows the unreacted Tollens' reagent. The test-tube on the right shows the result of a reaction with an aldehyde.

Practice Questions — Fact Recall

Q1 What does Brady's reagent test for?

Q2 Describe how you could use Brady's reagent and melting point data to determine the identity of an unknown compound.

Q3 What is Tollens' reagent?

Q4 Give the formula of the positive ion present in Tollens' reagent.

7. Carboxylic Acids

Learning Objectives:
- Be able to explain the water solubility of carboxylic acids in terms of hydrogen bonding and dipole-dipole interaction.
- Be able to describe the reactions of carboxylic acids with metals, carbonates and bases.

Specification Reference 4.1.3

You should recognise these crazy compounds from AS-Level (and the previous few topics) but here's a bit more detail about them and their reactions.

What are carboxylic acids?

Carboxylic acids contain the carboxyl functional group –COOH.

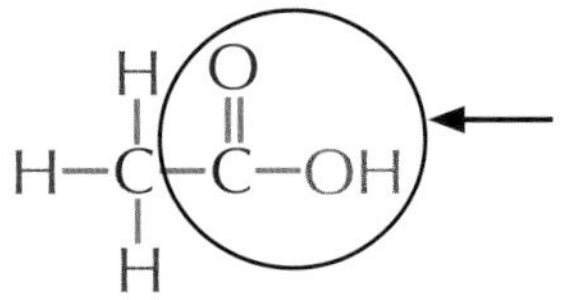

This is the carboxyl functional group.

Tip: A carboxyl group contains a carbonyl group and a hydroxyl group on the same carbon atom.

To name them, you find and name the longest alkane chain, take off the 'e' and add '–oic acid'. The carboxyl group is always at the end of the molecule and when naming it's more important than other functional groups — so all the other functional groups in the molecule are numbered starting from this carbon.

Tip: You've already covered how to name carboxylic acids at AS-level so this should just be a recap.

┌─ **Example** ──────────────────────────

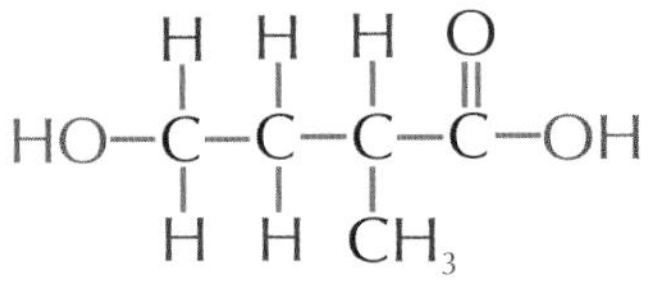

The longest continuous carbon chain is 4 carbon atoms, so the stem is butane.

Numbering of the carbons starts at the COOH group so there's a COOH group on carbon-1, a methyl group on carbon-2 and a hydroxyl group on carbon-4.

So, this is 4-hydroxy-2-methylbutanoic acid.

Solubility of carboxylic acids

Carboxylic acids are **polar** molecules, since electrons are drawn from the carbon atoms in the carbonyl groups towards the more **electronegative** oxygen atoms. This makes small carboxylic acids very soluble in water, as they form hydrogen bonds with the water molecules (see Figure 1).

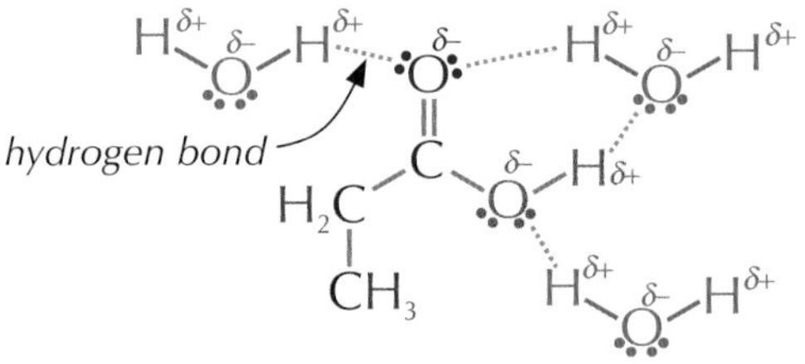

Exam Tip
If you're asked to draw hydrogen bonding in an exam don't forget to mark on the lone pairs of electrons and label the hydrogen bond and all the $\delta+$ and $\delta-$ atoms.

hydrogen bond

Figure 1: *Hydrogen bonds between propanoic acid and water molecules.*

Dissociation of carboxylic acids

Carboxylic acids are weak acids — in water they partially dissociate into a carboxylate ion and an H^+ ion.

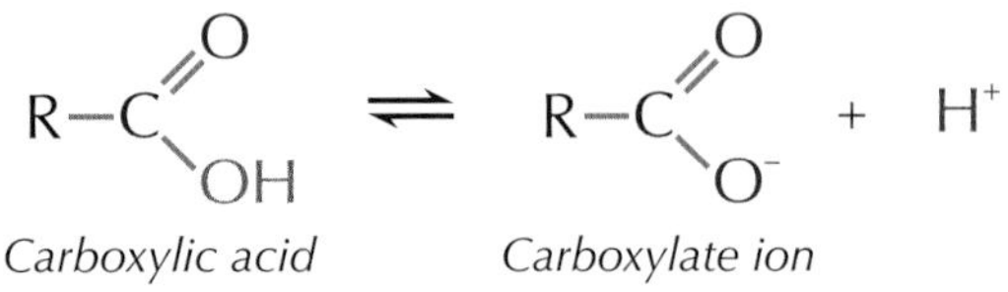

Carboxylic acid   *Carboxylate ion*

Tip: See page 140 for more on the dissociation of weak acids.

This reaction is reversible but the equilibrium lies to the left because most of the molecules don't dissociate.

Reaction with carbonates, metals and bases

Carboxylic acids react with the more reactive metals to form a salt and hydrogen gas.

Example

$$2CH_3COOH_{(aq)} + Mg_{(s)} \rightarrow (CH_3COO)_2Mg_{(aq)} + H_{2(g)}$$

Ethanoic acid   *Magnesium ethanoate*

Carboxylic acids react with carbonates (CO_3^{2-}) to form a salt, carbon dioxide and water.

Example

$$2CH_3COOH_{(aq)} + Na_2CO_{3(s)} \rightarrow 2CH_3COONa_{(aq)} + H_2O_{(l)} + CO_{2(g)}$$

Ethanoic acid   *Sodium carbonate*   *Sodium ethanoate*

In reactions between carboxylic acids and metals, and carboxylic acids and carbonates, the gas evolved during the reaction fizzes out of the solution.

Carboxylic acids are neutralised by bases (like metal oxides and hydroxides) to form a salt and water.

Example

$$2CH_3COOH_{(aq)} + MgO_{(s)} \rightarrow (CH_3COO)_2Mg_{(aq)} + H_2O_{(l)}$$

Ethanoic acid   *Magnesium ethanoate*

Tip: Salts of carboxylic acids are called carboxylates and their names end with –oate.

Figure 2: *Calcium carbonate reacting with ethanoic acid. The reaction gives off bubbles of carbon dioxide.*

Tip: Simple carboxylic acids form 1– ions (e.g. CH_3COO^-). So you need one molecule to react with a 1+ ion (like sodium), but two to react with a 2+ ion (like magnesium).

Practice Questions — Application

Q1 Below are two carboxylic acids:

(i)
H–C–OH with O double bonded to C

(ii)
H–C–C–C–C–C–OH with H H H H O; OH and C_2H_5 substituents

a) Name these carboxylic acids.

b) Write a balanced equation for the reaction of carboxylic acid (i) with magnesium metal.

c) Write a balanced equation for the reaction of carboxylic acid (ii) with sodium carbonate (Na_2CO_3).

Q2 Write a balanced equation for the reaction between 2-methylbutanoic acid and $NaOH_{(aq)}$.

Q3 Write a balanced equation for the partial dissociation of propanoic acid in water.

Exam Tip
When you're naming molecules in the exam check your spelling. You'll lose marks even if there's only one letter out of place.

Tip: Remember to double check that your equations balance when you've finished.

Practice Questions — Fact Recall

Q1 Write down the functional group of carboxylic acids.

Q2 Explain why small carboxylic acids, like ethanoic acid, are highly soluble in water. Draw a diagram to help you explain your answer.

Q3 Describe what you would observe if a carboxylic acid reacted with magnesium metal.

8. Esters

You met esters and esterification at AS-Level but there are a few more reactions and properties you're going to have to learn for your A2-Level exams.

Learning Objectives:
- Be able to describe the esterification of carboxylic acids with alcohols, in the presence of an acid catalyst.
- Be able to describe the esterification of acid anhydrides with alcohols.
- Be able to describe the hydrolysis of esters in hot aqueous acid to form carboxylic acids and alcohols.
- Be able to describe the hydrolysis of esters in hot aqueous alkali to form carboxylate salts and alcohols.
- Know the uses of esters in perfumes and flavourings.

Specification Reference 4.1.3

Naming esters

An **ester** is formed by reacting an alcohol with a carboxylic acid (see next page). So the name of an ester is made up of two parts — the first bit comes from the alcohol, and the second bit from the carboxylic acid.

To name an ester, just follow these steps:

1. Look at the alkyl group that came from the alcohol. This is the first bit of the ester's name.
2. Now look at the part that came from the carboxylic acid. Swap its '-oic acid' ending for 'oate' to get the second bit of the name.
3. Put the two parts together.

Example

Methanoic acid reacts with ethanol to produce the ester shown below:

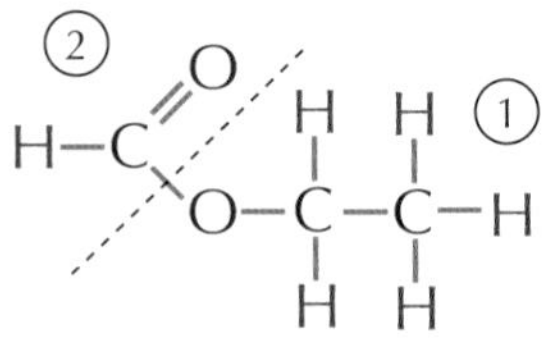

1. This part of the ester came from the alcohol. It's an ethyl group, so the first part of the ester's name is ethyl-.
2. This part of the ester came from the carboxylic acid. It was methanoic acid, so the second part of the ester's name is -methanoate.
3. So this ester is ethyl methanoate.

Tip: Be careful — the name of the ester is written the opposite way round to the formula.

The same rules apply even if the carbon chains are branched or if the molecule has a benzene ring attached. Always number the carbons starting from the carbon atoms in the C–O–C bond.

Examples

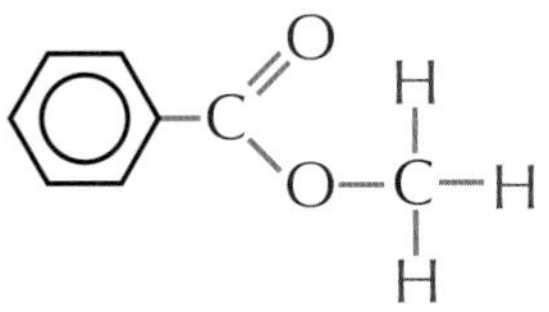

This ester has a methyl group that came from the alcohol so the name begins with methyl-.

There is a benzene ring that came from benzoic acid so the name ends in -benzoate.

So this is methyl benzoate.

This ester has an ethyl group that came from the alcohol and the carboxylic acid part was 2-methylbutanoic acid, so it is called ethyl 2-methylbutanoate.

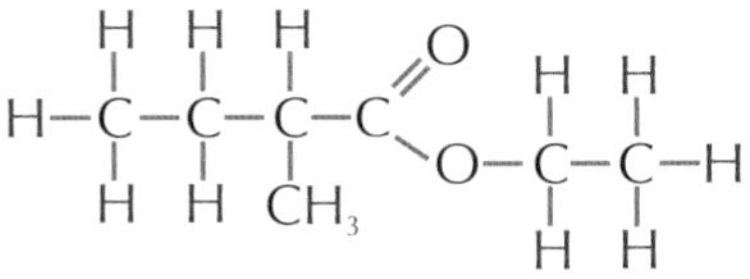

Tip: Here's how you'd number the carbons in ethyl 2-methylbutanoate:

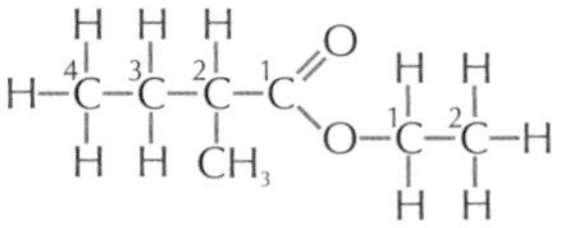

It doesn't matter that there are two C_1s (and C_2s) because one's in the bit that came from the alcohol and the other's in the bit from the acid.

Sometimes you may be asked to predict which alcohol and which carboxylic acid are needed to form a particular ester.

Example

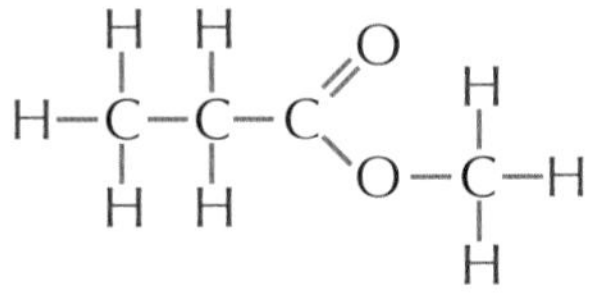

There are 3 carbons in the part of the molecule that came from the acid so the stem is propane. This part came from propanoic acid.

There is one carbon in the section that came from the alcohol so the stem is methane. This part of the molecule came from methanol.

Producing esters

Producing esters using alcohols and carboxylic acids

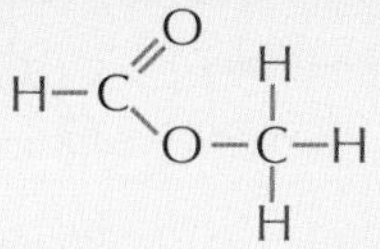

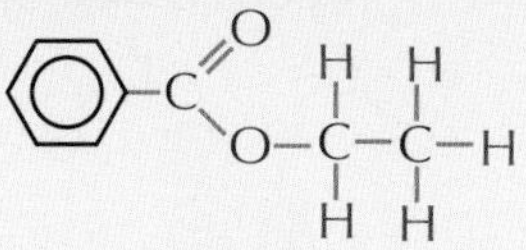

If you heat a carboxylic acid with an alcohol in the presence of a strong acid catalyst, you get an ester. It's called an **esterification** reaction.

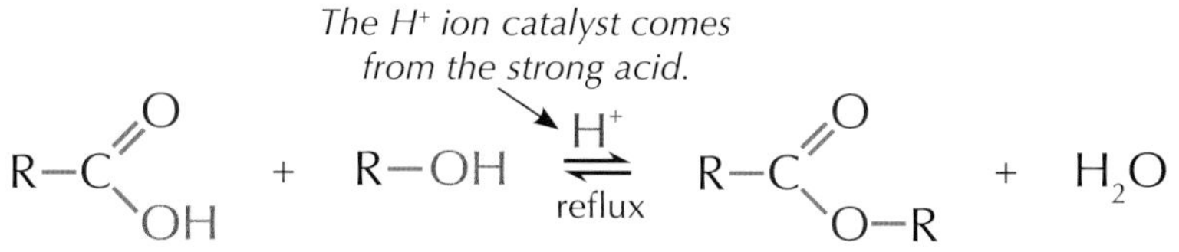

The H^+ ion catalyst comes from the strong acid.

$$R-C\overset{O}{\underset{OH}{}} \; + \; R-OH \;\underset{reflux}{\overset{H^+}{\rightleftharpoons}}\; R-C\overset{O}{\underset{O-R}{}} \; + \; H_2O$$

Carboxylic acid   *Alcohol*   *Ester*   *Water*

Concentrated sulfuric acid (H_2SO_4) is usually used as the acid catalyst but other strong acids such as HCl or H_3PO_4 can also be used.

┌─ **Example** ───

Ethanoic acid reacts with ethanol to produce ethyl ethanoate and water.

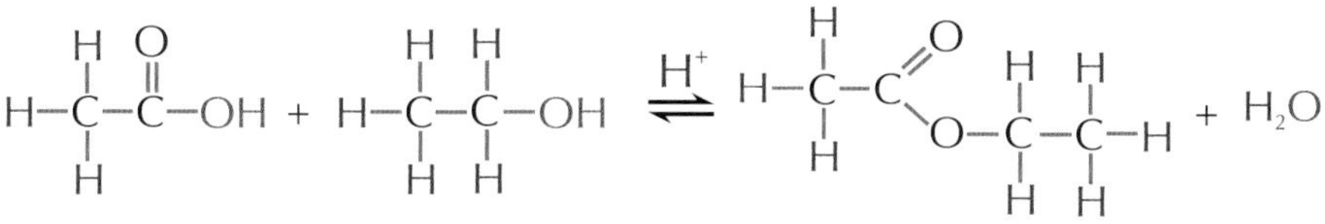

Ethanoic acid   *Ethanol*   *Ethyl ethanoate*   *Water*

The reaction is reversible, so you need to separate out the product as it forms. Small esters are very volatile, so for them you can just warm the mixture and distil off the ester. Large esters are harder to form so it's best to heat them under reflux and use distillation to separate the ester from the other compounds.

Producing esters from alcohols and acid anhydrides

An **acid anhydride** is made from two identical carboxylic acid molecules. The two carboxylic acid molecules are joined together via an oxygen with the carbonyl groups on either side. Acid anhydride formation is shown below.

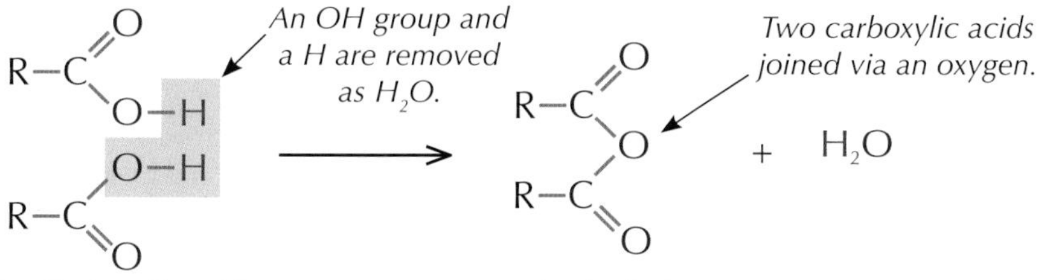

An OH group and a H are removed as H_2O.   *Two carboxylic acids joined via an oxygen.*

2 × Carboxylic acid   *Acid anhydride*

If you know the name of the carboxylic acid, acid anhydrides are easy to name — just take away 'acid' and add 'anhydride'. So methanoic acid gives methanoic anhydride, ethanoic acid gives ethanoic anhydride, etc.

Tip: This reaction is also a condensation reaction — molecules are combining by releasing a small molecule (e.g. water).

Exam Tip
These reactions are reversible, so don't forget the forwards-backwards arrows ($\rightleftharpoons$) when you're writing these equations in the exam.

Tip: If you can't remember what distillation or refluxing apparatus look like have a glance back at pages 17-18.

Tip: At first glance acid anhydrides can seem a bit daunting, but when you realise that they're just two carboxylic acids stuck together they don't look quite so bad.

Example

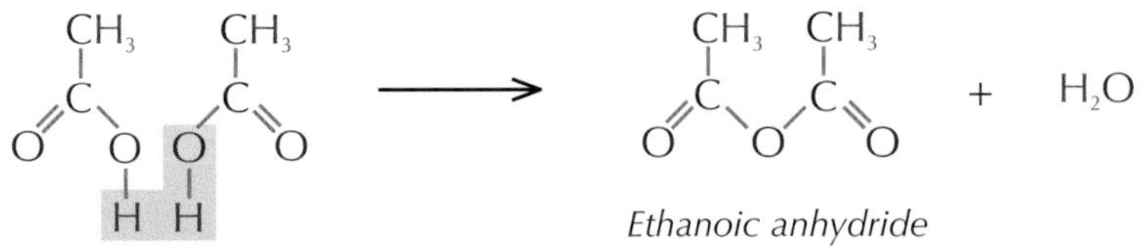

$2 \times$ Ethanoic acid → Ethanoic anhydride + H_2O

Tip: This way of making esters is simpler as the reaction isn't reversible — so you can just collect and separate the products at the end of the reaction. However, esters aren't generally produced on an industrial scale in this way as acid anhydrides are expensive.

Acid anhydrides can react with alcohols to make esters too. The acid anhydride is warmed with the alcohol. No catalyst is needed. The products are an ester and a carboxylic acid which can then be separated by distillation.

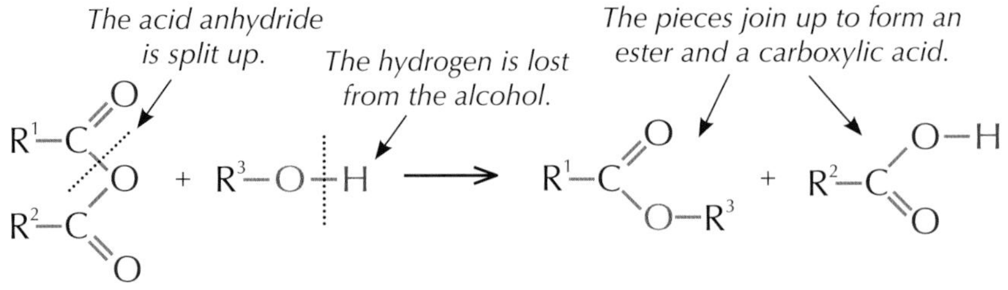

The acid anhydride is split up. *The hydrogen is lost from the alcohol.* *The pieces join up to form an ester and a carboxylic acid.*

Acid anhydride + Alcohol → Ester + Carboxylic acid

Example

Ethanoic anhydride reacts with methanol to form methyl ethanoate and ethanoic acid.

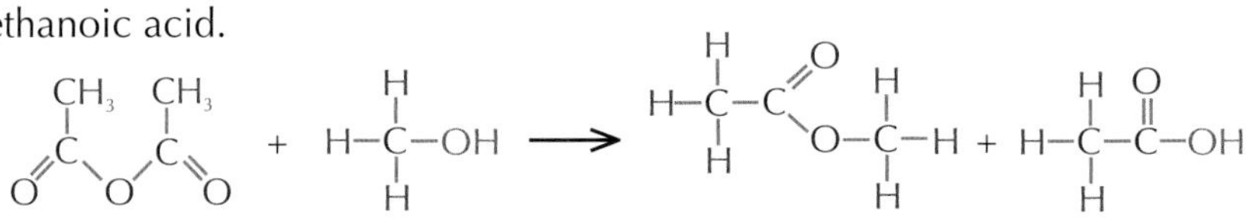

Ethanoic anhydride + Methanol → Methyl ethanoate + Ethanoic acid

Tip: Yes, I know... Learning the reactions of acid anhydrides is hard. The only thing to do is practise, practise, practise until you can do them standing on your head. Hard work never killed anyone (apart from my aunt Sally — but that's another story).

Practice Questions — Application

Q1 Write an equation to show the formation of butyl methanoate and methanoic acid from an acid anhydride and an alcohol.

Q2 Write an equation to show the formation of propyl pentanoate from an acid and an alcohol.

Hydrolysis of esters

Hydrolysis is when a substance is split up by water — but using just water can be very slow, so an acid or an alkali is often added to speed it up. There are two types of hydrolysis of esters — acid hydrolysis and base hydrolysis. With both types you get an alcohol, but the second product in each case is different.

Tip: Hydrolysis comes from two Greek words — 'hydro' meaning water and 'lysis' meaning to separate. So hydrolysis means separation using water. Simple.

Acid hydrolysis

Acid hydrolysis splits the ester into an acid and an alcohol — it's the reverse of the reaction on page 27. You have to heat the ester under reflux with a dilute acid, such as hydrochloric or sulfuric. The ester will then split back into the carboxylic acid and alcohol it was originally made from.

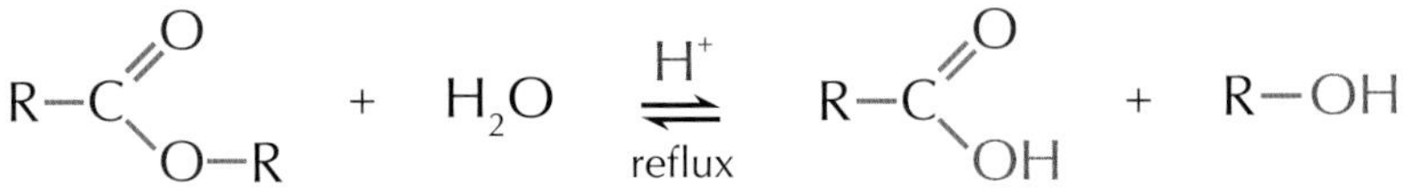

Ester + Water $\underset{\text{reflux}}{\overset{H^+}{\rightleftharpoons}}$ Carboxylic acid + Alcohol

Example

Acid hydrolysis of methyl ethanoate produces ethanoic acid and methanol:

$$H-\overset{\overset{\displaystyle H}{|}}{\underset{\underset{\displaystyle H}{|}}{C}}-\overset{\overset{\displaystyle O}{\|}}{C}\overset{\displaystyle O-\overset{\overset{\displaystyle H}{|}}{\underset{\underset{\displaystyle H}{|}}{C}}-H}{} \quad + \ H_2O \underset{\text{reflux}}{\overset{H^+}{\rightleftharpoons}} \ H-\overset{\overset{\displaystyle H}{|}}{\underset{\underset{\displaystyle H}{|}}{C}}-\overset{\overset{\displaystyle O}{\|}}{C}-OH \ + \ H-\overset{\overset{\displaystyle H}{|}}{\underset{\underset{\displaystyle H}{|}}{C}}-OH$$

Methyl ethanoate   Water   Ethanoic acid   Methanol

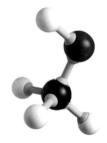

Figure 1: A molecular model of methanol.

As these acid hydrolysis reactions are reversible you need to use lots of water to push the equilibrium over to the right so you get lots of product. See pages 128-129 for more on reversible reactions and equilibria.

Base hydrolysis

For a base hydrolysis reaction you have to reflux the ester with a dilute alkali, such as sodium hydroxide. OH⁻ ions from the base react with the ester and you get a carboxylate ion and an alcohol.

$$R-\overset{\overset{\displaystyle O}{\|}}{C}\overset{\displaystyle O-R}{} \quad + \ OH^- \underset{}{\overset{\text{reflux}}{\rightleftharpoons}} \ R-\overset{\overset{\displaystyle O}{\|}}{C}\overset{\displaystyle O^-}{} \quad + \quad R-OH$$

Ester   Carboxylate ion   Alcohol

Tip: The carboxylate ion will form a salt with the positive ion from the alkali. For example, in this reaction sodium ethanoate would be formed if the alkali used was sodium hydroxide:

$$H-\overset{\overset{\displaystyle H}{|}}{\underset{\underset{\displaystyle H}{|}}{C}}-\overset{\overset{\displaystyle O}{\|}}{C}\overset{\displaystyle O^-Na^+}{}$$

Example

Base hydrolysis of methyl ethanoate produces ethanoate ions and methanol:

$$H-\overset{\overset{\displaystyle H}{|}}{\underset{\underset{\displaystyle H}{|}}{C}}-\overset{\overset{\displaystyle O}{\|}}{C}\overset{\displaystyle O-\overset{\overset{\displaystyle H}{|}}{\underset{\underset{\displaystyle H}{|}}{C}}-H}{} \ + \ OH^- \underset{}{\overset{\text{reflux}}{\rightleftharpoons}} \ H-\overset{\overset{\displaystyle H}{|}}{\underset{\underset{\displaystyle H}{|}}{C}}-\overset{\overset{\displaystyle O}{\|}}{C}\overset{\displaystyle O^-}{} \ + \ H-\overset{\overset{\displaystyle H}{|}}{\underset{\underset{\displaystyle H}{|}}{C}}-OH$$

Methyl ethanoate   Ethanoate ion   Methanol

Practice Question — Application

Q1 To the right is the ester methyl propanoate:
Write an equation to show:
a)   the acid hydrolysis of this ester,
b)   the base hydrolysis of this ester.

$$H-\overset{\overset{\displaystyle H}{|}}{\underset{\underset{\displaystyle H}{|}}{C}}-\overset{\overset{\displaystyle H}{|}}{\underset{\underset{\displaystyle H}{|}}{C}}-\overset{\overset{\displaystyle O}{\|}}{C}\overset{\displaystyle O-\overset{\overset{\displaystyle H}{|}}{\underset{\underset{\displaystyle H}{|}}{C}}-H}{}$$

Uses of esters

Esters have a sweet smell — it varies from gluey sweet for smaller esters to a fruity 'pear drop' smell for the larger ones. This means that they're great for making perfumes and for adding scents to products (e.g. washing powder). The food industry also uses esters to flavour things like drinks and sweets.

Tip: The fragrances and flavours of lots of flowers and fruits come from naturally occurring esters.

Practice Questions — Fact Recall

Q1 What two products are produced when an ester is broken down by:
a)   acid hydrolysis?
b)   base hydrolysis?
Q2 Give two common uses of esters.

Exam Tip
Make sure you learn the uses of esters as well as all the equations and mechanisms. They could be easy marks to pick up in the exam.

- Be able to describe a triglyceride as a triester of glycerol (propane-1,2,3-triol) and fatty acids.

- Be able to compare the structures of saturated fats, unsaturated fats and fatty acids, including cis and trans isomers, from systematic names and shorthand formulae.

Specification Reference 4.1.3

9. Fatty Acids and Triglycerides

The world would be pretty boring if we only dealt with small molecules all the time. So this topic's all about some slightly longer, marginally more complex and downright fancier molecules. Mmmmm... fats.

What are fatty acids?

Fatty acids are carboxylic acids — they have a long hydrocarbon chain with a carboxylic acid group at the end. If the hydrocarbon chain contains no double bonds then the fatty acid is **saturated**, but if it contains one or more double bonds then it's **unsaturated** (see Figure 1).

Saturated fatty acid

Unsaturated fatty acid

Double bonds

Figure 1: *Diagram showing the structure of saturated and unsaturated fatty acids.*

Tip: Sometimes you might see hydrocarbon chains written as R' or R''. The 's are to show that the hydrocarbon chains are different, so R is different to R' (and R' is different to R'').

Fatty acids can also be written like this:

where 'R' is a hydrocarbon chain.

Triglycerides

The animal and vegetable fats and oils we eat are mainly **triglycerides** (see Figure 2). Triglycerides contain the ester functional group –COO– three times — they are triesters.

Figure 3: *The fats and oils that we eat are mainly made up of triglycerides.*

Ester bond

Figure 2: *Diagram showing the structure of a triglyceride.*

Tip: This is the same reaction that you saw on page 27, but here three functional groups from each molecule are reacting at the same time — crazy...

Triglycerides are made by reacting glycerol (propane-1,2,3-triol) with fatty acids (see the next page). The three -OH groups on the glycerol molecule link up to fatty acids to produce a triglyceride molecule. Water is eliminated, so it's a type of **condensation reaction**.

Glycerol 3 × Fatty acid Triglyceride

Tip: Remember, the R groups can be any hydrocarbon chain. All three chains can be the same or they can all be different. It depends on the fat (or oil).

Naming fatty acids

Fatty acids are pretty complex molecules, which means that describing their structure clearly without drawing them can be a bit tricky. The best way is to use either their systematic names or their shorthand names.

Systematic naming

Fatty acids are long hydrocarbon chains with a –COOH group at the end. Here's how to name them systematically:

- Count how many carbon atoms there are.
  This is the stem of the molecule's name (see Figure 4).

- Find out where the double bonds are — count the carbons from the –COOH group end. Add these numbers to the stem.

- Add the suffix -anoic acid (saturated) or -enoic acid (unsaturated).

- If the molecule has more than one double bond, add a bit to the suffix to say how many it has (two is -dienoic acid, three is -trienoic acid, etc.).

This sounds a bit complicated, but an example or two should make it clearer:

Tip: Most fatty acids have a common name (for example 'oleic acid') but these names are no help if you want to know about the structure of the molecule.

┌─ **Examples** ───────────

- This fatty acid has 14 carbon atoms so the stem is tetradeca-.
- It has 0 double bonds so there are no numbers after the stem.
- The molecule is saturated so the suffix is -anoic acid
So this is tetradecanoic acid.

- This fatty acid has 16 carbon atoms so the stem is hexadeca-.
- It has 2 double bonds — one starting from carbon-3 and one starting from carbon-7. So there's a -3,7- after the stem.
- The molecule is unsaturated so the suffix is -enoic acid.
- It has two double bonds, so it must be a -dienoic acid.
So this is hexadeca-3,7-dienoic acid.

Stem	Number of carbon atoms
tetra-	4
penta-	5
hexa-	6
hepta-	7
octa-	8
nona-	9
deca-	10

Figure 4: *Stems for naming long carbon chains. You can add the stem names together to create the names of longer molecules. For example, a 14 carbon chain would be tetra- + deca- = tetradeca-.*

Tip: When a molecule's drawn in its skeletal formula, like these fatty acids, there's one carbon atom at each junction between bonds (and at the end of bonds). If you're struggling with skeletal formulas, dig out your AS-level notes.

Shorthand naming

There's a slightly quicker way of naming fatty acids which only uses numbers — the shorthand naming system.

To name fatty acids using the shorthand method, you need to:

- Write down the number of carbon atoms in the fatty acid.
- Count the number of double bonds in the molecule. Write this after the number of carbon atoms, separating them with a comma.
- Work out where in the carbon chain the double bonds are (if there are any). Add these numbers, in brackets, to the end of the name.

Here are the same examples again, but this time written in shorthand:

┌─ **Examples** ─────────────────────────

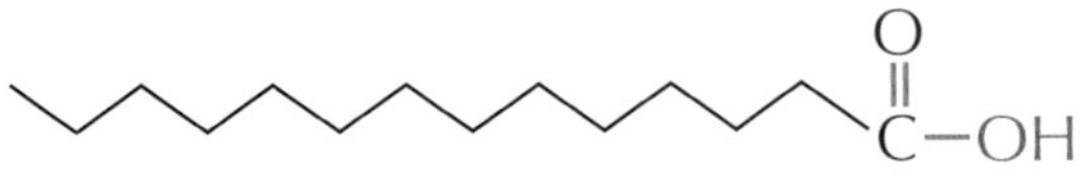

$$\text{H}_3\text{C}\diagdown\diagup\diagdown\diagup\diagdown\diagup\diagdown\diagup\diagdown\text{C}\overset{\text{O}}{=}\text{—OH}$$

- This fatty acid has 14 carbon atoms.
- It has 0 double bonds.

So this fatty acid is 14, 0.

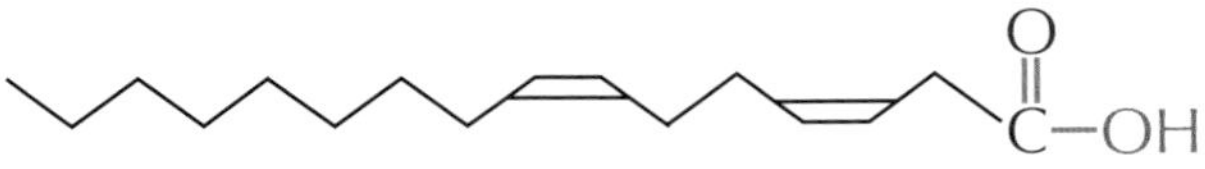

$$\diagdown\diagup\diagdown\diagup\diagdown\diagup=\diagup\diagdown=\diagdown\text{C}\overset{\text{O}}{=}\text{—OH}$$

- This fatty acid has 16 carbon atoms.
- It has 2 double bonds.
- The double bonds are found on carbons 3 and 7.

So this fatty acid is 16, 2(3, 7).

└──

Cis and trans fatty acids

Fatty acids can exist as **stereoisomers** — molecules with the same structural formula but different arrangements in space. This is because the C=C bond is rigid — the molecule can't rotate about this bond.

Almost all naturally-occurring fatty acids that are unsaturated have the cis configuration. This means that the hydrogens each side of the double bond are on the same side. This results in a bent molecule (see Figure 5), or with several double bonds, a curved molecule.

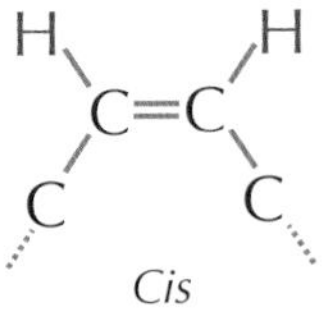

The fatty acid molecule is bent at the double bond.

Figure 5: *Cis fatty acid isomer.*

In trans fatty acids, the hydrogens are on opposite sides (see Figure 7). This gives long, straight molecules, similar to saturated fatty acids. They're almost always the product of human processing — hydrogen is added (hydrogenation) to unsaturated vegetable oils to saturate them, raising their melting point and creating solid fats.

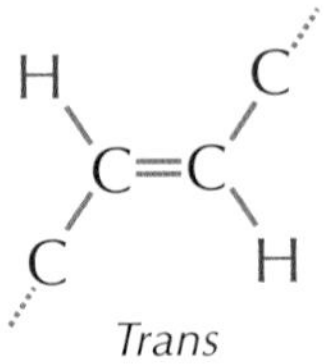

The fatty acid molecule is straight through the double bond.

Figure 7: *Trans fatty acid isomer.*

Exam Tip
Writing the names of fatty acids in shorthand may look simple but it's surprisingly easy to make a mistake. If you're asked to write down the shorthand name of a fatty acid in the exam <u>always</u> double check your answer.

Tip: You met cis-trans isomerism at AS-Level — look back at your notes if you need a reminder of how it works. It's a special case of E/Z isomerism (see page 65).

Figure 6: *Sunflower oil contains the cis fatty acid linoleic acid. This is an essential fatty acid that the body needs to stay healthy.*

Figure 8: *Yummy foods containing trans fatty acids (TFAs). Trans fatty acids have been linked to heart disease.*

Practice Questions — Application

Q1 State how many double bonds each of these fatty acids contains:

a) hexadecanoic acid

b) deca-2,4,8-trienoic acid

c) 20, 4(5, 8, 11, 14)

Q2 For the following fatty acids, give the:

i) systematic name,

ii) shorthand name.

a)

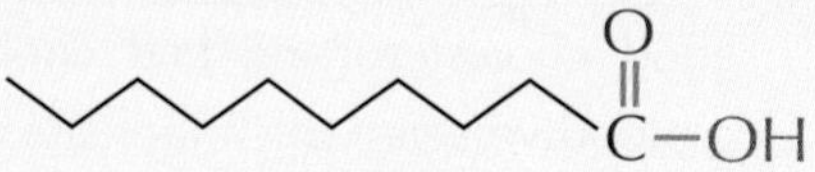

b)

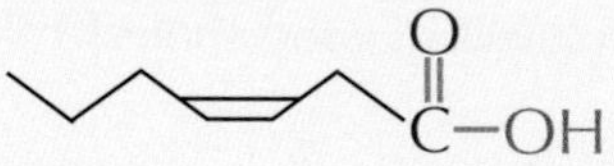

c)

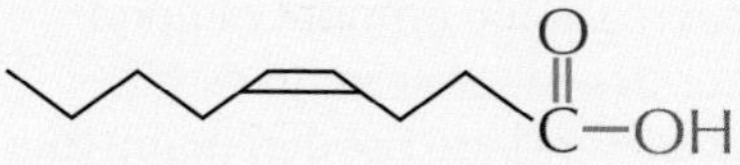

d)

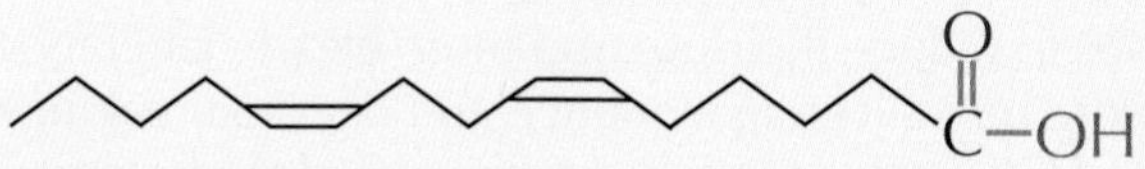

Q3 Write an equation for the production of the triglyceride below from glycerol.

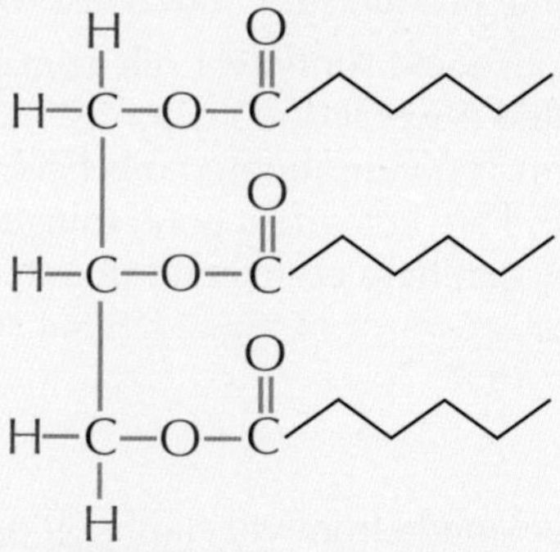

Q4 The cis isomer of octadeca-9-enoic acid has one double bond, which is in the cis configuration.

a) Describe the shape of this molecule.

b) Could this molecule be a naturally occurring fatty acid? Explain your answer.

Tip: Hmm... the molecule in question 3 looks a bit nasty. Don't worry though — making a triglyceride is just the same as making an ester (except that you need to make three functional groups instead of one).

Tip: Sometimes you might see cis- or trans- stuck on to the front of the fatty acid's name to tell you which isomer it is. For example, the fatty acid in question 4 could be called cis-octadeca-9-enoic acid (nice snappy name...).

Practice Questions — Fact Recall

Q1 What is an unsaturated fatty acid?

Q2 Draw the structure of a triglyceride using 'R' to represent the hydrocarbon chains.

Q3 What two reactants do you need to produce a triester?

Q4 Are trans fatty acids almost all naturally occurring or almost always the product of human processing?

10. Fats

Fats get a lot of bad press but they're not all bad. It's just that you've got to be careful which ones you choose to eat and how often you eat them. In general, trans fats and oils = bad, cis fats and oils = good.

Cholesterol and fats

Cholesterol is a soft, waxy material found in cell membranes and transported in your blood stream. It is partly produced by your body and partly absorbed from animal products that you eat, e.g. eggs, meat and dairy products. There are two types of cholesterol — 'good' cholesterol and 'bad' cholesterol.

Bad cholesterol can clog blood vessels, which increases the risk of heart attacks and strokes. Good cholesterol removes bad cholesterol, taking it to the liver to be destroyed. So high levels of good cholesterol can give protection from heart disease.

Recent research has shown that **trans fats** increase the amount of bad cholesterol and decrease the amount of good cholesterol. Trans fats are triglycerides made from trans fatty acids. They are almost all man-made and are used in many foods such as biscuits, cakes, chips and crisps. Because of recent health concerns, there have been moves to reduce their use and more clearly label foods that contain them (there's more on collecting evidence and decision making on pages 3-4 of the How Science Works section). Bad cholesterol is also increased by eating saturated fats (made from fatty acids with no double bonds). They occur in animal products but much less so in plants.

Plant oils such as olive and sunflower oils contain unsaturated fats. These can be polyunsaturated (several double bonds) or monounsaturated (one double bond per chain). Polyunsaturated oils have been shown to reduce "bad" cholesterol and are actually a good thing to eat in moderation to prevent heart disease. They can help counteract obesity if they're used instead of saturated fats.

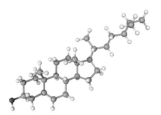

Figure 1: *Molecular model of cholesterol.*

Biodiesel

Biodiesel is a renewable fuel made from vegetable oil or animal fats that can be used in diesel engines. It is gaining popularity as a viable alternative to crude oil-based diesel.

Biodiesel is mainly a mixture of methyl and ethyl esters of fatty acids. It's made by reacting triglycerides (oils or fats) with methanol or ethanol in the presence of a potassium hydroxide (KOH) catalyst.

Figure 2: *A biodiesel fuel pump.*

Tip: This equation is very similar if you're making biodiesel from ethanol — you'll just get ethyl esters ($RCOOCH_2CH_3$) instead of methyl esters.

$$
\text{Fat/Oil} + 3CH_3OH \xrightarrow[\text{(catalyst)}]{KOH} \text{Glycerol (propane-1,2,3-triol)} + 3\,R\text{–C}\diagdown\!\!\!{}^{O}_{O\text{–}CH_3}
$$

R = long carbon chain

Methyl ester (biodiesel is a mixture of methyl and ethyl esters)

The vegetable oils used in the process can be new, low grade oil or waste oil from chip shops and restaurants. Animal fats that can be used include chicken fat, waste fish oil and lard from meat processing.

At present, biodiesel is mainly used mixed with conventional diesel, rather than in pure form. B20 fuel contains 20% biodiesel and 80% conventional diesel. Diesel engines generally need converting before they're able to run B100 fuel (100% biodiesel).

There is debate about how feasible large-scale use of biodiesel is — to produce significant quantities would mean devoting huge areas of land to growing biodiesel crops (e.g. rapeseed and soy beans) rather than food crops. The worry is that people in developing countries may decide to grow biodiesel crops instead of food crops because of the greater profit margins. This could mean that the amount of food available to local people decreases. (There's more on science and decision making in the How Science Works section on page 4.)

HOW SCIENCE WORKS

Exam Tip
If you're asked to talk about the advantages and disadvantages of the increased use of biodiesel, remember to talk about both. You'll lose marks if you don't.

Practice Question — Application

Q1 Below is a triester commonly found in vegetable oils.

$$\begin{array}{c} H \quad\quad O \\ | \qu\quad\quad || \\ H-C-O-C-(CH_2)_{14}CH_3 \\ | \qu\quad\quad O \\ \qu\quad\quad || \\ H-C-O-C-(CH_2)_{14}CH_3 \\ | \qu\quad\quad O \\ \qu\quad\quad || \\ H-C-O-C-(CH_2)_{14}CH_3 \\ | \\ H \end{array}$$

a) Write an equation for the conversion of this ester into biofuel.

b) Suggest a suitable catalyst for this reaction.

Practice Questions — Fact Recall

Q1 a) What is cholesterol?

b) Give one positive effect of having 'good cholesterol' in the body.

Q2 Explain why there have been moves to reduce the amount of trans fats in our food.

Q3 Why are polyunsaturated oils good for you when eaten in moderation?

Q4 How is biodiesel made?

Q5 Give one advantage and one disadvantage of using biodiesel.

Figure 3: *Lots of food companies have stopped using trans fats in their products.*

Learning Objectives:

- Be able to explain the basicity of amines in terms of proton acceptance by the nitrogen lone pair.

- Be able to describe the reactions of amines with acids to form salts.

- Be able to describe the preparation of aliphatic amines by substitution of halogenoalkanes with excess ethanolic ammonia.

- Be able to describe the preparation of aromatic amines by reduction of nitroarenes using tin and concentrated hydrochloric acid.

Specification Reference 4.1.4

Tip: If you need a reminder on the basic rules of how to name organic compounds, have a look back at your AS notes.

Tip: Bacisity is a measure of how good a base a compound is.

11. Amines

Well, a new functional group — I bet you're dizzy with excitement. Amines are produced from ammonia (NH_3) and this topic will tell you all about them...

What are amines?

If one or more of the hydrogens in ammonia (NH_3) is replaced with an organic group, you get an **amine**. If one hydrogen is replaced with an organic group, you get a primary amine — if two are replaced, it's a secondary amine, three means it's a tertiary amine and if a fourth organic group is added it's called a quaternary ammonium ion (see Figure 1).

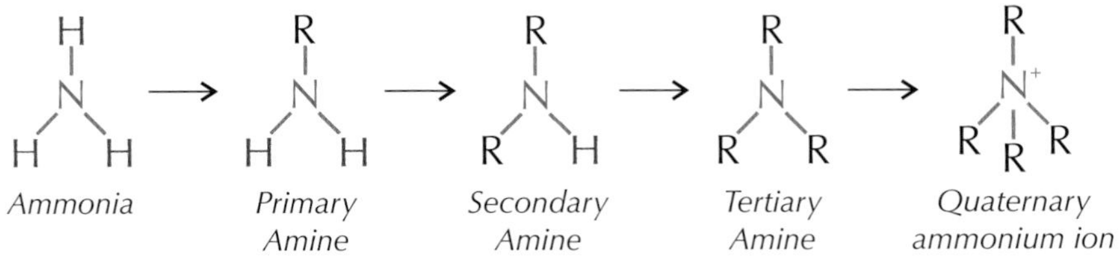

Figure 1: *Diagram showing the different types of amine.*

Small amines smell similar to ammonia, with a slightly 'fishy' twist. Larger amines smell very 'fishy'.

Naming amines

Naming amines is similar to naming other organic compounds. The suffix is -amine (or -amine ion if it's a quaternary ammonium ion). The prefix depends on what organic groups are attached. If the organic groups are all the same you also need to add di- for secondary amines, tri- for tertiary amines and tetra- for quaternary ammonium ions.

--- Examples ---

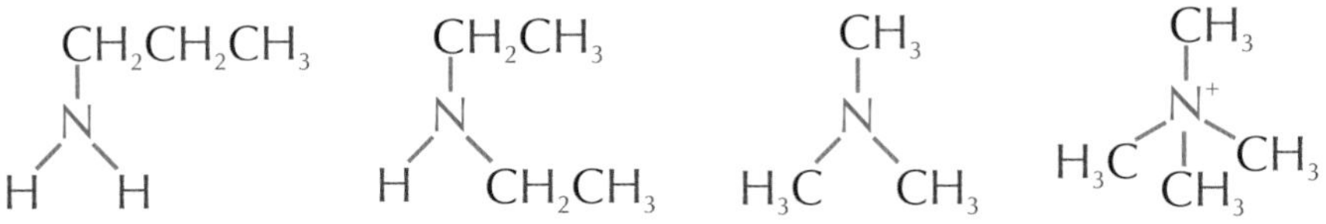

Propylamine   Diethylamine   Trimethylamine   Tetramethylamine ion

If the amine has more than one type of organic group attached, you list the different groups in alphabetical order.

--- Example ---

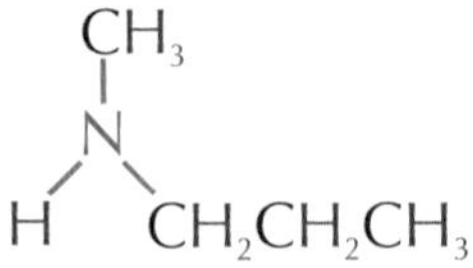

This is a secondary amine. It has a methyl group and a propyl group attached.
So this is methylpropylamine.

The bacisity of amines

In amines, the lone pair of electrons on the nitrogen atom can form a dative (coordinate) bond with an H^+ ion — the amine donates its lone pair of electrons and 'accepts' the proton (see Figure 2).

Dative bonds are covalent bonds where both electrons have come from the same atom.

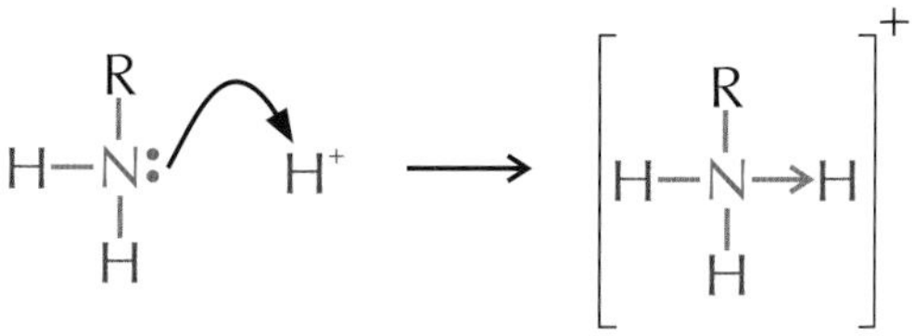

$$H-\underset{\underset{H}{|}}{\overset{\overset{R}{|}}{N}}\colon \curvearrowright \quad H^+ \quad \longrightarrow \quad \left[H-\underset{\underset{H}{|}}{\overset{\overset{R}{|}}{N}}\to H \right]^+$$

Figure 2: *Formation of a dative bond between a primary amine and an H^+ ion.*

Bases can be defined as proton acceptors or electron donors. An amine can accept a proton (H^+ ion) by donating its lone pair of electrons — so amines are bases.

Amine salts
Amines are neutralised by acids to make ammonium salts.

┌─ **Examples** ─────────────────────────

Methylamine reacts with hydrochloric acid to form methylammonium chloride:

$$CH_3NH_2 + HCl \rightarrow CH_3NH_3^+Cl^-$$

Ethylamine reacts with sulfuric acid to form diethylammonium sulfate:

$$2CH_3CH_2NH_2 + H_2SO_4 \rightarrow (CH_3CH_2NH_3^+)_2SO_4^{2-}$$

Figure 3: *A student testing an amine solution using litmus paper. The paper has turned blue, showing that the solution is alkaline.*

Producing Amines
Producing aliphatic amines from haloalkanes
Amines can be made by heating a haloalkane with an excess of ethanolic ammonia (that's just ammonia dissolved in ethanol).

Tip: Aliphatic amines are amines without a benzene ring. Amines with a benzene ring are called aromatic amines.

┌─ **Example** ──────────────────────────

Ethylamine can be produced by heating bromoethane with ammonia:

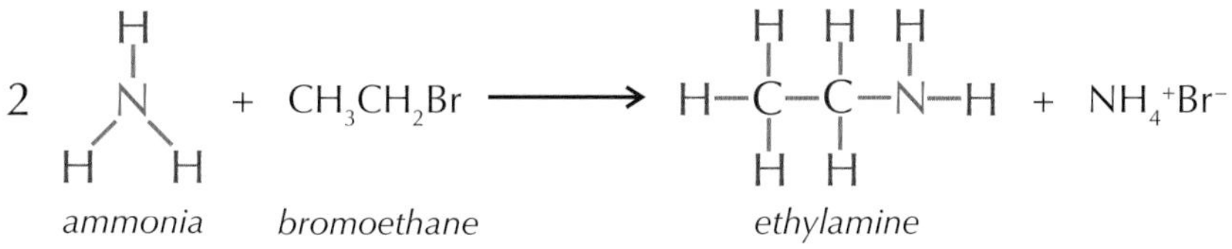

$$2 \quad \underset{\underset{H \quad H}{}}{N} \quad + \quad CH_3CH_2Br \quad \longrightarrow \quad H-\underset{\underset{H}{|}}{\overset{\overset{H}{|}}{C}}-\underset{\underset{H}{|}}{\overset{\overset{H}{|}}{C}}-\underset{}{\overset{\overset{H}{|}}{N}}-H \quad + \quad NH_4^+Br^-$$

ammonia   *bromoethane*   *ethylamine*

But, things aren't that simple. You'll actually get a mixture of primary, secondary and tertiary amines, and quaternary ammonium salts, as more than one hydrogen is likely to be substituted.

┌─ **Example** ──────────────────────────

When producing ethylamine you'll actually get a mixture of ethylamine, diethylamine, triethylamine and tetraethylamine ions:

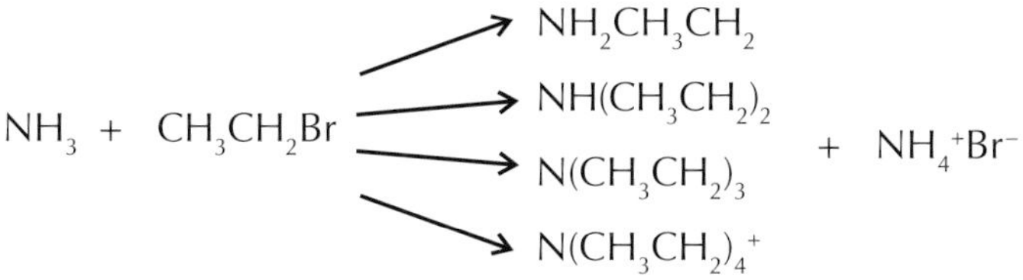

$$NH_3 + CH_3CH_2Br \quad \begin{array}{l} \nearrow NH_2CH_3CH_2 \\ \rightarrow NH(CH_3CH_2)_2 \\ \rightarrow N(CH_3CH_2)_3 \\ \searrow N(CH_3CH_2)_4^+ \end{array} \quad + \quad NH_4^+Br^-$$

Tip: If you use an excess of ammonia the bromoethane molecules are more likely to bump into ammonia molecules than secondary or tertiary amines, so you'll increase the yield of the primary amine. If you use an excess of bromoethane, the reverse is true and you'll increase the yield of the quaternary ammonium ions.

You can separate the products using distillation if you're trying to make one particular amine.

Exam Tip
If you're asked to draw a dative covalent bond in the exam don't forget to put the species in brackets and add the charge (if there is one).

Producing aromatic amines by reducing a nitro compound

Aromatic amines are produced by reducing an aromatic nitro compound, such as nitrobenzene. There are two steps to the method:

- First you need to heat a mixture of a nitro compound, tin metal and concentrated hydrochloric acid under reflux — this makes a salt.
- Then to turn the salt into an aromatic amine, you need to add an alkali, such as sodium hydroxide solution.

Tip: You saw how to make nitrobenzene from benzene on page 11.

--- Example ---

Phenylamine can be made by reducing nitrobenzene:

- Mixing nitrobenzene with tin and concentrated HCl and heating under reflux produces the salt $C_6H_5NH_3^+ Cl^-$.
- Adding NaOH to this salt then releases phenylamine.

Here's the overall equation for the reaction:

$$NO_2 \text{ (Nitrobenzene)} + 6[H] \xrightarrow[\substack{\text{reflux} \\ 2.\ NaOH_{(aq)}}]{1.\ Sn,\ conc.\ HCl} NH_2 \text{ (Phenylamine)} + 2H_2O$$

Nitrobenzene   *Phenylamine*

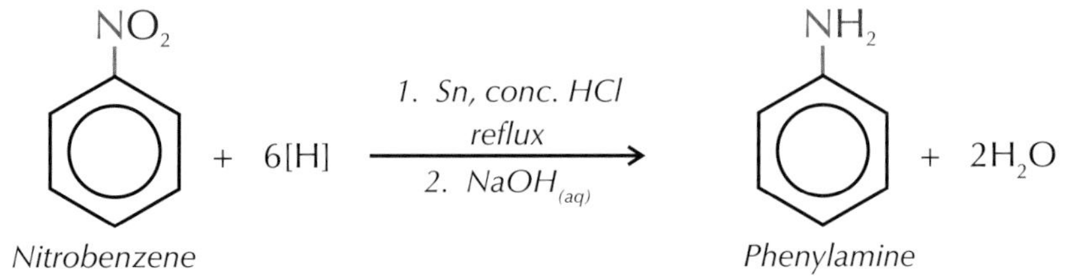

Tip: The [H] in the equation represents the reducing agent (which is the Sn/HCl mixture here).

Practice Questions — Application

Q1 Name these amines:

a) CH_2CH_3 — N — H, H

b) $CH_2CH_2CH_3$ — N — H, $CH_2CH_2CH_3$

c) CH_3 — N — H_3C, CH_2CH_3

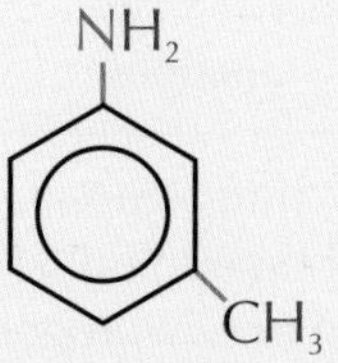

Tip: Don't forget that you list alkyl groups in alphabetical order when you're naming molecules. (You can ignore any di-s or tri-s at the front though.)

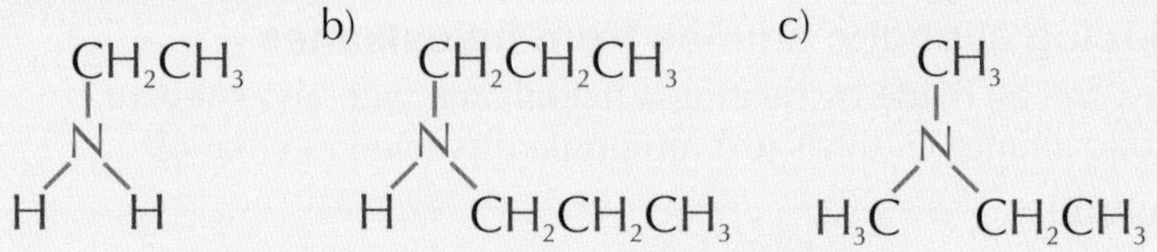

Q2 Write an equation for the reaction between trimethylamine ($N(CH_3)_3$) and hydrochloric acid.

Q3 Write an equation to show the formation of methylamine from chloromethane.

Q4 Write an equation to show the formation of 3-methylphenylamine from 3-methylnitrobenzene. The structure of 3-methylphenylamine is shown on the right.

Practice Questions — Fact Recall

Q1 What is a quaternary ammonium ion?

Q2 Explain why amines can act as bases.

Q3 a) How can an amine be produced from a haloalkane?

   b) Explain why a mixture of primary, secondary, tertiary and quaternary amines are produced in these reactions.

   c) How can the products of these reactions be separated?

Q4 Describe how aromatic amines can be produced.

12. Azo Dyes

Azo dyes are used to colour lots of products like food and paint. Azo molecules look a bit scary, but fear not — this topic will help you get to grips with them.

What are azo dyes?

Azo dyes are man-made dyes that contain the azo group, $-N=N-$. In most azo dyes, the azo group links two aromatic groups. Having two aromatic groups creates a very stable molecule — the azo group becomes part of the delocalised electron system (see page 6).

┌─ Example ─────────────────────────────────

Methyl orange is a typical azo compound with the azo group -N=N- linking two aromatic groups.

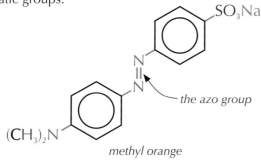

methyl orange

└──

Azo dyes all have characteristic colours which make them really useful colouring agents (see next page). The colours are the result of light absorption by the delocalised electron system. Different colours are made by combining different phenols and amines.

Producing azo dyes

The first step in creating an azo dye is to make a **diazonium salt** — diazonium compounds contain the group:

$$-\overset{+}{N}\equiv N-$$

The azo dye is then made by coupling the diazonium salt with an aromatic compound that is susceptible to electrophilic attack — like a phenol.

┌─ Example ─────────────────────────────────

Here's the method for creating a yellow-orange azo dye:

Step 1: React phenylamine with nitrous acid to make a diazonium salt

Nitrous acid (HNO_2) is unstable, so it has to be made in situ from sodium nitrite and hydrochloric acid.

$$NaNO_2 + HCl \rightarrow HNO_2 + NaCl$$

Nitrous acid reacts with phenylamine and hydrochloric acid to form benzenediazonium chloride. The temperature must be below 10 °C to prevent a phenol forming instead.

phenylamine   nitrous acid   benzenediazonium chloride

└──

Learning Objectives:

- Be able to describe the synthesis of an azo dye by reaction of an aromatic amine with nitrous acid (<10 °C), with formation of a diazonium ion, followed by coupling with a phenol under alkaline conditions.

- Know the use of reactions, such as the synthesis of azo dyes, in the formation of dyestuffs.

Specification Reference 4.1.4

Figure 1: *The German chemist, Peter Griess. Griess discovered azo dyes in 1862.*

Tip: 'In situ' means in the reaction here.

Step 2: Make the azo dye by coupling the diazonium salt with a phenol

First, the phenol has to be dissolved in sodium hydroxide solution to make sodium phenoxide solution. It's then stood in ice, and chilled benzenediazonium chloride is added.

Here's the overall equation for the reaction:

benzenediazonium chloride + phenol + NaOH

chilled in ice

→ yellow-orange azo compound —N=N—...—OH + NaCl + H₂O

The azo dye precipitates out of the solution immediately.

In this reaction phenol acts as a coupling agent. The lone pairs on its oxygen increase the electron density of the benzene ring, especially around carbons 2, 4 and 6. This gives the diazonium ion (a weak electrophile) something to attack.

Exam Tip
This equation is written down the page here so that it fits nicely. In the exam you can write it from left to right (if there's space). But whichever way you do it you'll get the marks as long as it's clear what you mean.

Tip: Remember — electrophile means 'electron lover'.

Uses of azo dyes

Azo dyes produce bright, vivid colours, most of them in the yellow to red spectrum, though many other colours are possible too. Azo dyes make up about 70% of all dyes used in food and textiles.

Many azo dyes are used as food colourings (and so they have corresponding E numbers). Examples include tartrazine (E102), yellow 2G (E107), allura red (E129) and brilliant black BN (E151), but there are many, many others.

Because the molecules are very stable, azo dyes provide lightfast (i.e. strong light won't fade them), permanent colours for clothing. They are added to materials like clay to produce paint pigments. Some azo dyes are used as indicators, for example methyl orange, because they change colour at different pHs.

In recent years there has been a lot of concern about the use of artificial additives in food. Some azo compounds that were previously used in foods have since been banned for health reasons — enzymes in the body can break some of them down to produce toxic or carcinogenic compounds. Others have been linked to hyperactivity in children.

Figure 2: *Worker at a factory in India that manufactures azo dyes.*

Practice Question — Application

Q1 Below is the structure of azorubine, a synthetic red food dye.

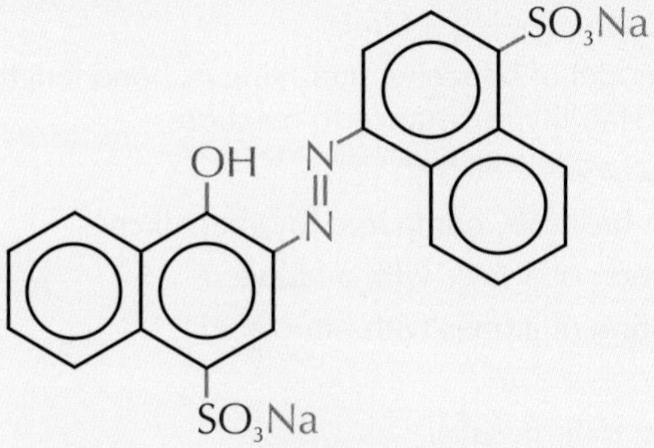

Azorubine

a) Draw the structure of the phenol and the diazonium salt that could be reacted to produce azorubine.

b) Write the equation for the production of the diazonium salt drawn in part a).

c) Write an equation for the formation of azorubine.

Exam Tip
You might get given quite complex molecules like this to answer questions on in the exam. Don't panic. You just have to identify the main functional groups and treat them like you would any other smaller molecule.

Practice Questions — Fact Recall

Q1 What are azo dyes?

Q2 Explain why the presence of benzene rings in azo dyes leads to a very stable structure.

Q3 Write down an equation for the production of nitrous acid (HNO_2).

Q4 Why must diazonium salts be made at a temperature below 10 °C?

Q5 Give two uses of azo dyes.

Q6 Recently some azo compounds have been banned for use in foods. Explain why.

Section Summary

Make sure you know...

- The Kekulé and delocalised models of benzene.
- The evidence that supports the delocalised model of benzene, including its bond lengths, its enthalpy change of hydrogenation and its stability (resistance to reaction).
- How to name aromatic compounds.
- Why it's difficult to get benzene to react with bromine, compared to other alkenes.
- The mechanism for the electrophilic substitution of arenes with a halogen.
- The mechanism for the electrophilic substitution of arenes with nitric acid.
- What phenols are and how to name them.
- That phenol will react with bases and sodium to form salts.
- Why phenol reacts more easily with bromine than benzene does.
- How phenol reacts with bromine to form 2,4,6-tribromophenol.
- That phenols are used to make polymers, antiseptics, disinfectants and resins for paints.
- What aldehydes and ketones are and how to name them.
- That you can oxidise alcohols using acidified potassium dichromate(VI) ($K_2Cr_2O_7/H_2SO_4$).
- How primary alcohols can be oxidised to form aldehydes or carboxylic acids.
- How aldehydes can be oxidised to form carboxylic acids.
- How secondary alcohols can be oxidised to form ketones.
- That you can reduce aldehydes and ketones to alcohols using $NaBH_4$.
- The mechanism for the nucleophilic addition reaction of an aldehyde or a ketone with $NaBH_4$.
- That you can use Brady's reagent (2,4-dinitrophenylhydrazine) to test for a carbonyl group.
- How to use Brady's reagent to identify a carbonyl compound from the melting point of the derivative.
- That you can use Tollens' reagent to distinguish between aldehydes and ketones.
- What carboxylic acids are and how to name them.
- That carboxylic acids are soluble in water because they form hydrogen bonds with water molecules.
- The reactions of carboxylic acids with metals, carbonates and bases.
- What esters are and how to name them.
- How to make esters using carboxylic acids and alcohols or acid anhydrides and alcohols.
- The reactions for the acid and base hydrolysis of esters.
- That esters are used in perfumes and flavourings.
- What fatty acids and triglycerides are.
- How to name fatty acids using the systematic and shorthand naming systems.
- That unsaturated fatty acids exist or cis and trans forms, and that trans fatty acids may cause an increases in 'bad' cholesterol in the body (which increases the risk of heart attacks and strokes).
- What biodiesel is and why it is increasingly being used instead of diesel.
- What amines are and how to name them.
- That amines are bases and can donate their lone pair to a proton to form a dative bond.
- The reactions of amines with acids to form ammonium salts.
- That you can make amines from halogenoalkanes and ammonia.
- How to make aromatic amines by reducing aromatic nitro compounds with tin and hydrochloric acid.
- How to make azo dyes.
- That azo dyes can be used as food colourings, paint pigments, clothing dyes and indicators.

Exam-style Questions

1   A scientist is trying to synthesise the explosive picryl chloride (1-chloro-2,4,6-trinitrobenzene) from benzene. The synthesis route used by the scientist is shown below.

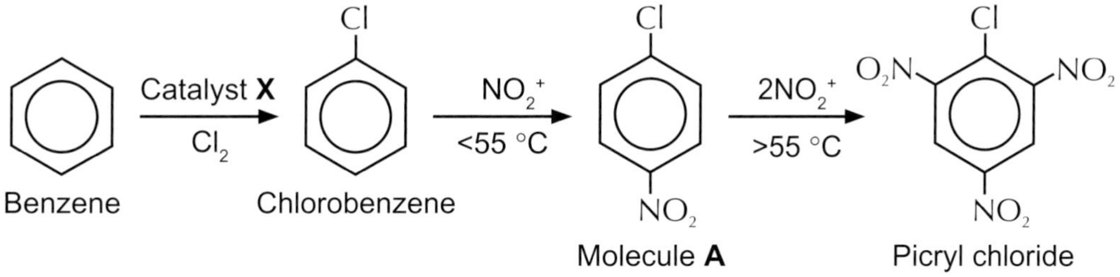

(a) (i) Give the catalyst (Catalyst **X**) required to produce chlorobenzene from benzene.

(1 mark)

(ii) Describe the role of Catalyst **X** in the reaction between benzene and Cl_2.

(3 marks)

(b) (i) Write an equation for the production of the NO_2^+ ion in the second step of this synthesis.

(1 mark)

(ii) Draw the mechanism for the reaction of NO_2^+ with chlorobenzene to produce Molecule **A**.

(4 marks)

(iii) Name Molecule **A**.

(1 mark)

(c)   The scientist heats the picryl chloride with tin and concentrated hydrochloric acid under reflux to form Molecule **B**.

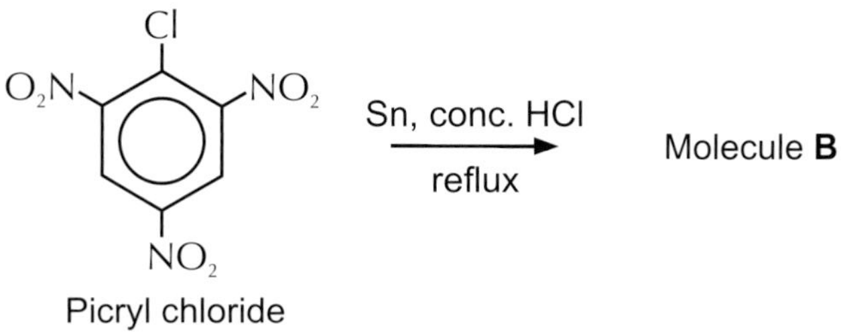

Picryl chloride

(i) Draw the structure of molecule **B**.

(1 mark)

(ii) Write an overall equation for this reaction.
Use [H] to represent the reducing agent.

(2 marks)

2   The following molecules are all derived from propane.

$$H-\overset{\overset{\displaystyle H}{|}}{\underset{\underset{\displaystyle H}{|}}{C}}-\overset{\overset{\displaystyle H}{|}}{\underset{\underset{\displaystyle H}{|}}{C}}-\overset{\overset{\displaystyle O}{\|}}{C}-H \qquad H-\overset{\overset{\displaystyle H}{|}}{\underset{\underset{\displaystyle H}{|}}{C}}-\overset{\overset{\displaystyle H}{|}}{\underset{\underset{\displaystyle H}{|}}{C}}-\overset{\overset{\displaystyle O}{\|}}{C}-OH \qquad H-\overset{\overset{\displaystyle H}{|}}{\underset{\underset{\displaystyle H}{|}}{C}}-\overset{\overset{\displaystyle O}{\|}}{C}-\overset{\overset{\displaystyle H}{|}}{\underset{\underset{\displaystyle H}{|}}{C}}-H$$

   Molecule **X**   Molecule **Y**   Molecule **Z**

(a)   Name molecules **X**, **Y** and **Z**.

(3 marks)

(b)   Molecule **Z** can be reduced to an alcohol using a hydride ion.
   (i)   Give a reducing agent that you could use for this reaction.

(1 mark)

   (ii)   Draw the mechanism for the reaction of Molecule **Z** with H⁻.

(4 marks)

   (iii) Write the equation for this reaction using [H] to represent the reducing agent.

(2 marks)

(c)   Molecule **Y** is a carboxylic acid.
   (i)   Explain why Molecule **Y** is soluble in water.

(2 marks)

   (ii)   Write an equation for the reaction of molecule **Y** with sodium carbonate (Na_2CO_3).

(2 marks)

(d) (i)   State the reagents and conditions needed to produce molecule **X** from propan-1-ol.

(2 marks)

   (ii)   A student carries out this reaction in a lab. They observed that during
   the reaction the mixture turned from orange to green.

   Identify the ions that were responsible for the colour of the solution
   before and after the reaction took place.

(2 marks)

(e)   Compounds **X**, **Y** and **Z** are treated with Brady's reagent and Tollens' reagent.

   Explain how you could distinguish between molecules **X**, **Y** and **Z**
   using the results of these reactions.

(3 marks)

3   Explain why scientists now believe that the delocalised model for the structure of
   benzene (C_6H_6) is more accurate than the Kekulé model.
   Include in your answer a description of the evidence supporting the delocalised model.

   In your answer, you should use appropriate technical terms, spelled correctly.

(6 marks)

4   A food scientist is doing some research into what makes food taste stale.
He has isolated a sample of an aromatic carbonyl compound that he believes is
present in many stale foods.

(a)   Explain how the scientist could identify his compound
using 2,4-dinitrophenylhydrazine (2,4-DNPH).

(3 marks)

(b)   The structure of the compound that the scientist has isolated is shown below.

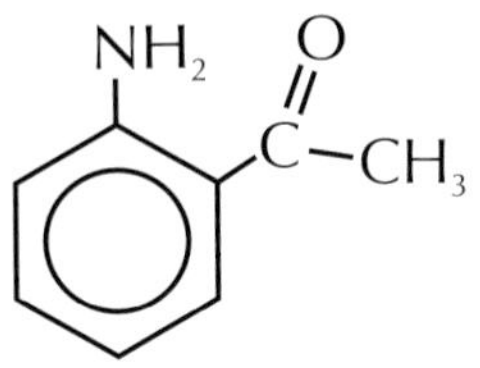

(i)   Identify all of the functional groups present in this compound,
other than the benzene ring.

(2 marks)

(ii)   The scientist observes that the compound he has isolated can act as a base.
Explain why this is the case.

(2 marks)

5   The azo dye below, Molecule **K**, can be used as an indicator.

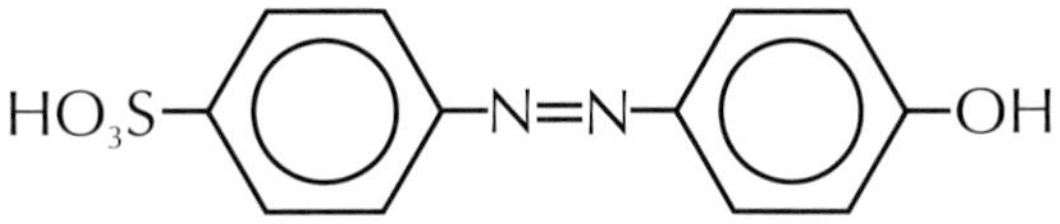

Molecule **K**

(a) (i)   Draw the structure of the diazonium salt used to prepare Molecule **K**.

(1 mark)

(ii)   What conditions must be used when preparing the diazonium salt
from an aromatic amine?

(2 marks)

(b)   In the second step of the process used to prepare the azo dye,
phenol is dissolved in sodium hydroxide solution.

Write an equation for the reaction of phenol with NaOH.

(1 mark)

(c)   Write down the overall equation for the production of Molecule **K** from
the diazonium salt drawn in part **(a) (i)**, phenol and sodium hydroxide.

(2 marks)

(d)   State one use of azo dyes other than as indicators.

(1 mark)

6   All of the fats and oils that we eat contain triglycerides.
The structure of one triglyceride, Triglyceride **T**, is shown below.

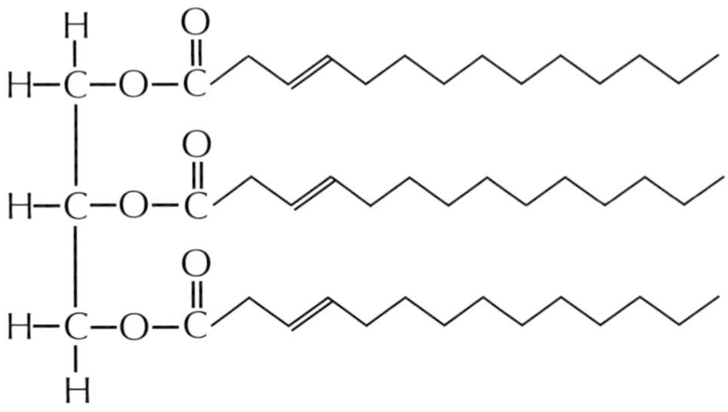

Triglyceride **T**

(a) (i)   Write an equation for the formation of Triglyceride **T**.
Use 'R' to represent the long hydrocarbon chains of the fatty acids.

(2 marks)

(ii)   Give the systematic name of the fatty acid used to produce Triglyceride **T**.

(1 mark)

(b)   The fatty acid used to synthesise Triglyceride **T** is a trans fatty acid.

(i)   Explain what this means for the shape of the fatty acid molecule.

(1 mark)

(ii)   Explain why it may be bad for your health to eat foods which are high in trans fats.

(3 marks)

(c)   Triglyceride **T** can be used to make biodiesel.

(i)   Write an equation for the production of biodiesel from methanol and Triglyceride **T**.
Use 'R' to represent the long hydrocarbon chains of the fatty acids.

(2 marks)

(ii)   Suggest a catalyst that could be used to carry out this reaction.

(1 mark)

(iii) Give one advantage of switching fuels from diesel to biodiesel.

(1 mark)

(d)   Triglyceride **T** contains three ester functional groups. This means that
it can be hydrolysed to split it back up into fatty acids and glycerol.

Name the reagents and conditions needed to carry out the acid hydrolysis
of Triglyceride **T**.

(2 marks)

1. Addition Polymers

Learning Objective:
- Be able to identify the monomer(s) required to form a given section of an addition polymer and vice versa.

Specification Reference 4.2.2

Lots of small molecules (called monomers) can join together to form really long molecules (called polymers). Polymers that are formed from alkenes are called addition polymers. You met these at AS-level but here's a recap...

What are addition polymers?

The double bonds in alkenes can break and then join together to make long chains called **addition polymers**. It's like they're holding hands in a big line. The individual, small alkenes are called **monomers** and the process of making an addition polymer is called addition polymerisation.

Example

Polyphenylethene is made by the addition polymerisation of phenylethene:

Double bond breaks

Lots of monomers join together

phenylethene
(monomer)

section of polyphenylethene
(polymer)

Tip: Polyphenylethene is more commonly known as polystyrene.

Figure 1: Two different forms of polyphenylethene. Expanded polyphenylethene is used in packaging and high density polyphenylethene is used to make plastic models.

Repeating units

Addition polymers are made up of repeating units (a bit of molecule that repeats over and over again). The repeating unit looks very similar to the monomer but the double bond has opened out. You need to be able to draw repeating units from the structure of a monomer and vice versa.

Examples

Polychloroethene is made from chloroethene. To draw the repeating unit of polychloroethene just replace the double bond in chloroethene with a single bond and add a bond to each of the carbons:

These bonds join on to the next repeating unit.

chloroethene
(monomer)

repeating unit of
polychloroethene

Because of the loss of the double bond, addition polymers, like alkanes, are unreactive.

The repeating unit of polypropene is shown below. To draw the monomer of polypropene just remove the empty bonds (which join on to the next repeating unit) and replace the central carbon-carbon bond with a double bond:

Tip: The names of polymers can be written with or without the brackets — e.g. poly(propene) or polypropene.

repeating unit of polypropene

propene (monomer)

Practice Questions — Application

Q1 Draw the monomers that formed these repeating units:

a)

b)

c)

Tip: There isn't too much to learn about addition polymers but you're going to need to know about condensation polymers too — they're covered in the next topic.

Q2 Draw the repeating units of the polymers that would be formed from these monomers:

a)

b)

c)

Q3 Draw two repeating units of the polymer that would form from 1-chloro-2-fluoroethene. The structure of 1-chloro-2-fluoroethene is shown below:

Q4 Teflon® is a polymer commonly used to coat non-stick pans. The structure of a short stretch of Teflon® is shown below.

Figure 2: *A Teflon® coated frying pan.*

a) Draw the repeating unit of Teflon®.
b) Draw the structure of the monomer that's used to make Teflon®.

Practice Questions — Fact Recall

Q1 What types of monomers form addition polymers?
Q2 What name is given to the process of forming an addition polymer?
Q3 What is a repeating unit?
Q4 Are addition polymers reactive or unreactive?

2. Condensation Polymers

Addition polymers aren't the only types of polymers you need to know about at A2-level. You also need to know about condensation polymers — they're a bit different. Read on to find out more...

What are condensation polymers?

Condensation polymerisation usually involves two different types of monomer. Each monomer has at least two functional groups. The functional groups react to form a link, creating polymer chains. Each time a link is formed, a small molecule is lost (often water) — that's why it's called condensation polymerisation.

     Examples of **condensation polymers** include polyamides, polyesters and polypeptides (or proteins). In polyesters, an ester link (–COO–) is formed between the monomers. In polyamides and polypeptides, amide links (–CONH–) are formed between the monomers. In polypeptides, these amide links are usually called peptide bonds.

Polyamides

Reactions between dicarboxylic acids and diamines make **polyamides**. The carboxyl groups of dicarboxylic acids react with the amino groups of diamines to form **amide links**. A water molecule is lost each time an amide link is formed — it's a condensation reaction (see Figure 1).

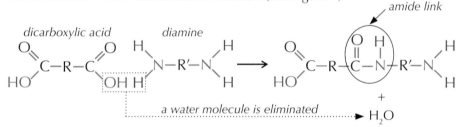

Figure 1: *The formation of an amide link.*

Dicarboxylic acids and diamines have functional groups at both ends, which means that they can each form two amide links and long chains can form.

Examples

Nylon 6,6 is made from hexane-1,6-dicarboxylic acid and 1,6-diaminohexane:

hexane-1,6-dicarboxylic acid   *1,6-diaminohexane*

$+ 2nH_2O$

nylon 6,6

Nylon fibre is very strong, elastic and quite abrasion-resistant (it won't wear away easily).

Learning Objectives:

- Be able to describe condensation polymerisation to form:
  (i) polyesters, e.g. Terylene™ from benzene-1,4-dicarboxylic acid and ethane-1,2-diol, poly(lactic acid) from 2-hydroxypropanoic acid (lactic acid).
  (ii) polyamides, e.g. nylon-6,6 from 1,6-diaminohexane and hexane-1,6-dicarboxylic acid, Kevlar® from benzene-1,4-diamine and benzene-1,4-dicarboxylic acid.

- Know the use of polyesters and polyamides as fibres in clothing.

- Be able to identify the monomer(s) required to form a given section of a condensation polymer and vice versa.

- Be able to compare condensation polymerisation with addition polymerisation.

- Be able to suggest the type of polymerisation from:
  (i) a given monomer or pair of monomers.
  (ii) a given section of a polymer molecule.

Specification Reference 4.2.2

Tip: The formation of polyamides is very similar to the formation of polyesters (next page) and polypeptides (covered on page 56).

Kevlar® is made from benzene-1,4-dicarboxylic acid and benzene-1,4-diamine:

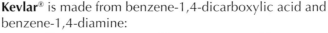

Figure 2: Kevlar® is used to make bulletproof clothing.

Kevlar® is really strong and light — five times stronger than steel. It's not stretchy, and is quite stiff. It's most famous for its use in bulletproof vests.

Polyesters

The carboxyl groups of dicarboxylic acids can react with the hydroxyl groups of diols to form **ester links** — it's another condensation reaction (see Figure 3).

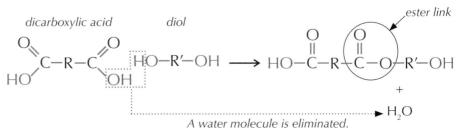

Figure 3: The formation of an ester link.

Polymers that are joined by ester links are called **polyesters**. Polyester fibres are used in clothing — they are strong (but not as strong as nylon), flexible and abrasion-resistant.

Figure 4: SEM of synthetic polyester fibres.

Examples

Terylene™ (PET) is formed from benzene-1,4-dicarboxylic acid and ethane-1,2-diol.

Terylene™ is used in clothes to keep them crease-free and make them last longer.

Figure 5: The containers that microwave meals come in are made of Terylene™.

Poly(lactic acid) (PLA) is made from lactic acid (2-hydroxypropanoic acid). Lactic acid monomers can form polymers on their own because they contain both a hydroxy group and a carboxylic acid group.

lactic acid
(2-hydroxypropanoic acid)

poly(lactic acid)
(PLA)

Poly(lactic acid) is a biodegradable and renewable polymer.

Tip: See page 54 for more on poly(lactic acid) and its uses.

Figure 6: *A cup made out of poly(lactic acid) or PLA. This cup is made from renewable materials and is biodegradable.*

Identifying monomers and polymers

In your exam, you might be asked to identify the monomers that formed a particular condensation polymer. To do this just follow these steps:

- Remove the bond in the middle of the amide or ester links — that's the bond between the C=O group and the NH group in polyamides and the bond between the C=O group and the oxygen in polyesters.
- Add OH groups on to the C=O groups to make carboxyl groups.
- For polyamides, add hydrogens on to the NH groups to make NH$_2$ groups
- For polyesters, add hydrogens on to the oxygens to make OH groups and add OH groups on to any terminal carbon atoms.

┌─ **Example** ─────────────────────────────────────

Draw the monomers that formed this condensation polymer:

This is a polyamide so if you remove the bond in the middle of the amide link you get:

and

Adding an OH group on to the C=O groups gives you:

And adding a hydrogen on to each of the NH groups gives you:

So these must be the monomers that joined to form the polymer.

Tip: This example is a polyamide. You do exactly the same for a polyester but you end up with a dicarboxylic acid and a diol.

Exam Tip
Don't be caught out — there won't necessarily be two different monomers. There could be one monomer with a COOH <u>and</u> an NH group on it.

You could also be asked to identify the polymer formed from two monomers, in which case you'd do the opposite — remove a hydrogen from the OH or NH$_2$, remove the OH group from the carboxyl group and draw the bond to form the amide or ester link.

Practice Questions — Application

Tip: If you think that a polymer was made from only one monomer, you'll need to look at both ends of the repeating unit to work out what type of polymer (polyester or polyamide) it is.

Q1 Identify whether the following are formulas of polyesters or polyamides and draw the monomer(s) they were formed from.

a)

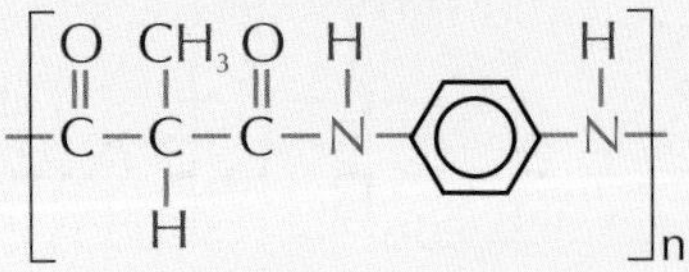

b)

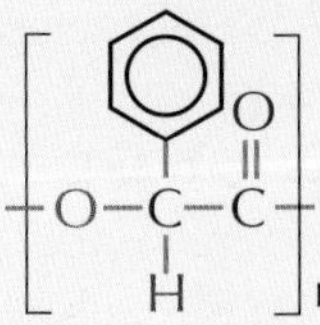

c)

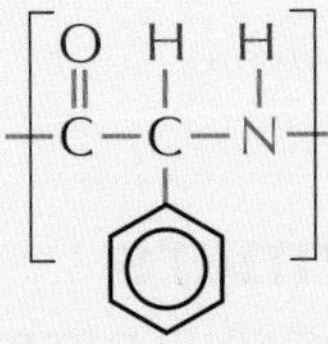

d)

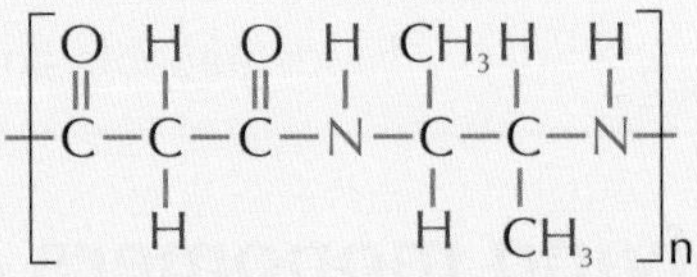

e)

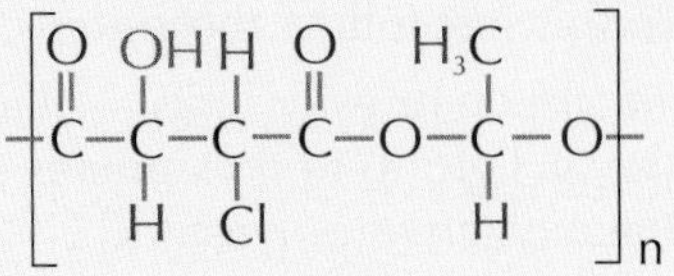

Exam Tip
In the exam, you could also be asked to compare condensation polymers with addition polymers (which were covered on pages 47-48). So you need to know the details of both types of polymerisation.

Q2 Draw the repeating units of the polymers that would be formed from these monomers:

a)

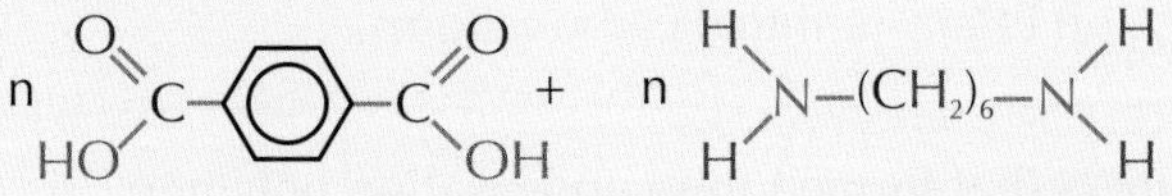

b)

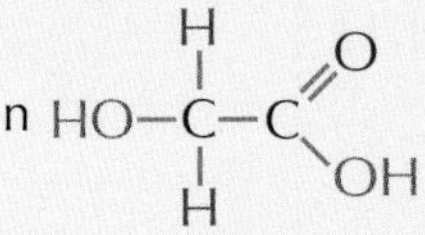

c)

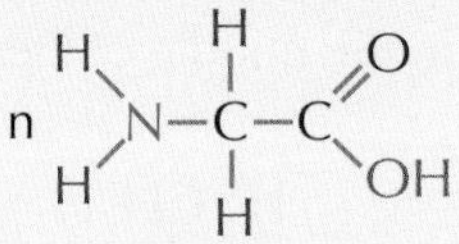

d)

Practice Questions — Fact Recall

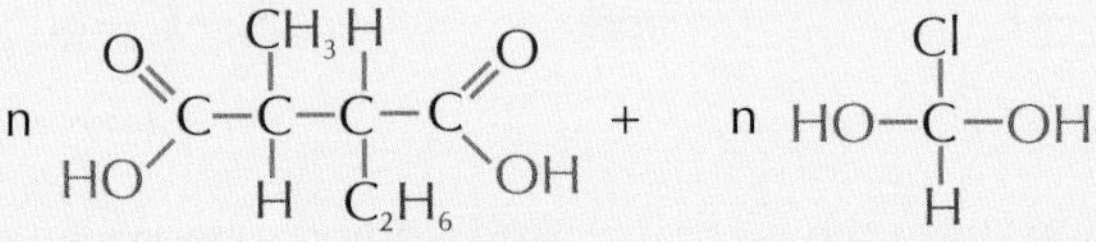

Q1 What small molecule is released when condensation polymers form?

Q2 Name the types of molecules that can join together to form:

a) polyamides   b) polyesters

Q3 Name the type of link that joins the monomers together in:

a) polyamides   b) polyesters

Q4 Give one use of polyester fibres.

3. Breaking Down Polymers

Breaking down polymers can be a tad tricky, which causes problems when it comes to disposing of them. This topic is all about the ways of breaking down polymers and what's being done to make using polymers more sustainable.

Hydrolysis of polyesters and polyamides

The ester or amide link in polyesters and polyamides can be broken down by **hydrolysis** — water molecules are added back in and the links are broken. The products of the hydrolysis are the monomers that were used to make the polymer — you're basically reversing the condensation reaction that was used to make them:

$$\text{n(monomers)} \underset{hydrolysis}{\overset{condensation}{\rightleftharpoons}} \text{polymer} + \text{water}$$

In practice, hydrolysis with just water is far too slow, so the reaction is done with an acid or alkali. Polyamides will hydrolyse more easily with an acid than an alkali. The general equation for the acid hydrolysis of a polyamide is shown below:

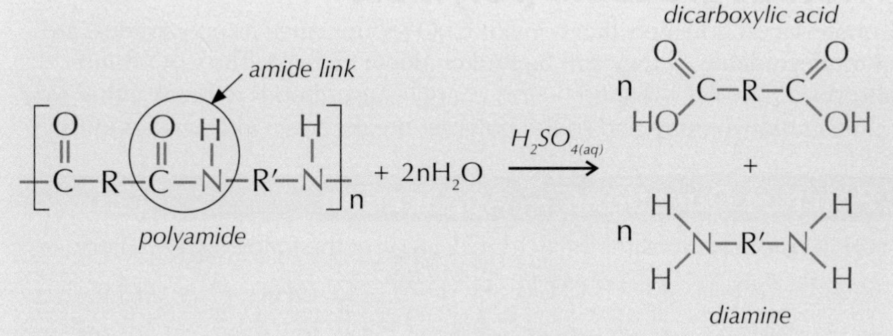

Polyesters will hydrolyse more easily with an alkali. A metal salt of the dicarboxylic acid is formed.

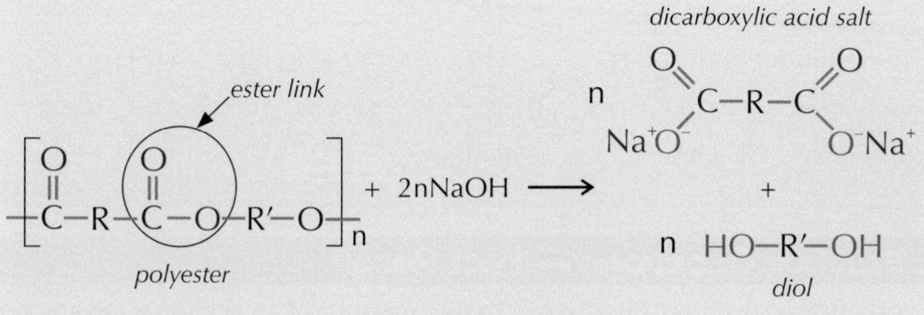

Biodegradability of polymers

Because amide links in polyamides and ester links in polyesters can be easily hydrolysed, polyamides and polyesters are biodegradable. These links are found in nature, so there are fungi and bacteria that are able to degrade them. It's not all hunky-dory though. It takes absolutely ages for synthetic polyamides and polyesters to decompose — e.g. nylon takes around 40 years.

Learning Objectives:

- Be able to explain the acid and the base hydrolysis of polyesters and polyamides.
- Be able to explain that condensation polymers may be (i) photodegradable as the C=O bond absorbs radiation.
  (ii) hydrolysed at the ester or amide group.
- Be able to outline the role of chemists in minimising environmental waste by development of degradable polymers, similar in structure to poly(lactic acid).

Specification Reference 4.2.2

Tip: If you were to acid hydrolyse a polyester you would get a diol instead of a diamine, but other than that the equation would be exactly the same.

Tip: If you were to hydrolyse a polyamide with an alkali you would get a diamine instead of a diol.

Tip: You did a lot about recycling polymers and developing biodegradable polymers at AS-level so have a quick skim over your AS-notes if you need a bit more info.

Figure 1: A scientist developing biodegradable plastic bags.

Tip: This is an example of how scientific advances can help us all to reduce our impact on the environment. See page 4 for more on science and decision making.

HOW SCIENCE WORKS

Tip: Biodegradable polymers break down naturally in the environment — but you can usually speed up the process a bit by heating them up.

Figure 2: Photodegradation is the reason why clothes fade when they're left out in the sunlight.

Developing biodegradable polymers

Although condensation polymers will break down by hydrolysis, the huge time this takes to happen in nature means that they still create waste problems. Addition polymers are even more of a problem — they are very stable molecules and won't be broken down by hydrolysis. Also, most polymers we use are made from monomers derived from crude oil which is not a renewable resource. To tackle these problems, chemists are trying to produce alternative polymers that biodegrade quickly and are renewable.

> **Example**
>
> **Poly(lactic acid)**
> Poly(lactic acid) (PLA — see page 51) is a polyester made from lactic acid. It's produced by fermenting maize or sugar cane, which are both renewable crops.
>
> PLA will biodegrade easily — it is hydrolysed by water if kept at a high temperature for several days in an industrial composter or more slowly at lower temperatures in landfill or home compost heaps.
>
> PLA has many uses, including rubbish bags, food and electronic packaging, disposable eating utensils and internal sutures (stitches) that break down without having to open wounds to remove them.

Photodegradable polymers

Condensation polymers that contain C=O groups, such as polyamides, are **photodegradable** — they can be broken down by light. The C=O bond absorbs ultraviolet radiation — this energy causes bonds to break either side of the carbonyl group and so the polymer breaks down into smaller units.

Practice Questions — Application

Q1 Write equations for the acid hydrolysis of the following polymers:

a)
$$\left[\begin{array}{c} \underset{H}{\overset{O}{\parallel}}C - \underset{}{\overset{H}{\underset{|}{C}}} - \underset{}{\overset{O}{\parallel}}C - \underset{H}{\overset{H}{\underset{|}{N}}} - \underset{}{\overset{CH_3}{\underset{|}{C}}} - \underset{CH_3}{\overset{H}{\underset{|}{C}}} - \underset{}{\overset{H}{\underset{|}{N}}} \end{array} \right]_n$$

b)
$$\left[\begin{array}{c} \underset{}{\overset{O}{\parallel}}C - \underset{H}{\overset{O}{\underset{|}{C}}} \underset{Cl}{\overset{H}{\underset{|}{C}}} - \underset{}{\overset{O}{\parallel}}C - O - \underset{H}{\overset{CH_3}{\underset{|}{C}}} - O \end{array} \right]_n$$

Q2 Write equations for the hydrolysis of the following polymers in the presence of NaOH.

a)
$$\left[\begin{array}{c} \underset{H}{\overset{O}{\parallel}}C - \underset{OH}{\overset{CH_3}{\underset{|}{C}}} - \underset{}{\overset{H}{\underset{|}{C}}} - \underset{}{\overset{O}{\parallel}}C - \underset{}{\overset{H}{\underset{|}{N}}} - \underset{}{\bigcirc} - \underset{OH}{\overset{H}{\underset{|}{N}}} \end{array} \right]_n$$

b)
$$\left[\begin{array}{c} \underset{H}{\overset{O}{\parallel}}C - \underset{H}{\overset{CH_3}{\underset{|}{C}}} - \underset{}{\overset{H}{\underset{|}{C}}} - \underset{}{\overset{O}{\parallel}}C - O - \underset{H}{\overset{H}{\underset{|}{C}}} - \underset{H}{\overset{H}{\underset{|}{C}}} - O \end{array} \right]_n$$

Practice Questions — Fact Recall

Q1 Why is hydrolysis performed in the presence of an acid or an alkali?

Q2 Are polyamides more easily hydrolysed with an acid or an alkali?

Q3 What are the products when polyesters are hydrolysed in the presence of an alkali?

Q4 What type of polymer is poly(lactic) acid (PLA) and why is it better for the environment than some other polymers?

Q5 What does the term photodegradable mean?

4. Amino Acids and Proteins

Proteins are an important part of all living organisms and they're made up of amino acids. This may sound like it belongs in a biology book but it's still chemistry — sometimes chemistry and biology overlap a bit.

Learning Objectives:

- Know the general formula for an α-amino acid as $RCH(NH_2)COOH$.
- Know that an amino acid exists as a zwitterion at a pH value called the isoelectric point.
- Know that different R groups in α-amino acids may result in different isoelectric points.
- Be able to describe the acid–base properties of α-amino acids at different pH values.
- Be able to explain the formation of a peptide (amide) linkage between α-amino acids by condensation and subsequent condensation polymerisation to form polypeptides and proteins.
- Be able to describe the acid and the alkaline hydrolysis of proteins and peptides to form α-amino acids or carboxylates.

Specification Reference 4.2.1

What are amino acids?

An **amino acid** has two functional groups — an amino group (NH_2) and a carboxyl group (COOH). There are a few different types of amino acid, but at A-level you only need to know about α-**amino acids**. α-amino acids have both groups attached to the same carbon atom — the 'α carbon'. The general formula of an α-amino acid is $RCH(NH_2)COOH$, where R is an alkyl side-chain which varies from one α-amino acid to the next. The general structure of an α-amino acid is given in Figure 1.

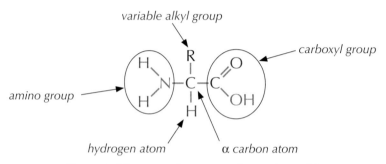

variable alkyl group

carboxyl group

amino group

hydrogen atom

α carbon atom

Figure 1: *The general structure of an amino acid.*

Amino acids are interesting molecules because they are **amphoteric** — this means they've got both acidic and basic properties. They can act as acids because the carboxyl group is acidic — it can donate a proton:

$$-COOH \rightleftharpoons -COO^- + H^+$$

They can act as bases because the amino group is basic — it can accept a proton:

$$-NH_2 + H^+ \rightleftharpoons -NH_3^+$$

Zwitterions

Amino acids can exist as **zwitterions**. A zwitterion is a dipolar ion — it has both a positive and a negative charge in different parts of the molecule. Zwitterions only exist near an amino acid's **isoelectric point**. This is the pH where the average overall charge on the amino acid is zero. It's different for different amino acids — for α-amino acids it depends on their R-group.

An amino acid becomes a zwitterion when its amino group is protonated to NH_3^+ and its COOH group is deprotonated to COO^-.

- In conditions more acidic than the isoelectric point, the $-NH_2$ group is likely to be protonated but the $-COOH$ group will be unchanged — so the amino acid will carry a positive charge but not a negative charge.

- In conditions more basic than the isoelectric point, the $-COOH$ group is likely to lose its proton but the $-NH_2$ group will be unchanged — so the amino acid will carry a negative charge but not a positive charge.

- Only at or near the isoelectric point are both the carboxyl group and the amino group likely to be ionised — forming a zwitterion (see Figure 3).

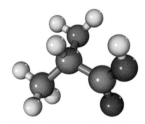

Figure 2: *Model of the amino acid alanine which has CH_3 as the R group.*

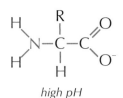

zwitterion

low pH
(acidic)

isoelectric point

high pH
(alkaline)

Figure 3: *Formation of a zwitterion.*

Changes in pH also influence the acid-base properties of α-amino acids:

- At pHs below the isoelectric point, α-amino acids act as bases and accept protons from the acid.
- At pHs above the isoelectric point, α-amino acids act as acids and donate protons to the base.
- At the isoelectric point, α-amino acids are amphoteric — they can act as acids and bases.

Dipeptides, polypeptides and proteins

Amino acids join together in a condensation reaction. A **peptide bond** is made between the amino acids. Here's how two amino acids join together to make a **dipeptide**:

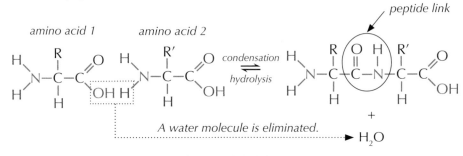

peptide link

amino acid 1   *amino acid 2*

condensation
hydrolysis

A water molecule is eliminated.

$+$

H_2O

Figure 4: *Formation of a peptide link between two amino acids.*

Polypeptides and **proteins** are made up of lots of amino acids joined together. Polypeptides are long chains of amino acids. Proteins are made up of one or more polypeptides folded into a precise 3D shape. Amino acids can polymerise because they have an amine group and a carboxylic acid group. Lots of amino acids can join together in a long chain via a series of condensation reactions — a water molecule is lost each time an amino acid joins on (see Figure 5).

Figure 6: *Molecular model of a section of a polypeptide.*

Amino acids have both an amine group and a carboxylic acid group.

peptide link

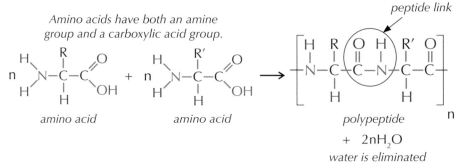

amino acid   *amino acid*   *polypeptide*

$+ \quad 2nH_2O$

water is eliminated

Figure 5: *Formation of a polypeptide.*

When two different amino acids join together to form a dipeptide, there are two possible products. This is because they could join either way around.

Example ───

When alanine and cysteine react in a condensation reaction, there are two possible products...

alanine + cysteine

or

+ H_2O + H_2O

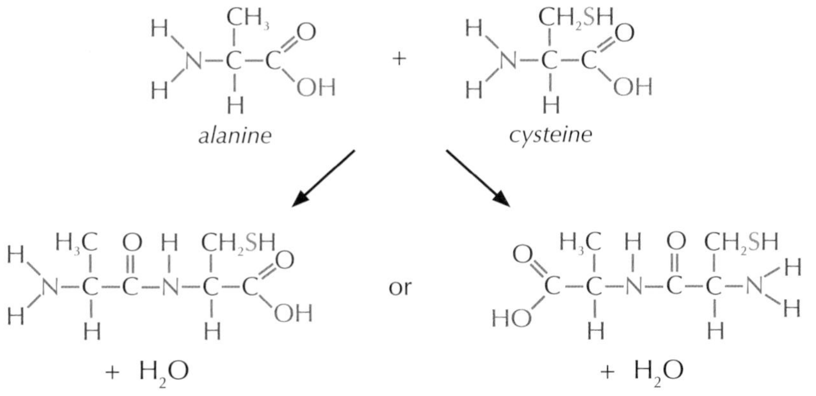

Tip: To draw the two possible products, draw the two amino acids with the amine groups on the left and stick them together to form the first dipeptide. Then, flip the amino acids over so the amine groups are on the right and stick them together to form the second dipeptide.

Hydrolysis of peptides

When you eat proteins, enzymes in your digestive system break the proteins down to individual amino acids by **hydrolysis**. This process can be simulated in the lab by heating proteins with hydrochloric acid for 24 hours. A shorter reaction time will give a mixture of smaller peptides rather than individual amino acids. The reaction helps biochemists to work out the sequence of amino acids in a protein. In the reaction, water molecules react with the peptide links and break them apart. The separate amino acids are then released (see Figure 7).

Tip: The hydrolysis of proteins is very similar to the hydrolysis of other condensation polymers covered on page 53.

Tip: This reaction is happening in your stomach right now.

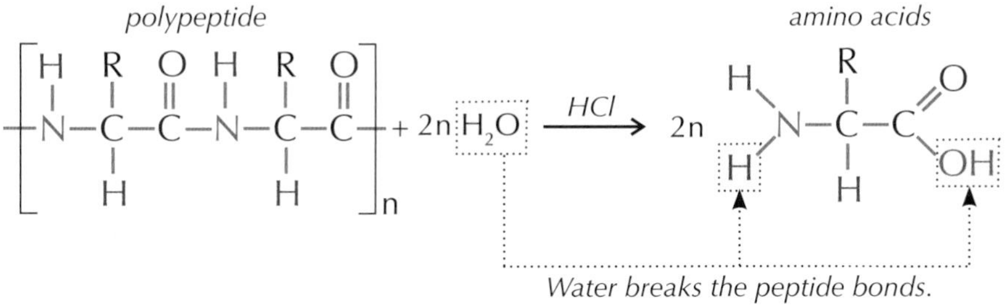

polypeptide   amino acids

+ 2n H_2O $\xrightarrow{HCl}$ 2n

Water breaks the peptide bonds.

Figure 7: Hydrolysis of a peptide bond with HCl.

Hydrolysis can also be carried out using alkalis, but in this case the hydrogen in the –COOH group is replaced by a metal to form a carboxylate salt of the amino acid, e.g. $RCH(NH_2)COO^-Na^+$ (see Figure 9).

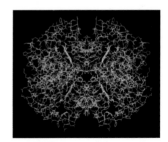

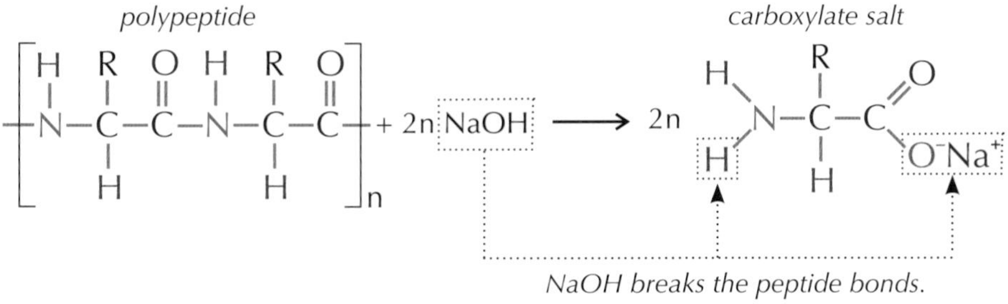

Figure 8: Proteins can be very complex. For example, this is a molecular model of the haemoglobin protein.

polypeptide   carboxylate salt

+ 2n NaOH $\longrightarrow$ 2n

NaOH breaks the peptide bonds.

Figure 9: Hydrolysis of a peptide bond with NaOH.

Tip: Other bases can be used to hydrolyse polypeptides too. For example, you could use KOH — then you'd end up with a K^+ ion in your carboxylate salt instead of an Na^+ ion.

Practice Questions — Application

Q1 Below are two amino acids (**A** and **B**):

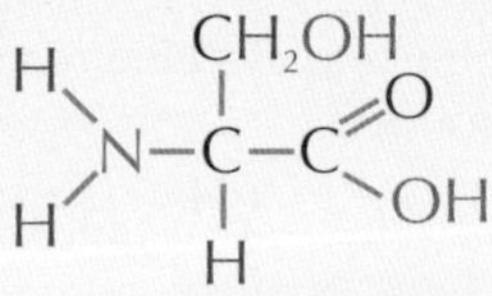

a) State why the isoelectric points of amino acids **A** and **B** are different.

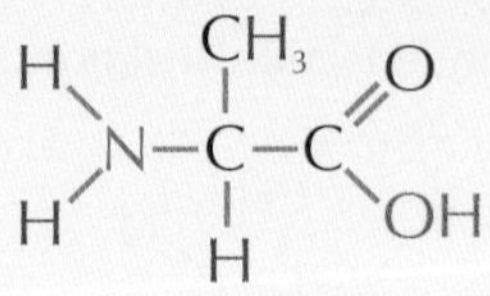

b) Draw the structure of the ions formed by species **A** at:
   (i) a low pH   (ii) its isoelectric point   (iii) a high pH

c) State whether species B acts as an acid and/or a base at:
   (i) a low pH   (ii) its isoelectric point   (iii) a high pH

d) Draw a dipeptide that could be formed by joining amino acids **A** and **B**.

Q2 The diagram below shows a dipeptide:

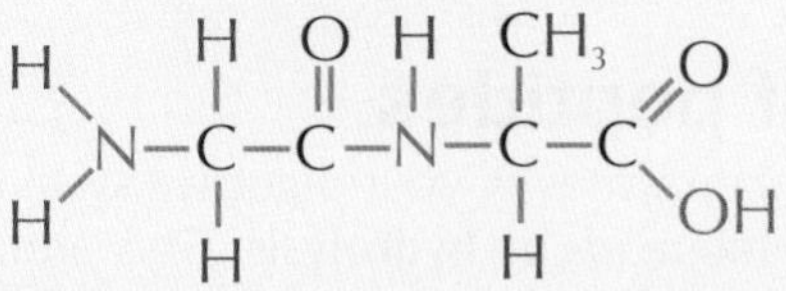

a) Draw the amino acids that formed this dipeptide.

b) Write an equation for the hydrolysis of this dipeptide with NaOH.

Practice Questions — Fact Recall

Q1 a) What is the general formula of an α-amino acid?

   b) What two key functional groups are found in amino acids?

Q2 Explain why amino acids are amphoteric.

Q3 a) What is a zwitterion?

   b) When do amino acids form zwitterions?

Q4 By what type of reaction are:

   a) amino acids joined to form dipeptides?

   b) dipeptides broken down to form amino acids?

Q5 What products are formed when a polypeptide is hydrolysed using an alkali?

Exam Tip
The R-groups on amino acids can get quite complicated and this can make them tricky to recognise — so keep an eye out for the characteristic amino group and carboxyl group.

Tip: You can find the monomers for polypeptides in exactly the same way as you did for polyamides and polyesters — see page 51 for more.

5. Organic Synthesis

Learning Objective:
- Be able to devise multi-stage synthetic routes for preparing organic compounds.

Specification Reference 4.2.3

Organic synthesis is the part of chemistry that deals with how to make organic compounds using different chemical reactions. Organic synthesis is one of the most important branches of chemistry as it provides ways to create materials and chemicals like pharmaceutical drugs, fertilisers and plastics.

Synthesis routes

Chemists have got to be able to make one compound from another. It's vital for things like designing medicines. It's also good for making imitations of useful natural substances when the real things are hard to extract. Chemists use **synthesis** routes to show the reagents, conditions and any special procedures needed to get from one compound to another. The reaction schemes on the next two pages show some of the synthesis routes you've come across in the AS- and A2-Level Chemistry course. These reactions are covered elsewhere in the book, or in your AS notes, so check back for extra details.

Synthesis routes for making organic compounds

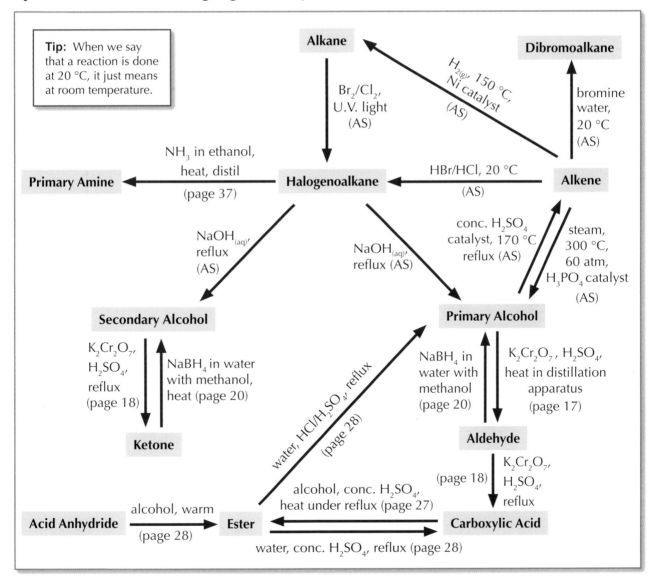

Tip: When we say that a reaction is done at 20 °C, it just means at room temperature.

Synthesis routes for aromatic compounds

There are not so many of these reactions to learn — so make sure you know all the itty-bitty details. If you can't remember any of the reactions, look back to the relevant pages and take a quick peek over them.

(page 10)

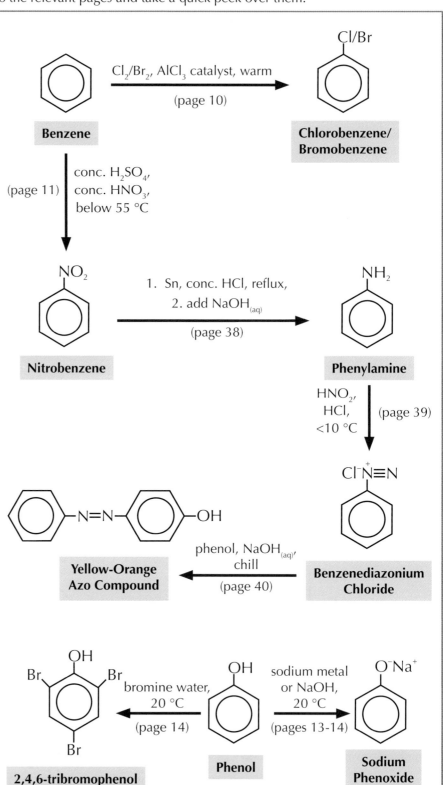

(page 11)
(page 38)
(page 39)
(page 40)
(page 14)
(pages 13-14)

Exam Tip
When you're writing down step-wise syntheses in the exam don't forget to put the conditions as well as the reagents. You might lose marks if you don't.

Exam Tip
There may be fewer reactions involving aromatic compounds but they're just as likely to come up in the exam as the reactions on the previous page — so make sure you learn both sets of synthesis routes.

Organic synthesis in the exam

In your Unit 4 chemistry exam you could be asked to provide a step-wise synthesis for the production of one chemical from another. You might have to use any of the reactions mentioned on the previous two pages so it's really important that you learn them all really well. If you're asked how to make one compound from another in the exam, make sure you include:

- Any special procedures, such as refluxing.
- The conditions needed, e.g. high temperature or pressure, or the presence of a catalyst.
- Any safety precautions, e.g. if there are things like hydrogen chloride around, you really don't want to go breathing them in, so do the reaction in a fume cupboard. Stuff like bromine and strong acids and alkalis are corrosive and you don't want to splash them on your skin, so wear gloves.

Exam technique

In the exam you may be asked to 'identify' the name of a reagent used in a synthesis step. A reagent is just a chemical that can be used straight out of a bottle or container, for example, hydrochloric acid (HCl) or sodium hydroxide (NaOH). You must be really careful about this...

Figure 1: *Reagents are chemicals that can be taken from bottles or containers.*

--- Example ---

Identify the reagent used to transform a bromoalkane into an alcohol.

Giving the reagent as OH^- in this case would be incorrect as you can't just take it out of a bottle. The correct answer would be $NaOH_{(aq)}$.

Practice Questions — Application

Q1 Write down the reagents and conditions you would use to carry out the following organic syntheses.

  a) Making ethanol from ethene using steam hydration.

  b) Forming bromomethane from methane.

  c) Turning ethanoic anhydride into ethyl ethanoate.

Q2 The following syntheses require two-steps. Write down the reagents and conditions you would use to carry out each step.

  a) Creating propanal from 1-bromopropane.

  b) Turning phenylamine into a yellow-orange azo compound.

  c) Making methyl butanoate from butanal.

Q3 In an organic synthesis, benzene was heated with H_2SO_4 and HNO_3 to make an intermediate, X. A tin catalyst and HCl were then added and the mixture was refluxed before adding NaOH to make the overall product, Y. Identify X and Y.

Q4 Give a three-step synthesis of dibromoethane starting from ethanal. In your second synthesis step you should form ethene. For each step, give the reagents and conditions you would use to carry out the reaction.

Q5 Give a three-step synthesis of propanone starting from propene. In your first synthesis step you should form 2-bromopropane. For each step, give the reagents and conditions you would use to carry out the reaction.

Exam Tip
For questions like these you don't have to give the mechanisms or equations for the reactions.

Exam Tip
You need to be specific when you're talking about reagents in the exam. Make sure you write down exactly what you need to use — writing 'an alcohol' when you really mean 'ethanol' just won't get you all of the marks.

- Be able to identify individual functional groups in an organic molecule containing several functional groups.
- Be able to predict properties and reactions for an organic molecule containing several functional groups.

Specification Reference 4.2.3

Exam Tip
You need to learn all of these functional groups off by heart — they won't be given to you in the exam.

Tip: Phenol is an aromatic alcohol.

Tip: You only add the di- or tri- bit on to amines if the alkyl groups are the same. See pages 36-38 for more on amines.

Tip: Compounds are aromatic if they contain a benzene ring and aliphatic if they don't.

6. Functional Groups

Functional groups are the most important parts of a molecule, so it's vital that you know how to identify them. This topic is all about the different functional groups and how they are used to classify compounds.

What are functional groups?

Functional groups are the parts of a molecule that are responsible for the way the molecule reacts. These are the main ones you need to know (which are all covered elsewhere in the book)...

Functional Group	Found in	Prefix or suffix	Example
O‖ −C−OH	carboxylic acids	-oic acid	ethanoic acid CH_3COOH
O‖ O‖ −C−O−C−	acid anhydrides	-oic anhydride	ethanoic anhydride $(CH_3CO)_2O$
O‖ −C−O−	esters, polyesters	-oate	ethyl ethanoate $CH_3COOCH_2CH_3$
O‖ −C−N−	amides	-amide	ethanamide CH_3CONH_2
O‖ −C−H	aldehydes	-al	ethanal CH_3CHO
O‖ −C−	ketones	-one	propanone CH_3COCH_3
−OH	alcohols	hydroxy- -ol	ethanol CH_3CH_2OH
◯−OH	phenols	hydroxyphenyl- -phenol	phenol C_6H_5OH
−NH$_2$	primary amines	amino- -amine	methylamine CH_3NH_2
−NH	secondary amines	di- -amine	dimethylamine $(CH_3)_2NH$
−N−	tertiary amines	tri- -amine	trimethylamine $N(CH_3)_3$
−NO$_2$	nitro compounds	nitro-	nitrobenzene $C_6H_5NO_2$
◯−	aromatic compounds	phenyl- -benzene	phenylamine $C_6H_5NH_2$
C=C	alkenes	-ene	propene $CH_3CH=CH_2$

The functional groups in a molecule tell you about its properties and reactions.

┌─ **Example** ─────────────

A −COOH group will (usually) make the molecule acidic and will mean that it can react with an alcohol to form an ester.

Molecules containing ester groups will have distinctive smells.

Classifying and naming compounds

Organic molecules can get pretty complicated, often with many functional groups. You need to be able to pick out the functional groups on an unknown molecule, name them and name the molecule in a systematic way.

The main functional group is used as the suffix and the other functional groups are added as prefixes. The table on the previous page shows the order of importance of the functional groups, with COOH being the most important, down to phenyl, which is the least. (Note — alkenes are treated differently, with 'ene' always appearing in the suffix.) If you need to include more than one functional group prefix, then list them in alphabetical order.

Tip: This 'order of priority' was made by IUPAC just to help make sure that scientists were all naming molecules in the same way.

Tip: Suffixes go at the end of a name (e.g. propanone has the suffix -one). Prefixes go at the beginning of a name (e.g. nitrobenzene has the prefix nitro-).

Examples

Look at compound A, shown on the right.

a) What class of chemicals does compound A belong to?

b) Give the systematic name of compound A.

A

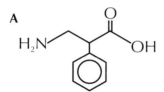

a) It's got a COOH group and an NH$_2$ group, so it must be an amino acid (see page 55).

b) COOH is the main functional group, so number the carbon atoms from this side. There's a 3-carbon chain, so it's a propanoic acid. The phenyl group is on the 2nd carbon atom. The amino group is on the 3rd carbon atom.

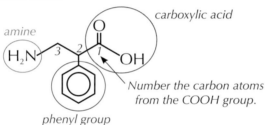

carboxylic acid

amine

Number the carbon atoms from the COOH group.

phenyl group

So the full name would be... 3-amino-2-phenylpropanoic acid.

Tip: Compound A is shown using a skeletal formula where only the carbon bonds and functional groups are shown. If you have trouble understanding skeletal formula (I know I do), try drawing the molecule out with a displayed formula. It'll make it easier to see what's what and to name the molecule.

Look at compounds B and C, shown below. For each compound:

a) circle and name the functional groups.

b) work out the molecular formula.

Exam Tip
Labelling the molecule like this can really help when it comes to naming molecules in your exam.

B

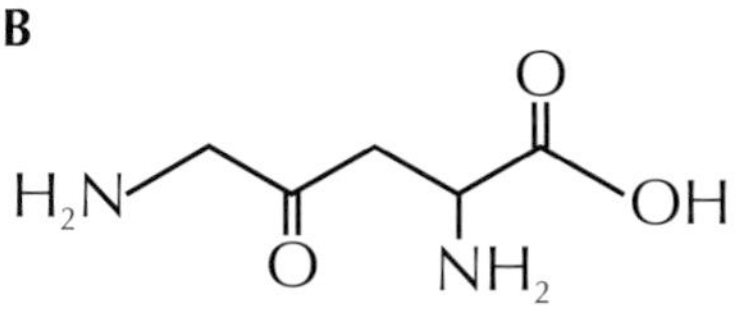

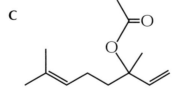

C

a) The functional groups on each of these compounds are as follows...

B

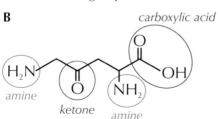

carboxylic acid

amine

ketone

amine

C

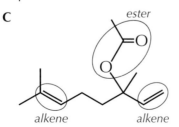

ester

alkene

alkene

Tip: Sometimes you put a -yl suffix on the end when you're naming a functional group. E.g. the C=C group found in alkenes is called an alkenyl group and the COOH group found in carboxylic acids is called a carboxyl group.

b) To work out the molecular formula from a skeletal formula, you need to work out how many C and H atoms there are. H atoms are the trickiest to find — remember, each C atom will have 4 bonds. Once you know how many C and H atoms there are, just add up the rest of the atoms and put it all together.

Tip: In a molecular formula, you just need to say how many of each atom there are.

B

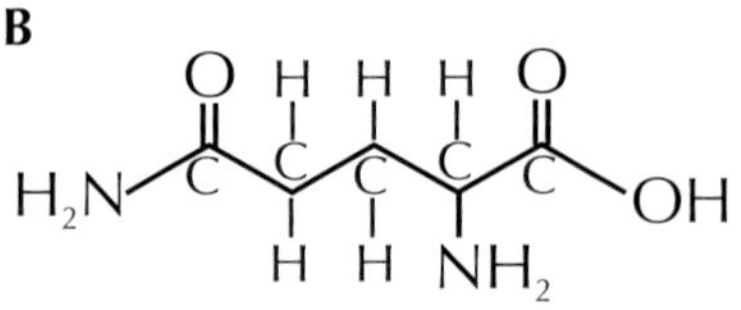

$C_5H_{10}N_2O_3$

C

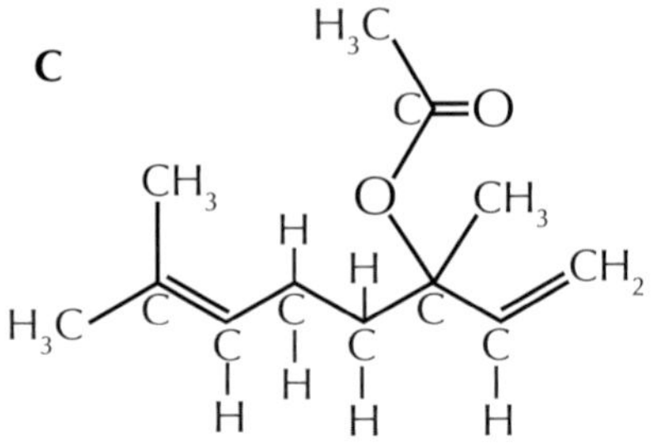

$C_{12}H_{20}O_2$

Practice Questions — Application

Q1 Give the systematic names for the following compounds:

a)

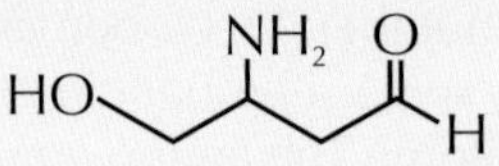

b)

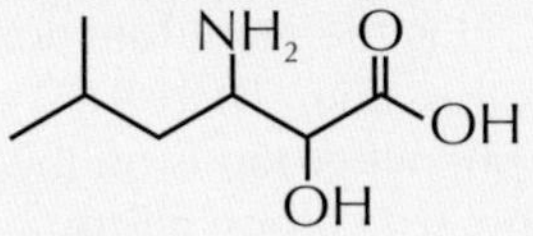

Q2 Below is a selection of organic compounds:

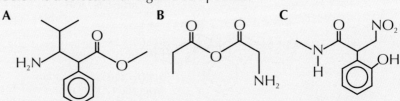

A   **B**   **C**

Exam Tip
Remember, if you're struggling to name a molecule in the exam, try drawing its structure out in full — it'll make it much easier to see the longest carbon chain (and the positions of all the functional groups).

a) Circle and name the functional groups in each of these molecules.

b) Work out the molecular formula of each of these molecules.

c) Which of these compounds could form an ester when reacted with an alcohol?

b) Which of these compounds is likely to have a sweet smell?

Practice Questions — Fact Recall

Q1 Draw the following functional groups:

a) ester group   b) nitro group   c) phenyl group   d) alkene group

Q2 In what types of molecules would you find these functional groups?

a)

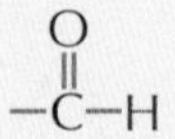

$$\underset{-C-H}{\overset{O}{\parallel}}$$

b)

$$\underset{-C-O-C-}{\overset{O\quad\ O}{\parallel\quad\ \parallel}}$$

c)

$$-NH$$

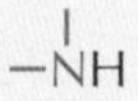

d)

$$\underset{-C-}{\overset{O}{\parallel}}$$

Q3 Put the following functional groups in order of importance:

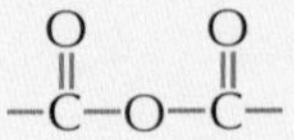

$$-NH_2 \qquad \underset{-C-N-}{\overset{O}{\parallel}} \qquad -OH \qquad \underset{-C-OH}{\overset{O}{\parallel}}$$

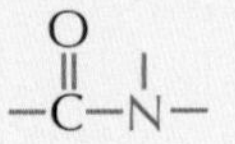

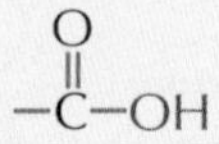

7. Stereoisomerism and Chirality

You need to know about two types of stereoisomers — optical isomers and E/Z isomers. If you don't know what they are, fret not — all will be revealed.

E/Z isomerism

Stereoisomerism is when two molecules have the same structural formula but different arrangements of atoms in space. **E/Z isomerism** is a type of stereoisomerism. It occurs when both of the double-bonded carbon atoms in an alkene have two different atoms or groups attached to them. You can twist and rotate a molecule any way you like around a single bond, but a double bond has a fixed position — you can't rotate the rest of the molecule around it. Because of the lack of rotation around the double bond you get an 'E-isomer' and a 'Z-isomer'.

Each of the groups linked to the double-bonded carbons is given a priority. If the two carbon atoms have their 'higher priority groups' on opposite sides, then it's an E-isomer. If the two carbon atoms have their 'higher priority groups' on the same side, then it's a Z-isomer — see Figure 1.

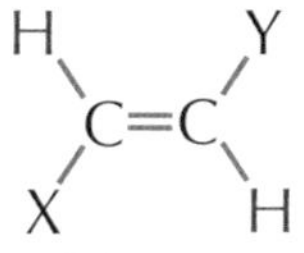

$$\begin{array}{cc} H \quad Y & H \quad H \\ C=C & C=C \\ X \quad H & X \quad Y \\ \textbf{\textit{E-isomer}} & \textbf{\textit{Z-isomer}} \end{array}$$

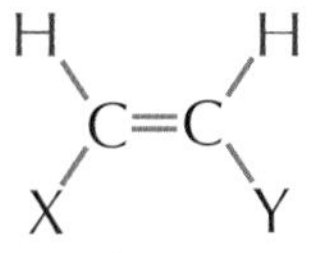

Figure 1: *E- and Z-isomers. X and Y are the higher priority groups.*

> **Example**
>
> In 1,2-dibromoethene ($C_2H_2Br_2$), both of the double-bonded carbon atoms have an H and a Br group attached to them.
>
> $$\begin{array}{cc} H \quad Br \\ C=C \\ Br \quad H \\ \textit{E-isomer} \end{array}$$
>
> When the high priority groups (Br and Br) are across the double bond from each other it's the E-isomer.
>
> This molecule is E-1,2-dibromoethene.
>
> $$\begin{array}{cc} Br \quad Br \\ C=C \\ H \quad H \\ \textit{Z-isomer} \end{array}$$
>
> When the high priority groups are both above or both below the double bond it's the Z-isomer.
>
> This molecule is Z-1,2-dibromoethene.

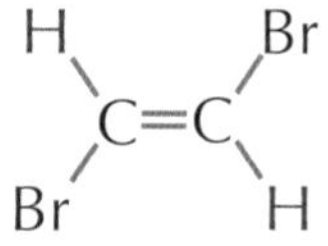

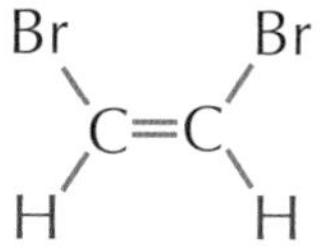

Optical isomerism

Optical isomerism is another type of stereoisomerism. Optical isomers have a **chiral** carbon atom. A chiral (or asymmetric) carbon atom is one that has four different groups attached to it.

> **Example**
>
> The molecule below, 1-aminoethanol, has a chiral carbon atom. 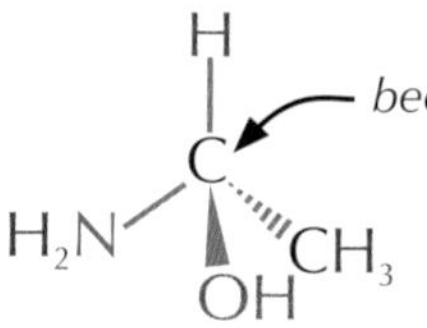
>
>
>
> *This carbon is chiral because it has four different groups attached to it.*
>
> $H_2N \quad C \quad CH_3$
> OH

Learning Objectives:

- Be able to explain that optical isomerism and E/Z isomerism are different types of stereoisomerism.
- Be able to describe optical isomers as non-superimposable mirror images about an organic chiral centre (four different groups attached to a carbon atom).
- Be able to identify chiral centres in a molecule of given structural formula.

Specification Reference 4.2.1

Tip: The group with the highest priority is the one that has the highest molecular mass.

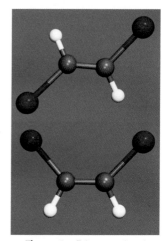

Figure 2: *E-isomer (top) and Z-isomer (bottom) of 1,2-dibromoethene.*

Tip: The best way to get your head around optical isomerism is to get some molecular models and have a go at making the isomers yourself. Give it a go — you know you want to.

It's possible to arrange the groups in two different ways around chiral carbon atoms so that two different molecules are made — these molecules are called **enantiomers** or optical isomers. The enantiomers are mirror images and no matter which way you turn them, they can't be superimposed.

Tip: If molecules can be superimposed, they're achiral — and there's no optical isomerism.

─ Example ────────────

Here are the two enantiomers of 1-aminoethanol. It doesn't matter how many times you turn and twist them, they can't be superimposed.

One enantiomer is usually labelled D and the other L — luckily you don't have to worry about which is which. Chiral compounds are very common in nature, but you usually only find one of the enantiomers — for example, all naturally occurring amino acids are L-amino acids (except glycine which isn't chiral) and most sugars are D-isomers.

Optical isomers are optically active — they rotate plane-polarised light. The two enantiomers of an optically active molecule will rotate the plane-polarised light in opposite directions. One enantiomer rotates it in a clockwise direction, and the other rotates it in an anticlockwise direction.

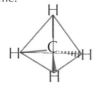

Figure 3: *Left handed and right handed scissors. These pairs of scissors are mirror images of each other — look closely and you'll see that they can't be superimposed on each other.*

Molecules with more than one chiral carbon

Some molecules contain more than one chiral carbon and as a result have more than two optical isomers.

Tip: Some amino acids have two chiral carbons. See page 55 for more on amino acids.

─ Example ────────────

The molecule on the right is 3-methylpentan-2-ol. It contains two chiral carbons, marked with asterisks.

$$H-\overset{\overset{\displaystyle H}{|}}{\underset{\underset{\displaystyle H}{|}}{C}}-\overset{\overset{\displaystyle H}{|}}{\underset{\underset{\displaystyle OH}{|}}{\overset{*}{C}}}-\overset{\overset{\displaystyle CH_3}{|}}{\underset{\underset{\displaystyle H}{|}}{\overset{*}{C}}}-\overset{\overset{\displaystyle H}{|}}{\underset{\underset{\displaystyle H}{|}}{C}}-\overset{\overset{\displaystyle H}{|}}{\underset{\underset{\displaystyle H}{|}}{C}}-H$$

As a result, there are four different optical isomers of this molecule:

Original molecule.   *Just top carbon mirror imaged.*   *Just bottom carbon mirror imaged.*   *Both carbons mirror imaged.*

Drawing optical isomers

You have to be able to draw optical isomers. Just follow these steps each time:

1. Locate the chiral centre — look for the carbon atom with four different groups attached.
2. Draw one enantiomer in a tetrahedral shape — put the chiral carbon atom at the centre and the four different groups in a tetrahedral shape around it. Don't try to draw the full structure of each group — it gets confusing.

Tip: If you draw lines joining up the Hs in tetrahedral molecules, the shape you get is a tetrahedron, hence the name:

3. Draw the mirror image of the enantiomer — put in a mirror line next to the enantiomer and then draw the mirror image of the enantiomer on the other side of it.

Don't panic. There are some examples below to help you get to grips with this.

Examples

Draw the two enantiomers of 2-hydroxypropanoic acid.
The structure of 2-hydroxypropanoic acid is shown below.

$$H-\overset{\overset{\displaystyle H}{|}}{\underset{\underset{\displaystyle H}{|}}{C}}-\overset{\overset{\displaystyle H}{|}}{\underset{\underset{\displaystyle OH}{|}}{C}}-\overset{\overset{\displaystyle O}{\|}}{C}-OH$$

1. Locate the chiral centre — the chiral carbon in this molecule is the carbon with the groups H, OH, COOH and CH_3 attached.

$$H-\overset{\overset{\displaystyle H}{|}}{\underset{\underset{\displaystyle H}{|}}{C}}-\overset{\overset{\displaystyle H}{|}}{\underset{\underset{\displaystyle OH}{|}}{C}}-\overset{\overset{\displaystyle O}{\|}}{C}-OH$$
chiral centre

Tip: The chiral centre and the chiral carbon atom are the same thing.

2. Draw one enantiomer in a tetrahedral shape — put the chiral carbon atom at the centre and the groups H, OH, COOH and CH_3 in a tetrahedral shape around it.

$$H_3C-\overset{\overset{\displaystyle H}{|}}{\underset{\underset{\displaystyle OH}{}}{C}}\cdots COOH$$

Tip: Remember, those dashed lines mean the bond is pointing into the page and the solid wedged lines mean the bond is pointing out of the page towards you.

3. Then draw a mirror image beside it.

$$H_3C-\overset{\overset{\displaystyle H}{|}}{\underset{\underset{\displaystyle OH}{}}{C}}\cdots COOH \qquad HOOC\cdots\overset{\overset{\displaystyle H}{|}}{\underset{\underset{\displaystyle OH}{}}{C}}-CH_3$$

If you're just given the structural formula of a molecule in the exam, the easiest way to spot any chiral centres is to draw out the displayed formula first.

Example

Draw the two enantiomers of butan-2-ol ($CH_3CH_2CHOHCH_3$).

Draw out the displayed formula and locate the chiral centre.

$$H-\overset{\overset{\displaystyle H}{|}}{\underset{\underset{\displaystyle H}{|}}{C}}-\overset{\overset{\displaystyle H}{|}}{\underset{\underset{\displaystyle H}{|}}{C}}-\overset{\overset{\displaystyle H}{|}}{\underset{\underset{\displaystyle OH}{|}}{C}}-\overset{\overset{\displaystyle H}{|}}{\underset{\underset{\displaystyle H}{|}}{C}}-H$$
chiral centre

Tip: Don't forget, the chiral carbon is the one with four <u>different</u> groups attached to it.

Draw one enantiomer in a tetrahedral shape, then draw a mirror image beside it.

$$H_3CH_2C-\overset{\overset{\displaystyle H}{|}}{\underset{\underset{\displaystyle OH}{}}{C}}\cdots CH_3 \qquad H_3C\cdots\overset{\overset{\displaystyle H}{|}}{\underset{\underset{\displaystyle OH}{}}{C}}-CH_2CH_3$$

Practice Questions — Application

Q1 State whether the following molecules are E-isomers or Z-isomers.

a)

$$H_3C \quad\quad H$$
$$\diagdown\quad\diagup$$
$$C{=}C$$
$$\diagup\quad\diagdown$$
$$H_3CH_2C \quad\quad CH_3$$

b)

$$H_3C \quad\quad CH_2Br$$
$$\diagdown\quad\diagup$$
$$C{=}C$$
$$\diagup\quad\diagdown$$
$$H_3CH_2C \quad\quad CH_3$$

Q2 Draw the E- and Z-stereoisomers of the following molecule.

$$\begin{array}{ccccccc} & H & CH_3 & & Cl & H & \\ & | & | & & | & | & \\ H- & C- & C- & C= & C- & C- & H \\ & | & | & & & | & \\ & H & H & CH_3 & & H & \end{array}$$

Q3 Circle the chiral carbon(s) in each of these molecules.

a)

$$\begin{array}{ccccc} & H & H & H & \\ & | & | & | & \\ H- & C- & C- & N- & H \\ & | & | & & \\ & H & Br & & \end{array}$$

b)

$$\begin{array}{ccccccc} & H & Cl & CH_3 & H & \\ & | & | & | & | & \\ H- & C- & C- & C- & C- & H \\ & | & | & | & | & \\ & H & H & CH_3 & H & \end{array}$$

c)

$$\begin{array}{cccc} & H_3C & H & H \\ & | & | & | \\ H_3C- & C- & C- & C-H \\ & | & | & | \\ & H & Br & H \end{array}$$

d)

$$\begin{array}{cccccc} & H & H & H & H & Cl \\ & | & | & | & | & | \quad H \\ H- & C- & C- & C- & C- & C=C{<}_H \\ & | & | & | & | & \\ & H & F & H & CH_3 & \end{array}$$

Q4 Draw the two enantiomers of the following molecules.

a)

$$\begin{array}{cccccc} & H & H & H & CH_3 & H \\ & | & | & | & | & | \\ H- & C- & C- & C- & C- & C-H \\ & | & | & | & | & | \\ & H & H & H & H & OH \end{array}$$

b)

$$\begin{array}{ccc} & Cl & H \\ & | & | \\ Cl- & C- & C-Br \\ & | & | \\ & H & CH_3 \end{array}$$

c)

$$\begin{array}{ccc} & H & H \\ & | & | \\ HO- & C- & C-OH \\ & | & | \\ & H & F \end{array}$$

d)

$$\begin{array}{cccc} & H & H & H \\ & | & | & | \\ H- & C- & C- & N-H \\ & | & | & \\ & H & C_2H_5 & \end{array}$$

Q5 Here is an equation for the reaction between butanone and HCN.

$$\begin{array}{ccccc} & H & H & O & H \\ & | & | & \| & | \\ H- & C- & C- & C- & C-H \quad + \quad HCN \quad \rightarrow \\ & | & | & & | \\ & H & H & & H \end{array}$$

butanone

$$\begin{array}{cccc} & H & H & OH \\ & | & | & | \\ H- & C- & C- & C-CH_3 \\ & | & | & | \\ & H & H & C{\equiv}N \end{array}$$

2-hydroxy-2-methylbutanenitrile

Draw the two optical isomers that can be formed via this reaction.

Practice Questions — Fact Recall

Q1 What is a stereoisomer?

Q2 When do you get E-/Z-isomerism in a molecule? Explain your answer.

Q3 What is optical isomerism?

Q4 What is a chiral carbon?

Q5 What does it mean if a molecule is 'optically active'?

Tip: When you're drawing out the enantiomers for molecules just write out the structural formula of each group — don't try and draw the displayed formula for each one or your diagram will become too confusing.

8. Chirality and Drug Development

When you prepare a chiral molecule in the lab, you often end up with something called a racemic mixture. This can cause problems when it comes to developing drugs. The next few pages tell you why...

Racemates

A **racemate** (or **racemic mixture**) contains equal quantities of each **enantiomer** of an optically active compound. Racemates don't show any optical activity — the two enantiomers cancel each other's light-rotating effect. Chemists often react two achiral things together and get a racemic mixture of a chiral product. This is because when two molecules react there's an equal chance of forming each of the enantiomers.

--- Example ---

Here's the reaction between butane and chlorine:

butane   *2-chlorobutane*

A chlorine atom replaces one of the H groups, to give 2-chlorobutane. Either of the H groups can be replaced, so the reaction produces a mixture of the two possible enantiomers.

Each hydrogen has a fifty-fifty chance of being replaced, so the two optical isomers are formed in equal amounts — you get a racemic mixture.

In contrast, chiral compounds produced naturally by enzymes in living things are often produced as one optical isomer only. This is because biological molecules are formed in the active sites of enzymes, which are a particular shape — so usually only one enantiomer will fit.

Racemates and drug development

The fact that a chemical reaction in a lab usually produces a racemic mixture can cause problems when chiral pharmaceutical drugs are being made.

Drugs work by changing chemical reactions that are taking place in the body. Most drugs do this by binding to an active site — usually on an enzyme or a specific receptor molecule. A drug must be exactly the right shape to fit into the correct active site — only one enantiomer will do. The other enantiomer could fit into a different active site, and might cause harmful side-effects or have no effect at all. So, usually, synthetic chiral drugs have to be made so that they only contain one enantiomer. This has the benefit that only half the dose is needed. It also reduces the risk of the drug companies being sued over side effects.

HOW SCIENCE WORKS

Learning Objectives:

- Be able to explain that molecules prepared synthetically in the laboratory often contain a mixture of optical isomers, whereas molecules of the same compound produced naturally by enzymes in living systems will often be present as one optical isomer only.

- Be able to explain that the synthesis of pharmaceuticals often requires the production of a single optical isomer.

- Be able to explain that the synthesis of a pharmaceutical that is a single optical isomer: (i) increases costs due to difficulty in separating the optical isomers. (ii) reduces possible side effects and improves pharmacological activity.

- Be able to explain that modern synthesis of a pharmaceutical with a single optical isomer is often carried out: (i) using enzymes or bacteria that promote stereoselectivity. (ii) using chemical chiral synthesis or chiral catalysts. (iii) using natural chiral molecules, such as L-amino acids or sugars, as starting materials.

Specification Reference 4.2.3

Tip: For more on decision-making in science see page 4.

Example

Ethambutol, a drug used to treat TB, is produced as a single enantiomer because the other causes blindness.

The problem is that optical isomers are very tricky to separate — producing single-enantiomer drugs is expensive.

It's still sometimes possible to use a racemic mixture of the drug to treat patients. However, the patient may have to take double the dose to achieve the same effect as taking an enantiomerically pure version of the drug. There are some benefits to using racemic mixtures as drugs though — there's no need to separate out the enantiomeric products, which will reduce the difficulty and cost of producing the drug.

Example

The painkiller Ibuprofen is sold as a racemic mixture — the inactive enantiomer is harmless and the cost of separating the mixture is very high.

Tip: You have to take double the dose of a racemic mixture because only half of the drug molecules will be the enantiomer that has the right effect.

Figure 1: *Molecular model of a molecule of Ibuprofen. The arrow points to the chiral carbon.*

chiral carbon

Producing single enantiomer drugs

Different techniques can be used to produce single enantiomer drugs. These include:

- Using natural enzymes or bacteria in the process which tend to produce only one isomer.

- Using naturally-occuring single optical isomer compounds as starting materials, e.g. sugars, amino acids.

- Using chemical chiral synthesis — this basically involves using carefully chosen reagents and conditions which will ensure only one isomer is produced. Chemical chiral synthesis methods usually rely on chemically modifying the molecule in a way that physically blocks most approaches to it, so that it can only be 'attacked' from one side. For example, you could turn your reagent into a cyclic molecule, or bond the molecules to a polymer support and let the other reactants flow over them.

- Using chiral catalysts — these do the same job as the other techniques (producing only one isomer), but have the advantage that only a small amount is needed because they can be reused. (This is useful because getting hold of large amounts of any single-enantiomer compound tends to be expensive.)

Tip: Often a combination of these techniques is used to ensure that only one enantiomer is produced in a reaction.

Practice Questions — Fact Recall

Q1 What is a racemic mixture?

Q2 When a chiral molecule is prepared in a lab, why do you usually end up with a racemic mixture?

Q3 Why is it necessary for most synthetic chiral drugs to be made so that they contain only one enantiomer?

Q4 Give one advantage of using racemic mixtures as drugs.

Q5 What is chemical chiral synthesis and how does it work?

Q6 Suggest three techniques, other than chemical chiral synthesis, which can be used to produce single enantiomer drugs.

Section Summary

Make sure you know...

- How addition polymers are formed through the polymerisation of alkenes.
- That condensation polymerisation forms polymers through the loss of water molecules.
- That condensation polymers are held together by ester or amide linkages.
- That polyamides such as nylon 6,6 and Kevlar® are formed through the condensation polymerisation of dicarboxylic acids and diamines.
- That polyesters such as Terylene™ and poly(lactic) acid are formed through condensation polymerisation when carboxylic acid and alcohol functional groups react.
- How to identify the monomer(s) that a given addition or condensation polymer was formed from.
- How to identify the polymer that a given monomer (or monomers) would form.
- The similarities and differences between addition polymerisation and condensation polymerisation.
- How to identify whether addition or condensation polymerisation will/has taken place from given monomers or a section of polymer.
- That condensation polymers can be broken down by hydrolysis.
- How polyesters and polyamides can be hydrolysed in the presence of acids and bases.
- Why it is important for biodegradable polymers such as poly(lactic acid) (PLA) to be developed.
- That some condensation polymers are photodegradable because $C=O$ bonds absorb UV radiation.
- That amino acids are molecules that contain an amino group and a carboxylic acid group.
- That α-amino acids have the amino and carboxylic acid groups on the same carbon.
- That the general formula of an α-amino acid is $RCH(NH_2)COOH$.
- That amino acids are amphoteric — they have acidic and basic properties.
- That amino acids can exist as zwitterions — ions with both positive and negative charges in different parts of the molecule.
- That zwitterions form at a pH value known as the isoelectric point.
- That the isoelectric points of α-amino acids vary depending on the R side-chain.
- That at pH values below the isoelectric point amino acids act as bases, but at pH values above the isoelectric point they act as acids.
- How amino acids join together in condensation reactions to form dipeptides and polypeptides.
- How polypeptides and dipeptides can be hydrolysed back into amino acids.
- How to devise multi-stage synthetic routes for preparing different organic compounds.
- How to systematically name organic molecules which have lots of functional groups.
- How to predict the properties and reactions of an organic molecule based on its functional groups.
- That stereoisomers are molecules with the same structural formula but a different arrangement of atoms in space.
- That optical isomerism and E/Z isomerism are two different types of stereoisomerism.
- What optical isomers are and how to identify chiral centres.
- How to draw optical isomers.
- That a racemic mixture contains equal amounts of each enantiomer of a chiral compound.
- That synthetically prepared chiral molecules are often produced as racemic mixtures.
- Why it is often necessary for drugs to be sythesised as single enantiomers.
- That producing single enantiomer drugs can be expensive and difficult.
- The different techniques for producing single-enantiomer drugs.

Exam-style Questions

1   A research chemist is investigating the reactions of 2-methyl-2-buten-1-ol, the structure of which is shown below:

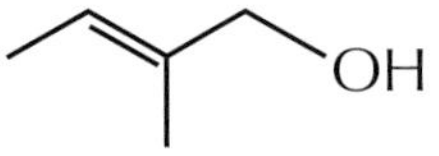

(a)   2-methyl-2-buten-1-ol exhibits stereoisomerism.

     (i)   Explain what is meant by the term stereoisomer and state the type of stereoisomerism shown by 2-methyl-2-buten-1-ol.

                        (2 marks)

     (ii)   What feature of 2-methyl-2-buten-1-ol enables it to show stereoisomerism?

                        (1 mark)

(b)   Under certain conditions, 2-methyl-2-buten-1-ol will polymerise to form an addition polymer. Draw the repeat unit of the polymer formed when 2-methyl-2-buten-1-ol polymerises.

                        (1 mark)

(c)   A two-stage synthesis reaction can be used to convert 2-methyl-2-buten-1-ol into 2-methylbutan-1,3-diol, via molecule K. The structures of molecule K and 2-methylbutan-1,3-diol are shown below.

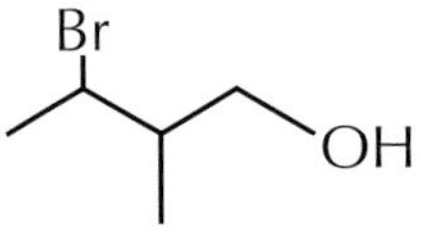

         molecule K 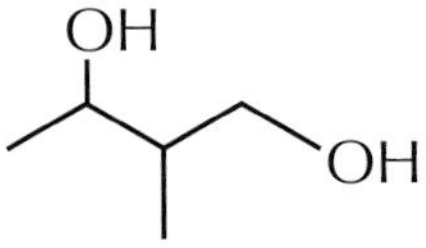   *2-methylbutan-1,3-diol*

     (i)   State the reagents and conditions required for each step in this synthesis.

                        (2 marks)

     (ii)   Does 2-methylbutan-1,3-diol exhibit stereoisomerism? Explain your answer.

                        (2 marks)

(d)   2-methylbutan-1,3-diol can be used in a second synthesis reaction to form the condensation polymer shown below:

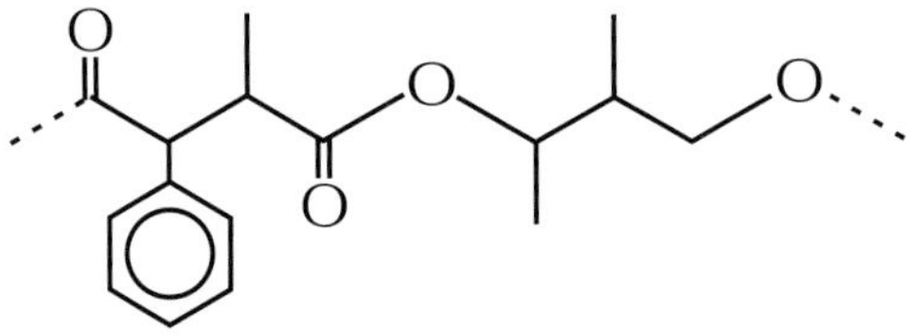

     (i)   Draw the structure of the molecule which would react with 2-methylbutan-1,3-diol to form this polymer.

                        (1 mark)

     (ii)   State what type of condensation polymer this is.

                        (1 mark)

     (iii) Explain what is meant by the term photodegradation and explain why this polymer is photodegradable.

                        (3 marks)

2   This question is about amino acids and their properties. The structures of three different amino acids are shown below:

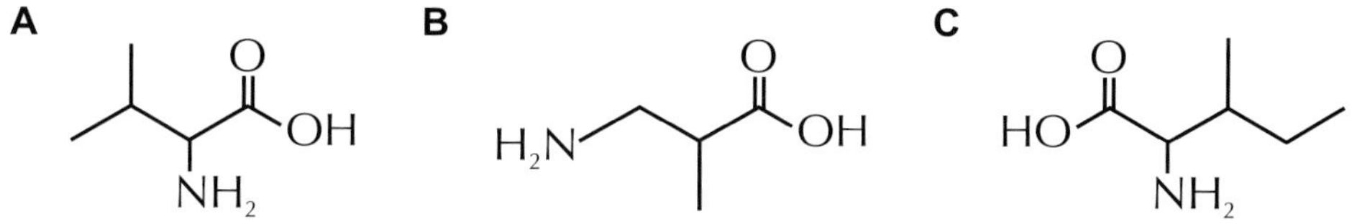

A   **B**   **C**

(a) (i)   Which of the amino acids (**A**, **B** and **C**) are α-amino acids? Explain your answer.

(2 marks)

(ii)   Write down the general formula of an α-amino acid.

(1 mark)

(b)   The common name for amino acid **A** is valine. Like many other amino acids, valine shows optical isomerism.

(i)   Using IUPAC rules, give the systematic name for amino acid **A**.

(1 mark)

(ii)   Draw the two optical isomers of valine.

(2 marks)

(iii)   Draw the molecule that would be formed if valine was heated under reflux with ethanol in the presence of an acid catalyst.

(1 mark)

(c)   The structure of amino acids varies depending on the pH.

(i)   Draw the structure of amino acid **B**:

- at a pH below its isoelectric point
- at its isoelectric point
- at a pH above its isoelectric point

(3 marks)

(ii)   At which of these pHs does amino acid **B** act as a base?

(1 mark)

(d)   Amino acids can polymerise to form polypeptides.

(i)   Name the type of polymerisation that gives rise to polypeptides.

(1 mark)

(ii)   Draw the dipeptide that would be formed from two molecules of amino acid **C** and circle the peptide link.

(2 marks)

(iii)   Draw the species that would be formed if sodium hydroxide was added to this dipeptide.

(1 mark)

3   Naproxen is a drug that is commonly used as an anti-inflammatory in the treatment of arthritis. The structure of naproxen is shown below:

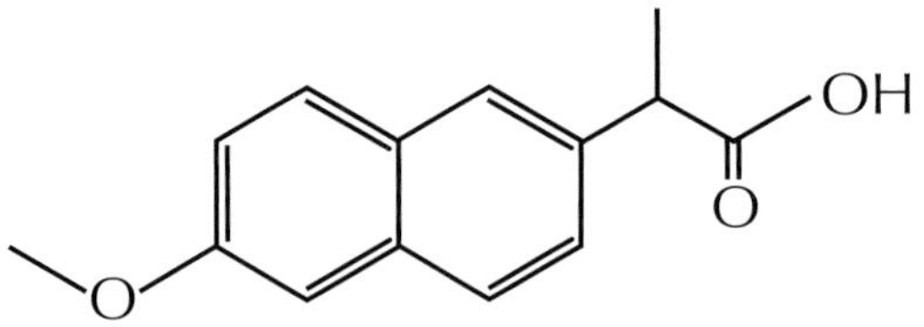

(a)   Naproxen contains several functional groups and shows optical isomerism.

   (i)   Draw out the structure of naproxen and indicate the chiral centre with an asterisk, *.

(1 mark)

   (ii) Circle the carboxylic acid functional group in naproxen.

(1 mark)

(b)   Naproxen is synthesised as a single enantiomer.

   (i)   State three techniques that can be used to produce a single enantiomer drug like naproxen.

(3 marks)

   (ii) Suggest two advantages of using single enantiomer drugs.

(2 marks)

   (iii) Suggest one disadvantage of using single enantiomer drugs.

(1 mark)

4   Nomex® is a fire-resistant polymer made from the two monomers shown below:

A

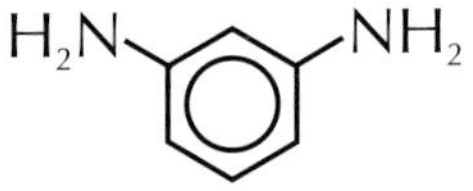

B

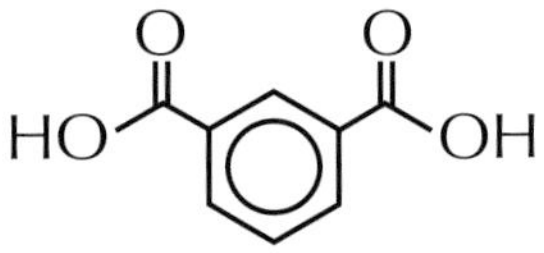

(a)   Outline a two-step synthesis for the formation of monomer **A** from benzene, identifying the product formed in the first step and stating suitable reagents and conditions for each step.

(3 marks)

(b)   Monomer **B** is formed from a diol. Draw the structure of this diol and state the reagents and conditions needed to convert it to monomer **B**.

(2 marks)

(c)   Draw the repeat unit of Nomex® and state what type of condensation polymer Nomex® is.

(2 marks)

1. Chromatography

An analytical technique is a method of analysing a substance to learn more about it. This topic deals with one specific analytic technique — chromatography. It's used to separate and identify chemicals in mixtures.

The basics

Chromatography is used to separate stuff in a mixture — once it's separated out, you can often identify the components. There are quite a few different types of chromatography (you might have tried paper chromatography) but the ones you need to know about for A-level are thin-layer chromatography (TLC) and gas chromatography (GC) — there's more about GC in the next topic. Both types of chromatography have two phases which help to separate out mixtures:

- A **mobile phase** — where the molecules can move. This is always a liquid or a gas.

- A **stationary phase** — where the molecules can't move. This must be a solid, or a liquid on a solid support.

The mobile phase moves through the stationary phase. As this happens, the components in the mixture separate out.

Thin-layer chromatography

In thin-layer chromatography (TLC):

- The mobile phase is a liquid solvent, such as ethanol, which passes over the stationary phase.

- The stationary phase is a thin layer of solid (0.1-0.3 mm), e.g. silica gel or alumina powder, on a glass or plastic plate.

Here's how you separate a mixture using TLC:

1. Draw a pencil line near the bottom of the plate — this is called the base line. Put a spot of the mixture to be separated on the line.

2. Dip the bottom of the plate (but not the spot) into a solvent.

3. As the solvent spreads up the plate, the different substances in the mixture move with it, but at different rates — so they separate out.

4. When the solvent's nearly reached the top, take the plate out and mark the distance that the solvent has moved (**solvent front**) in pencil.

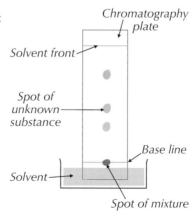

Figure 1: A thin-layer chromatography plate.

Then you can leave the plate in a safe place to dry out before you analyse it. The plate, with its pattern of spots, is called a **chromatogram**.

Learning Objectives:

- Be able to describe chromatography as an analytical technique that separates components in a mixture between a mobile phase and a stationary phase.

- Know that the mobile phase in chromatography may be a liquid or a gas.

- Know that the stationary phase in chromatography may be a solid (as in thin-layer chromatography, TLC) or either a liquid or solid on a solid support (as in gas chromatography, GC).

- Know that a solid stationary phase separates by adsorption.

- Be able to explain the term R_f value, and interpret one-way chromatograms in terms of R_f values.

Specification Reference 4.3.1

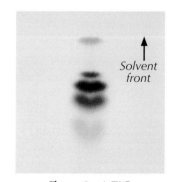

Figure 2: A TLC chromatogram.

How far each bit of the mixture travels depends on how strongly it's attracted to the stationary phase. The attraction between a substance and the surface of the stationary phase is called **adsorption**. A substance that is weakly adsorbed will spend more time dissolved in the solvent (moving up the plate) than stuck to the surface, so it will travel quickly. A substance that is strongly adsorbed will spend more time stuck to the plate than moving with the solvent, so it will travel slowly.

R_f values

An **R_f value** is the ratio of the distance travelled by a spot to the distance travelled by the solvent. You can calculate them using this formula:

$$R_f \text{ value} = \frac{\text{distance travelled by spot}}{\text{distance travelled by solvent}}$$

When you're measuring how far a spot has travelled, you just measure from the base line (point of origin) to the vertical centre of the spot.

You can work out what was in a mixture by calculating an R_f value for each spot and looking them up in a database, or table, of known values.

Example

A sugar solution containing a mixture of three sugars is separated using TLC. The chromatogram is shown on the right.

a) Calculate the R_f value of spot X.

To find the R_f value of spot X all you have to do is stick the numbers into the formula:

$R_f \text{ value} = \dfrac{\text{distance travelled by spot}}{\text{distance travelled by solvent}}$

$= 2.5 \text{ cm} \div 10.4 \text{ cm} = \textbf{0.24}$

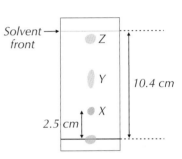

b) Figure 3 shows the R_f values of three sugars under the conditions used in the experiment. Use the table to identify the sugar present in spot X.

Spot X has an R_f value of 0.24. Fructose also has an R_f value of 0.24. So fructose is the sugar present in spot X.

Sugar	R_f value
Glucose	0.20
Fructose	0.24
Xylose	0.30

Figure 3: R_f values of sugars.

Practice Question — Application

Q1 A student used thin-layer chromatography to separate out a mixture of three amino acids. The chromatogram that she produced is shown on the right.

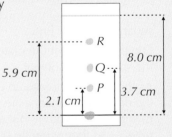

a) Calculate the R_f values of the three spots, P, Q and R.

b) Use the table in Figure 4 to identify the amino acid present in each spot.

Amino acid	R_f value
Glycine	0.26
Alanine	0.39
Tyrosine	0.46
Valine	0.61
Leucine	0.74

Figure 4: R_f values of amino acids.

Practice Questions — Fact Recall

Q1 What is chromatography used for?

Q2 Explain why mixtures separate during thin-layer chromatography.

Q3 Give the formula for calculating R_f values.

2. Gas Chromatography

The second type of chromatography you need to know about is gas chromatography. It's more high-tech than thin-layer chromatography, but the idea's just the same — a mobile phase, a stationary phase and things separating.

What is gas chromatography?

If you've got a mixture of volatile liquids (ones that turn into gases easily), then **gas chromatography** (GC) is the way to separate them out so that you can identify them. In gas chromatography:

- The **stationary phase** is a viscous liquid, such as an oil, or a solid.
- A liquid stationary phase can be used to coat inside of a long tube, which acts as a solid support for it.
- Alternatively, tiny beads can be coated with the stationary phase and packed into the tube. In this case it's the beads that act as the support material.
- The tube is coiled to save space, and built into an oven.
- The **mobile phase** is an unreactive carrier gas such as nitrogen or helium.

The sample to be analysed is injected into the machine, where it is vaporised (turned into a gas). The mobile phase (the stream of carrier gas) then carries it through the tube and over the stationary phase (see Figure 1).

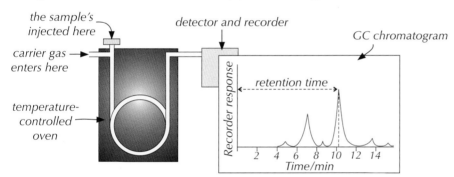

Figure 1: *Gas chromatography equipment and a chromatogram.*

If you have a liquid stationary phase, the components of the mixture will constantly dissolve in it, evaporate into the mobile phase and then redissolve as they travel through the tube. The solubility of each component of the mixture determines how long it spends dissolved in the stationary phase and how long it spends moving along the tube in the mobile phase. A substance with a high solubility will spend more time dissolved, so will take longer to travel through the tube to the detector than one with a lower solubility.

If you have a solid stationary phase, then the separation works in the same way as thin-layer chromatography (see page 76). How long each part of the mixture takes to travel through the tube will depend on how strongly it is adsorbed to the stationary phase.

The time taken from the injection of a sample to the detection of a substance is called the **retention time**. This can be used to identify the substance.

Gas chromatograms

A gas **chromatogram** is a graph showing a series of peaks at the times when the detector senses something other than the carrier gas leaving the tube. They can be used to identify the substances within a sample and their relative proportions.

Learning Objectives:

- Know that the mobile phase in chromatography may be a gas.
- Know that the stationary phase in gas chromatography (GC) may be either a liquid or solid on a solid support.
- Know that a liquid stationary phase separates by relative solubility.
- Be able to explain the term retention time and interpret gas chromatograms in terms of retention times and the approximate proportions of the components of a mixture.
- Be able to explain that analysis by gas chromatography has limitations, e.g. that similar compounds often have similar retention times and that unknown compounds have no reference retention times for comparison.

Specification Reference 4.3.1

Exam Tip
If you're writing about GC with a liquid stationary phase, then <u>solubility</u> is the word you need to use.

Figure 2: *A sample being injected into a gas chromatograph.*

Each peak on a chromatogram corresponds to a substance with a particular **retention time** (see Figure 3). Retention times are measured from zero to the centre of each peak, and can be looked up in a database, or reference table, to identify the substances present.

The area under each peak tells you the relative amount of each component that's present in the mixture (see Figure 3). For example, if a peak has three times the area of another peak, it tells you that there is three times as much of the first substance in the mixture (compared to the second substance).

Tip: If you ever need to estimate the area of a peak, you can treat it as a triangle and find the area of that.

Tip: If you're looking at the amount of each compound present, it's the <u>area</u> of the peaks (not the height) that's important — the tallest peak won't always represent the most abundant substance.

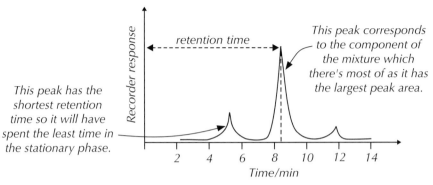

This peak has the shortest retention time so it will have spent the least time in the stationary phase.

This peak corresponds to the component of the mixture which there's most of as it has the largest peak area.

Figure 3: *A chromatogram showing the separation of three components in a mixture.*

You can use the retention times to identify the components of the mixture.

Example

If you wanted to know if a mixture contained octane, you could run a sample of the mixture through the system, then look up the retention time for octane run under those conditions and see if they're the same.

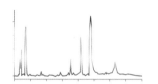

Figure 4: *Gas chromatogram. The horizontal axis shows the retention time of each component in the mixture.*

If you're looking up retention times in a reference table, you must make sure that the sample was run under the same conditions (e.g. at the same temperature and using the same stationary phase). Changing the conditions will alter the retention time.

HOW SCIENCE WORKS

The limitations of gas chromatography

Although a very useful and widely used technique, GC does have limitations when it comes to identifying chemicals.

Compounds which are similar often have very similar retention times, so they're difficult to identify accurately. A mixture of two similar substances may only produce one peak, so you won't be able to identify the substances. This also means that you can't tell how much of each one there is.

Tip: Handily, you can combine GC with mass spectrometry to make a much more powerful identification tool — there's more on this on page 83.

Tip: Sometimes you can separate the peaks out by changing the conditions and running the experiment again.

Example

On the right is a gas chromatogram for a mixture of alcohols.

Peak 2 is a bit wobbly. It looks like it's one big peak made up of smaller peaks that overlap. The mixture must contain some alcohols with very similar retention times.

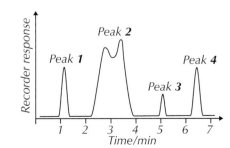

It looks like peak 2 probably represents two alcohols — but you can't tell for certain, or identify them. And you can't work out how much of each is in the sample, because you don't know how much each one is contributing to the big peak.

Another problem with GC is that you can only use it to identify substances that you already have reliable reference retention times for. (That means someone must have run a sample of the same pure substance under exactly the same conditions before.)

Tip: Scientists need to be aware of the limitations of the technology they use. They have to be careful when reporting results that they aren't misinterpreting the facts. There's more about reporting results on page 2 of the How Science Works section.

HOW SCIENCE WORKS

Practice Questions — Application

Q1 A scientist is using gas chromatography to purify an organic product. She knows that the pure product is more soluble in the liquid stationary phase than the impurities. Will the pure product reach the detector before or after the impurities? Explain your answer.

Q2 The gas chromatogram below shows the retention times of three components in a mixture.

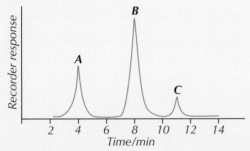

a) State which peak, A, B or C, corresponds to the component that spends the highest proportion of its time in the tube in the mobile phase.

b) One component of the mixture is hexene. Run under the same conditions, pure hexene has a retention time of 8 minutes. Which of the components, A, B or C, is hexene?

c) The smallest proportion of the mixture is made up of decene. Which of the components, A, B or C, is decene?

Q3 A gas chromatogram has two peaks. A student works out the areas of both peaks. He finds that Peak 1 has an area of 32 cm², and Peak 2 has an area of 16 cm². What percentage of the original mixture was made up of the chemical that caused Peak 2?

Exam Tip
Remember, in your exam answers it's 'retention time' that you need to talk about for gas chromatography and 'R$_f$ value' for thin-layer chromatography — don't get them mixed up.

Practice Questions — Fact Recall

Q1 Give an example of a mobile phase used in gas chromatography.

Q2 Briefly explain why the components in a mixture separate out during gas chromatography using a liquid stationary phase.

Q3 What is retention time?

Q4 What does the area under each peak tell you on a gas chromatogram?

Q5 Give two problems with using gas chromatography to identify the components of a mixture.

Figure 5: *A researcher using a gas chromatograph to separate and identify the chemicals in a sample.*

Learning Objective:

- Be able to analyse molecular ion peaks and fragmentation peaks in a mass spectrum to identify parts of structures (in organic compounds containing any of the following atoms: C, H, N and O).

Specification Reference 4.3.2

Figure 1: *Mass spectrometer.*

Tip: Most real-life mass spectra have a tiny peak one unit to the right of the M peak. It's called an M+1 peak and it's caused by the carbon isotope ^{13}C. The good news is that you don't need to worry about it at A-Level — it won't be on any mass spectrum you're given in the exam (so it's not on any of the ones in this book either).

Tip: The free radicals don't show up on the mass spectrum because they're not charged.

3. Mass Spectrometry

You should remember mass spectrometry from AS-level — this is just a refresher. A mass spectrum gives you loads of information about a molecule's structure.

Finding relative molecular mass

A **mass spectrum** is produced by a mass spectrometer. The molecules in a sample are bombarded with electrons and a molecular ion, $M^+_{(g)}$, is formed when the bombarding electrons remove an electron from the molecule. On a mass spectrum the y-axis gives the abundance of the ions, often as a percentage. The x-axis is the mass/charge ratio. This is just the molecular mass of the ion divided by its charge.

To find the relative molecular mass of a compound you look at the molecular ion peak (the M peak). For the spectra that you'll see, the M peak is the one with the highest mass/charge ratio. The mass/charge value of the molecular ion peak is the molecular mass of the compound (assuming the ion has 1+ charge, which it normally will have).

--- Example ---

Here's the mass spectrum of but-2-ene ($CH_3CHCHCH_3$):

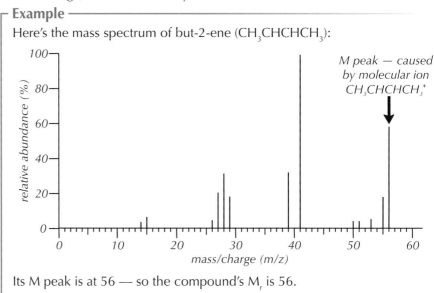

Its M peak is at 56 — so the compound's M_r is 56.

Fragmentation patterns

The bombarding electrons make some of the molecular ions break up into fragments. The fragments that are ions show up on the mass spectrum, making a fragmentation pattern. Fragmentation patterns are actually pretty useful because you can use them to identify molecules and even their structures.

--- Example ---

For butane ($CH_3CH_2CH_2CH_3$), the molecular ion is $CH_3CH_2CH_2CH_3^+$. The fragments it breaks into include CH_3^+ ($M_r = 15$) and $CH_3CH_2^+$ ($M_r = 29$).

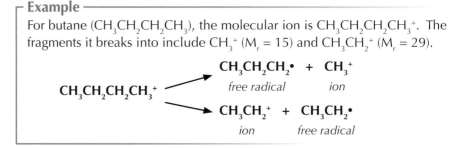

To work out the structural formula, you've got to work out what ion could have made each peak from its m/z value. (You assume that the m/z value of a peak matches the mass of the ion that made it.)

Exam Tip
The only way to get good at interpreting mass spectra is to practise. Beware... This is not a topic to try and learn the night before an exam — it just won't make sense.

Example

The mass spectrum below is for a molecule with the molecular formula C_3H_8O. Use the mass spectrum to work out the structure of the molecule:

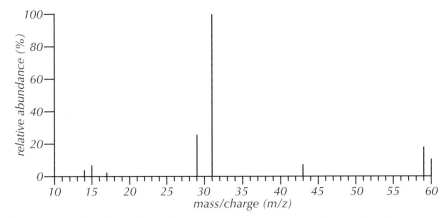

First you need to identify the fragments — you can use Figure 2 to help you identify some common ions. This molecule's got a peak at 15 m/z, so it's likely to have a CH_3 group. It's also got a peak at 29 m/z which could be a $CH_2CH_3^+$ ion and a peak at 43 m/z which could be $CH_2CH_2CH_3^+$. It has another peak at 17 m/z, so it probably contains an OH group.

Fragment	m/z
CH_3^+	15
$CH_2CH_3^+$	29
$CH_2CH_2CH_3^+$	43
OH^+	17
$C=O^+$	28

Figure 2: *Common fragment ions.*

To find the other fragments you just have to add combinations of 12 (the mass of carbon), 1 (hydrogen) and 16 (oxygen) until you come up with sensible fragment ions. Other ions are matched to the peaks here:

Tip: You can also try subtracting the mass of a fragment from the M_r and working out what's 'dropped off'.

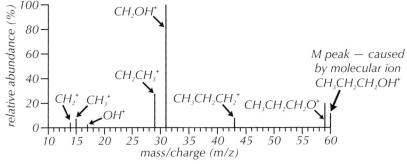

The next step is piecing them together to form a molecule with the correct molecular formula. Propan-1-ol has all the fragments on this spectrum.

Exam Tip
You won't actually get a table of fragment ions like the one in Figure 2 in the exam. But you can work out the m/z value of any fragment ion by finding its M_r (e.g. $CO^+ = 12 + 16 = 28$).

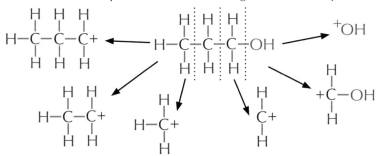

Propan-1-ol's molecular mass is 60. This should be the same as the m/z value of the M peak — it is. So, this is the mass spectrum of propan-1-ol.

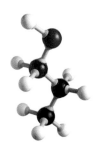

Figure 3: *A molecule of propan-1-ol.*

Differentiating between similar molecules

Even if two different compounds contain the same atoms, you can still tell them apart with mass spectrometry because they won't produce exactly the same set of fragments.

Example

Ethylamine and dimethylamine have the same empirical formula (C_2H_7N), so they also have the same M_r (45). But they have different molecular structures.

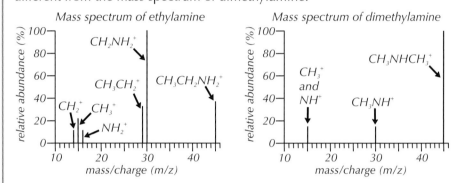

ethylamine   *dimethylamine*

Because their structures are different, they'll break up into different fragments in a mass spectrometer. So the mass spectrum of ethylamine is different from the mass spectrum of dimethylamine.

Mass spectrum of ethylamine   *Mass spectrum of dimethylamine*

Practice Questions — Application

Q1 The mass spectrum of hexan-3-one has a major peak in its spectrum at 57 m/z. Identify the fragment ion that caused this peak.

Q2 The spectrum below is for a molecule with the molecular formula C_3H_6O. Use the spectrum to find the structure of the compound.

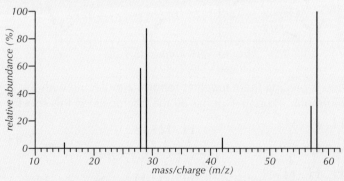

Q3 Identify two fragment ions that will be produced when butanal breaks up in a mass spectrometer, but not when butan-2-one does.

Practice Questions — Fact Recall

Q1 Explain how to find the M_r of a compound from its mass spectrum.

Q2 Give a common fragment ion that would cause a peak at 29 m/z.

4. Combining Chromatography with Mass Spectrometry

Just when you thought you'd seen the back of chromatography and mass spectrometry, you have to deal with both of them at once. Don't panic though — it's mostly about how they're used, which isn't too scary.

GC-MS

Gas chromatography (see pages 77-79) is very good at separating a mixture into its individual components, but not so good at identifying those components (see page 78). Mass spectrometry, on the other hand, is very good at identifying unknown compounds (see pages 80-81), but would give confusing results from a mixture of substances. If you put these two techniques together, you get an extremely useful analytical tool. Gas chromatography-mass spectrometry (or GC-MS for short) combines the benefits of gas chromatography and mass spectrometry to make a super analysis tool.

The sample is separated using gas chromatography, but instead of going to a detector, the separated components are fed into a mass spectrometer (see Figure 1). The spectrometer produces a mass spectrum for each component, which can be used to identify each one and show what the original sample consisted of. Computers can be used to match up the mass spectrum for each component of the mixture against a database, so the whole process can be automated.

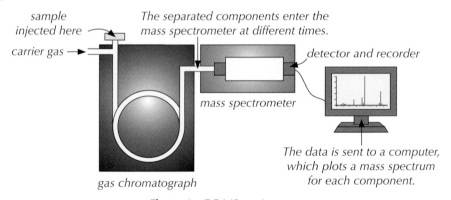

sample injected here
carrier gas
The separated components enter the mass spectrometer at different times.
detector and recorder
mass spectrometer
gas chromatograph
The data is sent to a computer, which plots a mass spectrum for each component.

Figure 1: *GC-MS equipment.*

The advantage of this method over normal GC is that the components separated out by the chromatography can be positively identified, which can be impossible from a chromatogram alone (because compounds which are similar often have very similar retention times — see page 78 for more).

HPLC-MS

You can also combine high performance liquid chromatography, or HPLC, with mass spectrometry to get HPLC-MS (see Figure 2). In HPLC, the stationary phase is a solid that is packed into a glass column, like tiny silica beads. The mobile phase (a solvent) and the mixture are pushed through the column under high pressure. This allows the separation to happen much faster than if the solvent just dripped through.

As with GC, HPLC is more useful for separating mixtures of substances than identifying them — combining it with mass spectrometry gives a better identification tool than either method alone.

Learning Objectives:

- Know that mass spectrometry can be combined with chromatography to provide a far more powerful analytical tool than chromatography alone.
- Understand that mass spectrometry can be combined with chromatography to generate mass spectra, which can be analysed or compared with a spectral database by computer for positive identification of a component.
- Know the use of GC-MS in analysis, e.g. in forensics, environmental analysis, airport security and space probes.

Specification Reference 4.3.1

Exam Tip
You don't need to know the detail of how HPLC works — just that, like GC, it's used to separate out mixtures.

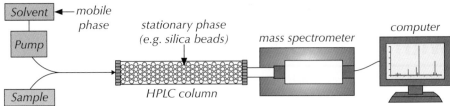

Figure 2: HPLC-MS equipment

Applications of GC-MS

GC-MS is a really important analytical tool, and not just in chemistry labs — check out the four uses below.

1. **Forensics** — GC-MS can be used to identify unknown substances found on victims or suspects or at crime scenes. For example, if GC-MS shows that a substance found at a crime scene is identical to one found on a suspect, then it is evidence that the suspect was at the crime scene. Or fire investigators can use the method to detect whether fires were started deliberately using substances such as petrol or paraffin.

2. **Airport security** — GC-MS can be used to look for specific substances — e.g. explosives or illegal drugs. The MS can be set to only look at a substance produced at a particular retention time on the GC to find out if it is present or not. The whole process is quick — it takes just a few minutes — and is accurate enough to be used in court as evidence.

3. **Space probes** — several space probes have carried GC-MS machines. Missions to the planets Venus and Mars, and to Saturn's moon Titan, have used the technique to examine the atmosphere and rocks.

4. **Environmental analysis** — the technique is used to detect and track pollutants such as pesticides in the environment. Foods can be tested in the same way to check that they do not contain harmful levels of substances such as pesticides.

Figure 3: GC-MS being used in a police lab to analyse evidence found at a crime scene.

Figure 4: Scientists collecting river water samples for environmental analysis.

Practice Question — Application

Q1 An environmental scientist ran a water sample through a GC-MS machine. He was looking for traces of the herbicide glyphosate.

a) What function does the gas chromatograph (GC) part of the scientist's GC-MS machine perform?

b) Explain how the scientist can confirm that the water is contaminated with glyphosate once he has the results from the GC-MS machine.

Practice Questions — Fact Recall

Q1 Outline how GC-MS works.

Q2 Why is GC-MS a better technique for identifying compounds in a mixture than GC alone?

Q3 Briefly describe how HPLC works.

Q4 a) Describe what GC-MS is used for in airport security.

b) Give two other applications of GC-MS.

Exam Tip
You might get a question about GC-MS where you have to analyse a gas chromatogram or a mass spectrum — examiners do tend to like mixing and matching topics...

5. NMR Spectroscopy

Here's a lovely new analytical technique for you to sink your teeth into. NMR (nuclear magnetic resonance) spectroscopy provides information on the different environments of atoms in molecules.

NMR spectroscopy and radio waves

Nuclear magnetic resonance (NMR) spectroscopy is an analysis technique that you can use to work out the structure of an organic molecule. The way that NMR works is pretty complicated, but you only need to know the basics.

A sample of a compound is placed in a strong magnetic field and exposed to a range of different frequencies of low-energy radio waves. The nuclei of certain atoms within the molecule absorb energy from the radio waves. The amount of energy that a nucleus absorbs at each frequency will depend on the environment that it's in (see below). The pattern of these absorptions gives you information about the positions of certain atoms within the molecule, and about how many atoms of that type the molecule contains. You can piece these bits of information together to work out the structure of the molecule.

The two types of NMR spectroscopy you need to know about are carbon-13 NMR (or ^{13}C NMR) and high resolution proton NMR (or ^{1}H NMR). Carbon-13 NMR gives you information about the number of carbon atoms that are in a molecule, and the environments that they are in. High resolution proton NMR gives you information about the number of hydrogen atoms that are in a molecule, and the environments that they're in.

Nuclear environments

A nucleus is partly shielded from the effects of an external magnetic field by its surrounding electrons. Any other atoms and groups of atoms that are around a nucleus will also affect the amount of electron shielding. So the nuclei in a molecule feel different magnetic fields depending on their environments.

Example

If a carbon atom bonds to a more electronegative atom (like oxygen) the amount of electron shielding around its nucleus will decrease.

These electrons provide the carbon atoms with shielding from a magnetic field.

These electrons are pulled further away from the carbon atom by the electronegative oxygen atom. The carbon atom is less shielded.

This means that carbon 1 and carbon 2 are in different environments.

Nuclei in different environments will absorb different amounts of energy at different frequencies. It's these differences in absorption of energy between environments that you're looking for in NMR spectroscopy.

An atom's environment depends on all the groups that it's connected to, going right along the molecule — not just the atoms it's actually bonded to. To be in the same environment, two atoms must be joined to exactly the same things.

Learning Objectives:

- Know that NMR spectroscopy involves interaction of materials with the low-energy radio wave region of the electromagnetic spectrum.

- Be able to describe the use of tetramethylsilane, TMS, as the standard for chemical shift measurements.

- Know that NMR spectroscopy is the same technology as that used in 'magnetic resonance imaging' (MRI) to obtain diagnostic information about internal structures in body scanners.

Specification Reference 4.3.2

Exam Tip
You won't be asked how an NMR spectrometer works (apart from the fact that it uses radio waves), but it'll help you to understand the spectra if you know the basics.

Figure 1: *An NMR spectrometer.*

Tip: Here's the ^{13}C NMR spectrum for TMS:

^{13}C NMR spectrum of TMS

← $\quad$ 0

chemical shift (δ)

Chemical shift

NMR spectroscopy measures differences in the energy absorbed by nuclei in different environments relative to a standard substance — the difference is called the **chemical shift** (δ). The standard substance is tetramethylsilane (TMS).

$H_3C-\underset{\underset{CH_3}{|}}{\overset{\overset{CH_3}{|}}{Si}}-CH_3$

tetramethylsilane (TMS)

This molecule has 12 hydrogen atoms in identical environments and 4 carbon atoms in identical environments. This means that, in both ^1H NMR and ^{13}C NMR, it will produce a single absorption peak. Chemical shift is measured in parts per million (ppm) relative to TMS. So the single peak produced by TMS is given a chemical shift value of 0. You might see a peak at $\delta = 0$ on a spectrum because TMS is added to the test compound for calibration purposes.

MRI scanning

Magnetic resonance imaging (MRI) is a scanning technique that's used in hospitals to study the internal structures of the body. MRI uses the same technology as NMR spectroscopy — the patient is placed inside a very large magnet and radio waves are directed at the area of the body being investigated.

Hydrogen nuclei in water molecules in the body absorb energy from the radio waves at certain frequencies. The frequency depends on the kind of tissue that the water is in, so an image of the different tissues can be built up.

The benefit of MRI is that it doesn't use damaging radiation like X-rays or gamma rays, but does give high quality images of soft tissue like the brain. The technique is used to diagnose and monitor tumours, examine bones and joints for signs of injury, and to study the brain and cardiovascular system.

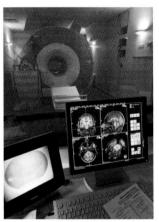

Figure 2: *An MRI scanner.*

Tip: To give you a hand, the structural formulas of the molecules in Q1 are shown below.

Butan-1-ol:
$CH_2OHCH_2CH_2CH_3$,
Pentan-3-ol:
$CH_3CH_2CHOHCH_2CH_3$
Propan-1,3-diol:
$CH_2OHCH_2CH_2OH$

Practice Question — Application

Q1 How many carbon environments are there in:
   a) butan-1-ol,   b) pentan-3-ol,   c) propan-1,3-diol?

Practice Questions — Fact Recall

Q1 What type of energy is absorbed by nuclei in NMR spectroscopy?
Q2 What unit is chemical shift (δ) measured in?
Q3 What is the standard substance used in NMR?
Q4 Describe what an MRI scanner is used for.

6. ^{13}C NMR Spectroscopy

Time for some more information about carbon-13 NMR. This topic's all about working out where the carbon atoms in an organic molecule are.

Interpreting ^{13}C NMR spectra

If you have a sample of a chemical that contains carbon atoms you can use a ^{13}C NMR spectrum of the molecule to help work out what it is. The spectrum gives you information about the number of carbon atoms that are in a molecule, and the environments that they are in.

Learning Objectives:
- Be able to analyse a carbon-13 NMR spectrum of a simple molecule.
- Know how to use a carbon-13 NMR spectrum to predict the different types of carbon present from chemical shift values.
- Know how to use a carbon-13 NMR spectrum to predict possible structures for a molecule.

Specification Reference 4.3.2

┌─ **Example** ─────────────────────────────────
Ethanol has two carbon environments...   ...and its ^{13}C NMR spectrum has two peaks.

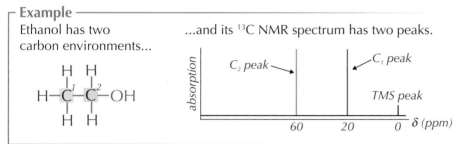

Here are the three steps to follow to interpret a ^{13}C NMR spectrum:

1. Count the number of peaks in the spectrum (excluding the TMS peak) — this is the number of carbon environments in the molecule.

2. Use a table of chemical shift data to work out what kind of carbon environment is causing each peak. A table of typical chemical shift data for carbon-13 NMR is shown in Figure 1.

3. Use this information to figure out the structure of the molecule.

Tip: Carbons next to more electronegative atoms (like oxygen) will have a higher chemical shift and be further to the left on the spectrum.

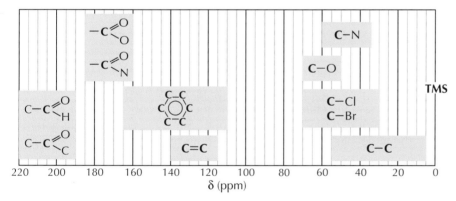

Figure 1: Chemical shift data for carbon-13 NMR.

Exam Tip
You'll get a table like this in the exam, so you don't need to learn it (phew). Just read up from any chemical shift value to find what groups could be causing a peak there.

┌─ **Example** ─────────────────────────────────
The carbon-13 NMR spectrum of a ketone with the molecular formula $C_5H_{10}O$ is shown below. Use the spectrum to identify the molecule.

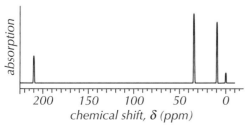

Tip: The best way to figure out the structure of a molecule is often to sketch out some possibilities. Then you can rule out any that don't have the right number of carbon environments or chemical shift values.

Tip: Don't forget that if there's a peak at $\delta = 0$ it's a TMS peak, so you can ignore it.

Tip: There are actually three ketones that have the formula $C_5H_{10}O$ (you could try sketching them all out) but pentan-3-one is the only one that has three carbon environments.

1. The spectrum has three peaks, so the molecule must have three carbon environments.
2. The peak at $\delta = 10$ ppm represents carbon atoms in C–C bonds. The peak at $\delta = 35$ ppm must also be due to carbons in C–C bonds. The carbons causing this peak have a different chemical shift to those causing the first peak, so they must be in a slightly different environment. The peak at $\delta = 210$ ppm is due to the carbon atom in the C=O group in the ketone.
3. You know you're looking for a ketone with the formula $C_5H_{10}O$ that has three different carbon environments. The only one that fits the bill is pentan-3-one:

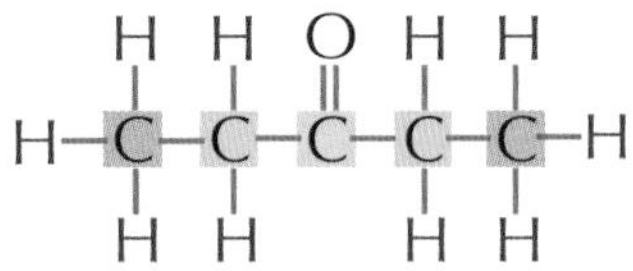

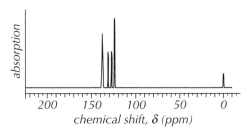

^{13}C NMR spectra of cyclic molecules

The number of peaks on the ^{13}C spectrum of a cyclic compound depends on the symmetry of the molecule. Here's an example to show how it works:

Tip: Benzene (C_6H_6) is completely symmetrical. It only has one peak on its ^{13}C NMR spectrum as all of its carbon atoms are in the same environment.

Example

The ^{13}C NMR spectrum of an aromatic molecule with the formula $C_6H_4Cl_2$ is shown below. Identify the molecule that produced this spectrum.

absorption
200
150
100
50
0
chemical shift, δ (ppm)

Exam Tip
Watch out for the scale on ^{13}C spectra in the exam — the chemical shift <u>increases</u> from <u>right to left</u>.

1. The spectrum has four peaks, so it must have four carbon environments.
2. All four peaks are between $\delta = 120$ ppm and $\delta = 140$ ppm. Looking at the chemical shift table these can only be due to alkene groups or carbons in a benzene ring. Since the question tells you that the molecule is aromatic, these carbons must be in a benzene ring.
3. There are only three aromatic molecules with the formula $C_6H_4Cl_2$ — they're all isomers of dichlorobenzene.

Tip: If a cyclic molecule is symmetrical, you can draw a mirror line (like the dashed lines on the molecules on the right) across it. Atoms or groups that are in the same place on opposite sides of the line will be in the same environment.

Cl
Cl

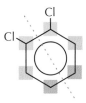

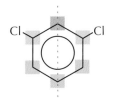

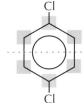

1,2-dichlorobenzene

Cl
Cl

1,3-dichlorobenzene

Cl
Cl

1,4-dichlorobenzene

If you look at the symmetry of the molecules you can see that 1,2-dichlorobenzene has three carbon environments, while 1,3-dichlorobenzene has four and 1,4-dichlorobenzene only has two. So the spectrum must have been produced by 1,3-dichlorobenzene.

Practice Questions — Application

Q1 How many peaks would you see on a ^{13}C NMR spectrum of:

a) butanal?

b) pentane?

c) 2-methylpropane?

d) 4-chlorocyclohexanone
(shown on the right)?

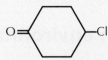
4-chlorocyclohexanone

Q2 The carbon-13 NMR spectrum of a compound with the molecular formula C_5H_{12} is shown below.

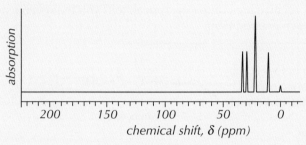

Tip: Use the chemical shift data table from page 87 to help you with these questions.

Use the spectrum to identify the molecule. Explain your reasoning.

Q3 The carbon-13 NMR spectrum of a molecule with the formula $C_4H_{10}O$ is shown below.

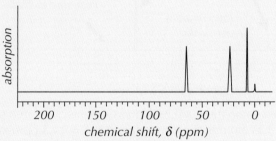

a) What type of carbon is causing the peak at $\delta = 65$?

b) Use the spectrum to identify the molecule. Explain your reasoning.

Tip: Matching peaks to groups isn't always easy, because some of the chemical shift ranges overlap (e.g. a peak at $\delta = 30$ could be caused by C–C, C–Cl or C–Br). You might have to use other information that you're given — for instance if you're told that the molecule's a hydrocarbon, then it couldn't have C–Cl or C–Br in it.

Practice Questions — Fact Recall

Q1 What does the number of peaks on the carbon-13 NMR spectrum of a compound correspond to?

Q2 Which way does the δ scale increase on a carbon-13 NMR spectrum?

- Be able to analyse a high resolution proton NMR spectrum of a simple molecule.

- Know how to use a ^1H NMR spectrum to predict the relative numbers of each type of proton present from relative peak areas, using integration traces or ratio numbers, when required.

- Know how to use a ^1H NMR spectrum to predict the different types of proton present, from chemical shift values.

- Be able to predict the chemical shifts of the protons in a given molecule.

Specification Reference 4.3.2

7. ^1H NMR Spectroscopy

This topic is all about ^1H NMR, also known as proton NMR. It works in pretty much the same way as ^{13}C NMR except this time the spectra tell you about the different hydrogen environments in a molecule.

Hydrogen environments

Each peak on a ^1H NMR spectrum is due to one or more hydrogen nuclei (protons) in a particular environment — this is similar to a ^{13}C NMR spectrum (which tells you the number of different carbon environments).

Working out the number of H atoms in an environment

In ^1H NMR, the relative area under each peak tells you the relative number of H atoms in each environment.

Examples

The spectrum below is the ^1H NMR spectrum of ethanoic acid (CH_3COOH).

ethanoic acid

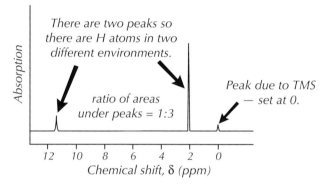

There are two peaks so there are H atoms in two different environments.

ratio of areas under peaks = 1:3

Peak due to TMS — set at 0.

There are two peaks — so there are two environments. The area ratio is 1 : 3 — so there's 1 H atom in the environment at δ = 11.5 ppm to every 3 H atoms in the other environment. If you look at the structure of ethanoic acid, this makes sense:

3 H atoms attached to CH_3COOH.

1 H atom attached to $COOCH_3$.

How many peaks will be present on the ^1H NMR spectrum of 1-chloropropanone? Predict the ratio of the areas of these peaks.

By looking at the structure of 1-chloropropanone we can see that there are two different hydrogen environments, which means there will be 2 peaks on the ^1H NMR spectrum.

There are 2 hydrogens in one environment and 3 hydrogens in the other so the ratio of the peak areas will be 2 : 3.

Two different hydrogen environments.

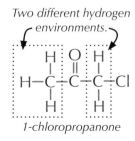

1-chloropropanone

Integration traces

H NMR spectra can get quite cramped and sometimes it's not easy to see the ratio of the areas — so an **integration trace** is often shown. The height increases shown on the integration trace are proportional to the areas of the peaks.

┌─ **Example** ─────────────────────────────

Here's the spectrum for ethanoic acid again:

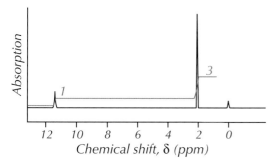

The integration trace (shown in green on the diagram) has a peak around 11.5 ppm and one around 2 ppm.

The heights of the vertical lines are in the ratio 1 : 3 — this means that for every one hydrogen in the first environment there are three in the second environment.

Tip: If the ratio of areas isn't given to you, you can use a ruler to measure the ratios off the integration trace. Measure the heights of the trace peaks and divide the measurements by the smallest peak height, et voilá — you've got your area ratio.

Chemical shift

You can use a table like the one shown in Figure 1 to identify which functional group each peak in a ^{1}H NMR spectrum is due to. Don't worry — you don't need to learn it. You'll be given one in your exam, so use it. The copy you get in your exam may look a little different, and have different values — they depend on the solvent, temperature and concentration.

Exam Tip
Have a look at a copy of the data sheet that you'll get in the exam before the day (you can download one from OCR's website). Then you'll know exactly what's on it.

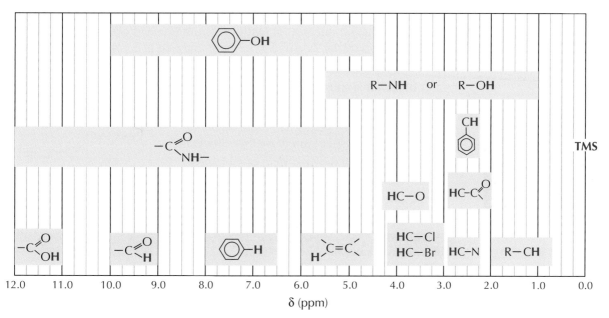

Figure 1: Chemical shift data for ^{1}H NMR.

─ **Example** ─

According to the table, ethanoic acid (CH_3COOH) should have a peak at 11 – 12 ppm due to an H atom in a -COOH group, and a peak at 2.0 – 2.9 ppm due to H atoms in a CH_3CO- group.

You can see these peaks on the ^{1}H NMR spectrum of ethanoic acid, on the right:

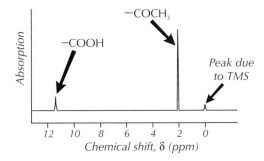

Practice Questions — Application

Q1 a) How many hydrogen environments are there in the molecule 1,2,2-tribromopropane?

  b) How many peaks will the ^{1}H NMR spectrum of 1,2,2-tribromopropane have?

Q2 Draw an alkane molecule that has two hydrogen environments.

Q3 The ^{1}H NMR spectrum of a haloalkane molecule is shown on the right.

  a) How many hydrogen environments are there in this molecule?

  b) What is the area ratio of the peaks on this spectrum?

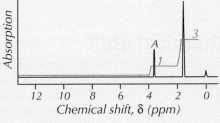

  c) This molecule contains a total of 8 hydrogen atoms. How many hydrogen atoms are there in each environment?

Q4 A scientist produces a ^{1}H NMR spectrum of a hydrocarbon. It has two peaks, one at $\delta = 1.7$ ppm and one at $\delta = 4.8$ ppm.

  a) What is causing the peak at $\delta = 1.7$ ppm?

  b) What is causing the peak at $\delta = 4.8$ ppm?

Q5 The ester methyl ethanoate is shown on the right.

  a) How many peaks will there be on the ^{1}H NMR spectrum of methyl ethanoate?

  b) What will the area ratio of the peaks on this spectrum be?

  c) Predict the approximate δ values of all the peaks in this spectrum.

Figure 2: *Methyl ethanoate is used a solvent in many fast-drying spray paints and spray glues.*

Practice Questions — Fact Recall

Q1 What does the number of peaks on a ^{1}H NMR spectrum tell you?

Q2 What does the area under the peaks on a ^{1}H NMR spectrum tell you?

Q3 What information would the height increases of the integration trace on a ^{1}H NMR spectrum give you?

8. More ¹H NMR Spectroscopy

You've finally reached the last topic about NMR spectroscopy, hurrah. This topic covers a bit more about ¹H NMR spectra, including how NMR spectra can help you to identify molecules — plus a bit about how they're made.

Splitting patterns

The peaks on a ¹H NMR spectrum may be split into smaller peaks (this is called spin-spin splitting). These split peaks are called **multiplets**. Peaks always split into the number of hydrogens on the neighbouring carbons, plus one. It's called the **n + 1 rule**. Some of the different **splitting patterns** you'll find in ¹H spectra are shown in Figure 1.

Type of peak	Structure of peak	Number of hydrogens on adjacent carbons
Singlet	⋀	0
Doublet	⋀⋀	1
Triplet	⋀⋀⋀	2
Quartet	⋀⋀⋀⋀	3

Figure 1: *Splitting patterns in ¹H NMR.*

Learning Objectives:

- Know how to use a ¹H NMR spectrum to predict the number of non-equivalent protons adjacent to a given proton from the spin-spin splitting pattern, using the n + 1 rule.

- Be able to predict the splitting patterns of the protons in a given molecule.

- Understand the need for deuterated solvents, e.g. CDCl₃, when running an NMR spectrum.

- Know how to identify O–H and N–H protons by proton exchange using D₂O.

- Know how to use the ¹H NMR spectrum of a molecule to predict possible structures for the molecule.

Specification Reference 4.3.2

Examples

Here's the ¹H NMR spectrum for 1,1,2-trichloroethane:

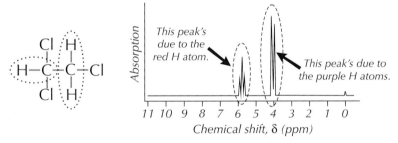

The peak due to the purple hydrogens is split into two because there's one hydrogen on the adjacent carbon atom. The peak due to the red hydrogen is split into three because there are two hydrogens on the adjacent carbon atom.

These splitting rules work just the same for cyclic (ring) compounds too. For example, look at the molecule oxetane (shown below). It has two hydrogen environments, so it has two peaks on its ¹H NMR spectrum:

The peak due to the blue hydrogens is a triplet because there are two hydrogens on the adjacent carbon.

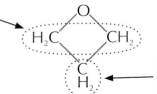

The peak due to the pink hydrogens is a quintet because there are four hydrogens on the adjacent carbons.

Tip: You don't need to know at A-level why ¹H NMR peaks split. It's all down to how the tiny magnetic fields of the hydrogen nuclei interact — it's pretty tricky stuff...

Tip: Multiplets don't stop at quartets — you can go even higher. Here are some of the names for other peak splitting patterns:

5 peaks = quintet
6 peaks = sextet
7 peaks = heptet
8 peaks = octet

Tip: If you want to work out the number of hydrogens on an adjacent carbon from a peak you have to <u>take 1 away</u> from the number of peaks.

Q1 A proton attached to carbon-1 causes a triplet on a ^{1}H NMR spectrum. How many hydrogens are on the carbon adjacent to carbon-1?

Q2 The structure of 2-chlorobut-2-ene has been drawn on the right with its hydrogen environments numbered. For each environment, say how its peak would be split on a ^{1}H NMR spectrum of the molecule.

Figure 2: Atomic model of deuterium. Deuterium has one neutron and one proton in its nucleus, whereas hydrogen has no neutrons.

Deuterated solvents

NMR spectra are recorded with the molecule that is being analysed in solution. But if you used a ordinary solvent, like water or ethanol, the hydrogen nuclei in the solvent would add peaks to the ^{1}H NMR spectrum and confuse things.

To overcome this, the hydrogen nuclei in the solvent are replaced with **deuterium** (D) — an isotope of hydrogen with one proton and one neutron (see Figure 2). Deuterium nuclei don't absorb the radio wave energy, so they don't add peaks to the spectrum. A commonly used example of a **'deuterated solvent'** is deuterated chloroform, $CDCl_3$ (see Figure 3).

Figure 3: Deuterated chloroform.

Identifying OH and NH protons

The chemical shift due to protons (H atoms) attached to oxygen (OH) or nitrogen (NH) is very variable — check out the huge ranges given in the table on page 91. They make a broad peak that isn't usually split (it's a singlet).

There's a clever little trick that chemists can use to identify OH and NH protons. You just run two spectra of the molecule — one with a little deuterium oxide, D_2O, added. If an OH or NH proton is present it'll swap with deuterium (to become an OD or ND group) and, hey presto, the peak that was caused by that group will disappear. (This is because deuterium doesn't absorb the radio wave energy).

Tip: If an ^{1}H NMR spectrum has a triplet and a quartet (like the one on the right) it's very likely that the molecule that produced the spectrum will contain a CH_2CH_3 group.

Tip: Peaks caused by H atoms bonded to an O or an N (e.g. OH in alcohols or NH_2 in amines) always appear as singlets.

┌─ **Example** ──────────

This is the structure of ethanol:

Here's the ^{1}H NMR spectrum of ethanol:

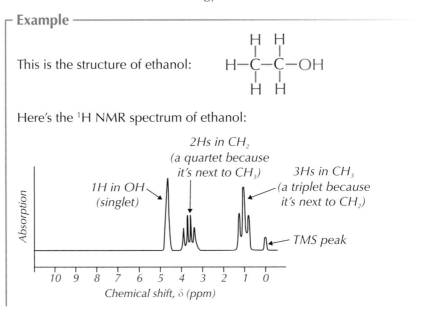

And here's the spectrum produced with a little D_2O added to the ethanol:

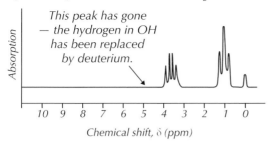

This peak has gone — the hydrogen in OH has been replaced by deuterium.

Predicting structure from ¹H NMR spectra

¹H NMR spectra provide you with an awful lot of information to analyse. Here's a run down of the things to look out for:

- The number of peaks tells you how many different hydrogen environments there are in your compound.
- You can use the chemical shift of each peak to work out what type of environment the hydrogen is in.
- The ratio of the peak areas tells you about the relative number of hydrogens in each environment.
- The splitting pattern of each peak tells you the number of hydrogens on the adjacent carbon. You can use the n + 1 rule to work this out.

And here's one last example to help you on your way...

<hr>

Example

The ¹H NMR spectrum of a carboxylic acid is shown below. Use the spectrum and the chemical shift data on page 91 to predict its structure.

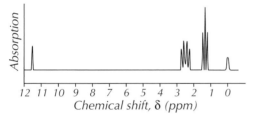

ratio of areas under peaks = 1 : 2 : 3

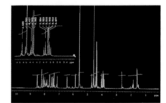

Figure 4: *¹H NMR spectrum. Splitting patterns on the spectra of large organic molecules can be very complicated. Thankfully you'll never have to deal with one like this.*

- There are three peaks so there are three different hydrogen environments.
- Using the chemical shift data, the peak at δ = 1.2 ppm should represent hydrogens in an R–CH group, the peak at δ = 2.4 ppm should represent hydrogens in a –CHCO– group, and the peak at δ = 11.5 ppm should represent a hydrogen in a –COOH group.
- From the area ratios, there's one proton in the environment at δ = 11.7 ppm for every two in the environment at δ = 2.4 ppm and every three in the environment at δ = 1.2 ppm. To fit this data the groups must be –COOH, –CH₂CO– and –CH₃.

Now you know the molecule must contain these groups:

$$-\overset{\overset{\displaystyle O}{\|}}{C}-OH \qquad -\overset{\overset{\displaystyle H}{|}}{\underset{\underset{\displaystyle H}{|}}{C}}-\overset{\overset{\displaystyle O}{\|}}{C}- \qquad H-\overset{\overset{\displaystyle H}{|}}{\underset{\underset{\displaystyle H}{|}}{C}}-$$

- The peak at δ = 1.2 ppm is a triplet, so these protons must have two neighbouring hydrogens. The peak at δ = 2.4 ppm is a quartet, so these protons have four neighbouring hydrogens. The peak at δ = 11.5 ppm is a singlet, so these protons have no neighbouring hydrogens.

Now all you have to do is fit the groups together
in a way that matches the splitting pattern:

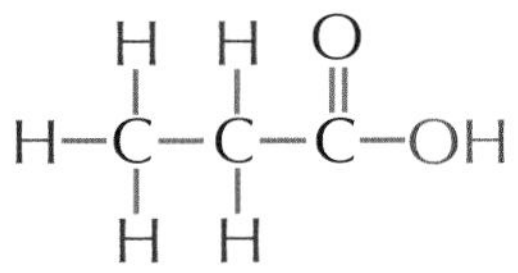

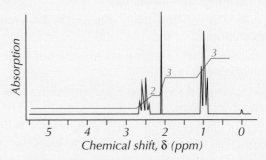

So this is the ^{1}H NMR spectrum of propanoic acid.

Practice Questions — Application

Q1 Use the ^{1}H NMR spectrum of compound **X** below, along with
the chemical shift data on page 91, to work out the structure of
compound **X**. HINT: Compound **X** has the molecular formula C_4H_8O.

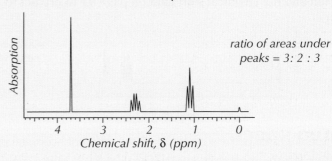

Q2 A high resolution proton NMR spectrum of an ester is shown below.
Use the spectrum along with the chemical shift data on page 91,
to work out the structure of the compound.

*ratio of areas under
peaks = 3: 2 : 3*

Practice Questions — Fact Recall

Q1 What is the n + 1 rule?

Q2 What's the technical name for a peak on an NMR spectrum that's
been split into four smaller peaks?

Q2 Suggest one solvent that could be used to dissolve a sample
for analysis by ^{1}H NMR.

Q3 You have a sample of a chemical that you think contains an OH group.
Explain how you can use NMR spectroscopy to confirm that it does.

9. Infrared Spectroscopy

Here's another analytical technique — you'll probably remember it from AS-Level. Infrared spectroscopy uses the different absorbencies of the bonds in functional groups to produce a spectrum which we can analyse to find out about a compound's structure.

Learning Objective:

- Be able to analyse infrared absorptions in an infrared spectrum to identify the presence of functional groups in organic molecules (limited to molecules containing C, H, N or O).

Specification Reference 4.3.2

The basics

In **infrared (IR) spectroscopy**, a beam of IR radiation is passed through a sample of a chemical. The IR radiation is absorbed by the covalent bonds in the molecules, increasing their vibrational energy. Bonds between different atoms absorb different frequencies of IR radiation. Bonds in different places in a molecule absorb different frequencies too — so the O–H group in an alcohol and the O–H in a carboxylic acid absorb different frequencies. Figure 1 shows what frequencies different bonds absorb — you don't need to learn this data, but you do need to understand how to use it. Wavenumber is the measure used for the frequency (it's just 1/wavelength).

Bond	Where it's found	Frequency / Wavenumber (cm⁻¹)	Type of absorption
C–O	alcohols, carboxylic acids and esters	1000 – 1300	strong
C=O	carboxylic acids, aldehydes, ketones, esters and amides	1640 – 1750	strong, sharp
C–H	most organic molecules	2800 – 3100	strong, sharp
O–H	carboxylic acids	2500 – 3300	medium, broad
N–H	amines and amides	3200 – 3500	medium
O–H	alcohols, phenols	3200 – 3550	strong, broad

Figure 1: *Bond absorption for different functional groups.*

Exam Tip
Don't worry about learning all this data — you'll be given a handy table with all of the groups and wavenumbers on it in the exam.

Tip: O–H groups tend to have broad absorptions because they take part in hydrogen bonding. All the O–H groups are hydrogen bonded to different extents so they all have slightly different absorptions. This results in the broad peak seen on the spectrum.

Infrared spectra

An infrared spectrometer produces a graph that shows you what frequencies of radiation the molecules are absorbing. So you can use it to identify the functional groups in a molecule. The peaks show you where radiation is being absorbed — the 'peaks' on IR spectra are upside-down.

Tip: The 'type of absorption' column tells you what the peak is going to look like. A strong peak is a big, easy-to-see peak, a medium peak is smaller. A sharp peak is quite narrow and a broad peak is really wide.

┌ Examples ───────────────

Ethyl ethanoate is an ester.
Here's its structure:

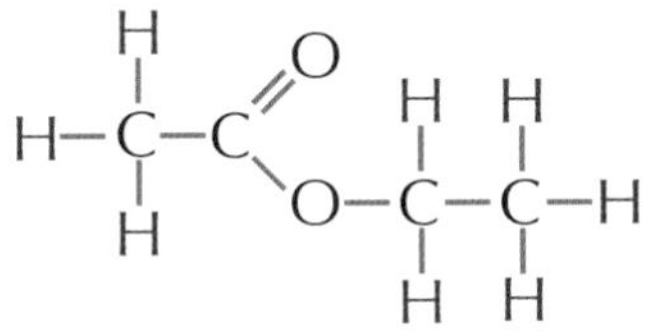

The infrared spectrum of ethyl ethanoate is shown on the next page.
There's a strong, sharp absorption at 1740 cm⁻¹ because of the C=O bond.

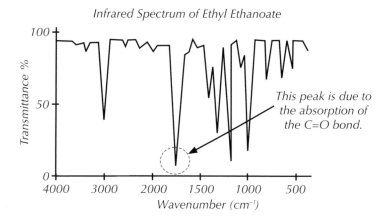

Infrared Spectrum of Ethyl Ethanoate

This peak is due to the absorption of the C=O bond.

Tip: The peaks on an IR spectrum show you the wavelengths of radiation that have been absorbed.

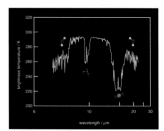

Figure 2: *Infrared spectrum of gases in the Earth's atmosphere. The big peak on the right of the spectrum is caused by the C=O bonds in CO_2.*

Here's the structure of propanamide:

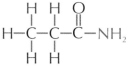

And here's its infrared spectrum:

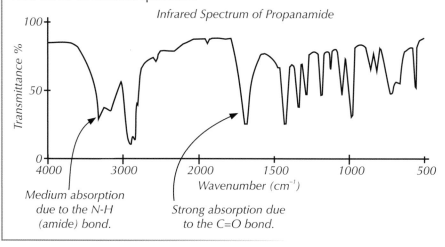

Infrared Spectrum of Propanamide

Medium absorption due to the N-H (amide) bond.

Strong absorption due to the C=O bond.

Exam Tip
Sometimes it can be quite difficult to spot the important peaks on IR spectrums but don't worry — the ones you'll have to analyse in the exam will be really obvious.

Practice Questions — Application

Q1 Identify the peak(s) on the IR spectrum below which indicate the presence of an amide group.

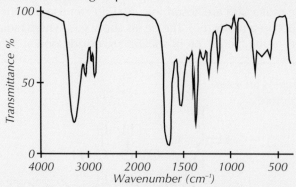

Tip: Use Figure 1 to help you with these questions.

Q2 The formula of Compound **Y** is $C_3H_7NO_2$. Its IR spectrum has a strong, sharp peak at 1680 cm⁻¹, a broad peak at 2800 cm⁻¹ and a medium peak at 3300 cm⁻¹. Give a possible structure for compound **Y**.

10. More on Spectra

Finally the end of the analysis module is in sight... This last topic's about how you can put together information from lots of different techniques to work out a molecule's structure.

Predicting structures from spectra

All the spectroscopy techniques in this section will give clues to the identity of a mystery molecule, but you can be more certain about a structure (and avoid jumping to wrong conclusions) if you look at data from several different types of spectrum.

Learning Objective:
- Be able to combine evidence from a number of spectra, including NMR, IR and mass spectra, to deduce structures of organic molecules (limited to molecules containing C, H, N or O).

Specification Reference 4.3.2

--- Example ---

The following spectra were all obtained from the same molecule. Deduce the structure of the molecule.

Mass spectrum

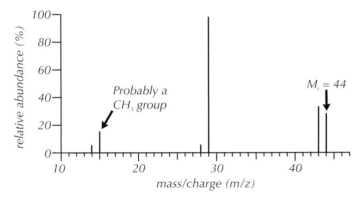

Probably a CH_3 group

$M_r = 44$

This tells you that the molecule has a molecular mass of 44 and is likely to contain a CH_3 group.

Exam Tip
Don't forget that in the exam you'll have NMR and infrared absorption data tables to use. There are versions of these data tables on pages 87, 91 and 97.

Infrared spectrum

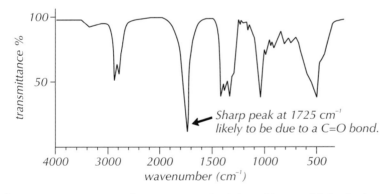

Sharp peak at 1725 cm^{-1} likely to be due to a C=O bond.

Figure 1: *Researchers using different types of spectra to identify a molecule.*

This IR spectrum strongly suggests a C=O bond in an aldehyde, ketone, amide, ester or carboxylic acid.

Since it doesn't also have a broad absorption between 2500 cm^{-1} and 3300 cm^{-1}, this molecule does not contain an O–H bond, so it can't be a carboxylic acid. Also, as there is no absorption between 3200 cm^{-1} and 3500 cm^{-1} there is no N–H bond either, so the molecule can't be an amide.

¹H NMR

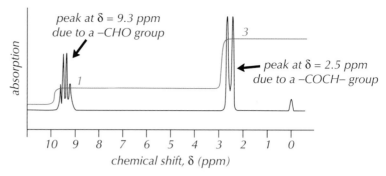

The ¹H NMR spectrum suggests a molecule with two hydrogen environments. The peak at δ = 9.3 ppm is due to a hydrogen in a –CHO group. (It can't be an amide group because the IR spectrum ruled that out, and it can't be a phenol group because that would give a molecule with an M_r higher than 44.) The peak at δ = 2.5 ppm is due to the hydrogen atoms in a –COCH– group. (It can't be R–NH, R–OH or HC–N because there aren't peaks matching these groups on the IR spectrum and it can't be a methylbenzene group because that would give a molecule with an M_r higher than 44.)

The area under the peaks is in the ratio 1 : 3, which means they must be –CHO and –COCH₃ groups. The splitting pattern shows that the protons must be on adjacent carbon atoms because they are splitting each other.

Tip: When you're solving a problem like this one, try starting off by quickly jotting down everything you can learn from each of the spectra. That way you shouldn't miss any information.

¹³C NMR

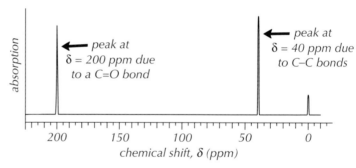

The ¹³C NMR spectrum shows that the molecule has two carbon environments. The peak at δ = 200 ppm corresponds to a carbon in a carbonyl group and the peak at δ = 40 ppm is due to a C–C bond. (It can't be caused by a C–N bond because there isn't a peak matching that on the IR spectrum, and it can't be a C–Cl or C–Br bond because that would give a molecule with an M_r higher than 44.)

Putting all this together we have a molecule with a mass of 44, which contains a CH₃ group next to an aldehyde group. So the structure of the molecule must be:

$$H-\overset{\displaystyle H}{\underset{\displaystyle H}{C}}-\overset{\displaystyle O}{C}-H$$

...which is the aldehyde ethanal.

Tip: When you've come up with your final answer it's a good idea to check it against all the spectra — just to make doubly sure that it fits.

You won't always get all four different kinds of spectra — sometimes you'll have to work out a structure from two or three different types.

Tip: The four different types of spectra are most useful for different things. A mass spectrum gives you the M_r of the molecule. IR spectra are really handy for identifying functional groups. NMR spectra are best for working out the fine structure of the molecule once you know its formula.

Example

The mass spectrum and ^{1}H NMR spectrum of an unknown alkene are shown below. Use the spectra to identify the alkene.

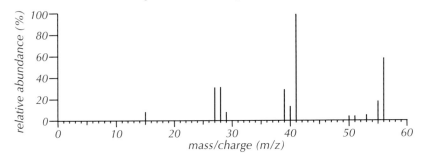

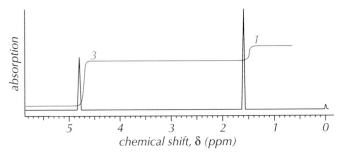

Mass spectrum

- The M peak is at m/z = 56, so the alkene has a molecular mass of 56.
- There's a peak at m/z = 15, so it probably contains a CH_3 group.

If the molecule is an alkene with an M_r of 56, its molecular formula must be C_4H_8. There are three alkene isomers with this molecular formula:

Tip: When you get to the stage where you're sure what the formula of the mystery compound is, it's a really good idea to sketch out all the isomers it could possibly be. It's usually easier to narrow down a list of options than to try drawing a molecule that fits from scratch.

but-1-ene   *but-2-ene*   *2-methylpropene*

Now you can use the ^{1}H NMR spectrum to work out which isomer it is.

^{1}H NMR

- The alkene molecule has two hydrogen environments.
- The area under the peaks is in the ratio 1 : 3.
- The peak at δ = 1.6 ppm must be due to an R–CH group (it's probably the CH_3 group). It's a singlet, so it can't be next door to any other hydrogens.
- The peak at δ = 4.8 ppm must be the C=C group (the alkene group). It's also a singlet, so it can't be next door to any other hydrogens either.

But-1-ene has four hydrogen environments, so it can't be that. But-2-ene and 2-methylpropene both have two hydrogen environments in a ratio of 1 : 3. But only 2-methylpropene has two singlets on its ^{1}H NMR spectrum. So the unknown alkene must be 2-methylpropene.

Exam Tip
There's usually just one mark for identifying the molecule in a question like this. The rest come from explaining all the info you can get from the spectra — so don't worry if you can't work out exactly what it is.

Q1 All four spectra shown below are for the same molecule. Use them to identify the molecule.

Tip: Use the tables on pages 87, 91 and 97 to help you answer these questions.

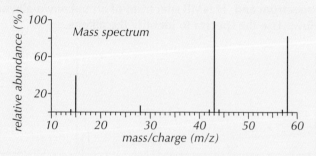

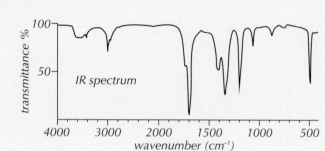

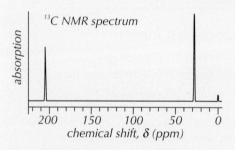

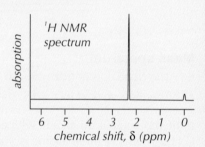

Q2 The IR spectrum and the ^{13}C NMR spectrum of a molecule with the formula $C_4H_8O_2$ are shown below. Use them to identify the molecule.

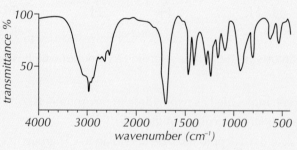

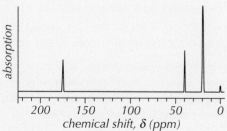

Section Summary

Make sure you know...

- That chromatography is used to separate out mixtures of chemicals.
- That in chromatography you always have a mobile phase and a stationary phase, and that the mixture separates out because the different components spend different amounts of time in each phase.
- That the mobile phase in chromatography can be a liquid or a gas.
- What the mobile phase and stationary phase are in thin-layer chromatography (TLC).
- That in TLC how far a substance travels depends on how strongly it's adsorbed to the stationary phase.
- What an R_f value is and how to calculate one using a TLC chromatogram.
- What the mobile phase and stationary phase are in gas chromatography (GC).
- That in GC how long a substance takes to travel through the machine depends on how soluble it is in a liquid stationary phase, or how strongly it is adsorbed to a solid stationary phase.
- What retention time is and how to find it using a gas chromatogram.
- How to interpret a gas chromatogram (including retention times and relative peak areas).
- The problems with using gas chromatography to identify substances.
- How to find the relative molecular mass of a molecule from its mass spectrum.
- How to work out the structure of a molecule from the pattern of fragment ions on its mass spectrum.
- That chromatography can be combined with mass spectrometry to give a way of separating mixtures and identifying chemicals that works better than chromatography on its own.
- How gas chromatography-mass spectrometry (GC-MS) and high performance liquid chromatography-mass spectrometry (HPLC-MS) equipment are used to separate and identify substances.
- Some of the real-life uses of GC-MS including forensics, airport security, environmental analysis and in space exploration vehicles.
- How nuclear magnetic resonance (NMR) spectroscopy works.
- How to work out how many carbon or hydrogen environments a molecule contains.
- That chemical shift (δ) depends on the molecular environment of a nucleus.
- Why tetramethylsilane (TMS) is used as a standard in NMR spectroscopy.
- That magnetic resonance imaging (MRI) scanning is a form of NMR used to diagnose illnesses by producing pictures of the inside of the body.
- That ^{13}C NMR (carbon-13 NMR) gives you information about the number of carbon atoms in a molecule and the environments they're in.
- How to use a ^{13}C NMR spectrum to work out the structure of a molecule.
- That ^{1}H NMR (proton NMR) gives you information about the number of hydrogen atoms in a molecule and the environments they're in.
- That integration traces and area ratios can tell you the relative number of hydrogen atoms in different environments.
- How to use peak splitting patterns on a ^{1}H NMR spectrum to work out how many hydrogens there are on the neighbouring carbons (using the n + 1 rule).
- Why samples for ^{1}H NMR spectroscopy have to be dissolved in deuterated solvents, like $CDCl_3$.
- How to use deuterium oxide (D_2O) to confirm that a molecule contains a hydrogen atom in an OH or NH group using ^{1}H NMR spectroscopy.
- How to use a ^{1}H NMR spectrum to work out the structure of a molecule.
- How to use infrared (IR) spectroscopy to work out what bonds a molecule contains.
- How to combine data from different analytical methods to find the structure of an unknown molecule.

Exam-style Questions

1   A forensic scientist is analysing a sample of chemicals taken from the scene of a fire. The scientist uses GC-MS to identify the compounds in the mixture.

(a)   Explain how GC-MS is used to identify the different components in a mixture.

(2 marks)

(b)   The sample contains several short-chain alkanes.
Suggest why the scientist could not use gas chromatography alone to identify the components of the mixture.

(2 marks)

(c)   Several of the substances that the scientist finds in the mixture are common components of petrol. The structures of two of these molecules, butane and methylbenzene, are shown below.

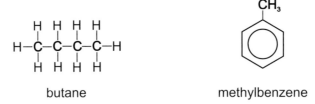

butane   methylbenzene

(i)   The mass spectrum of butane has a major peak at 43 m/z.
Identify the fragment ion that caused this peak.

(1 mark)

(ii)   The scientist runs a sample of methylbenzene through an NMR spectrometer.
How many peaks will appear on the ^{13}C NMR spectrum of this molecule?

(1 mark)

2   The infrared spectrum of an organic molecule is shown below.

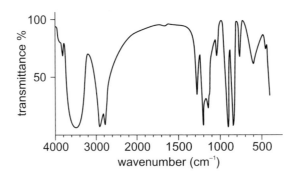

(a)   Use the infrared spectrum and the table on page 97 to say which homologous series the molecule belongs to. Explain your reasoning.

(2 marks)

(b)   The ^{1}H NMR spectrum of the same molecule is shown below.

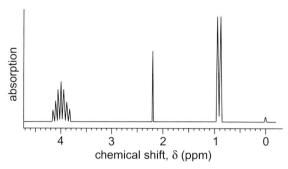

(i) Suggest a solvent that you could use to dissolve the sample for this spectrum.

(1 mark)

(ii) Use the chemical shift values and splitting patterns to identify the chemical.
Explain your reasoning. You may use the table on page 91 to help with this question.

(6 marks)

(iii) A second ^{1}H NMR spectrum was produced for the same molecule,
but this time a little D_2O was added to the sample.
Explain how this spectrum would look different to the first one.

(1 mark)

3   A scientist has a sample of a fruit flavouring that is used in soft drinks.
He uses thin-layer chromatography to separate out the components of the mixture.
The thin-layer chromatogram that he produces is shown below.

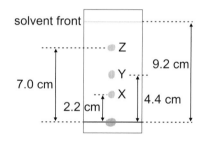

(a)   Explain why the components of the mixture separate as they travel up the plate.

(2 marks)

(b)   Calculate the R_f value of spot X.

(1 mark)

(c)   Spot Y is made up of the ester methyl 2-methylpropanoate.
The structure of this ester is shown below, with its carbon atoms labelled.

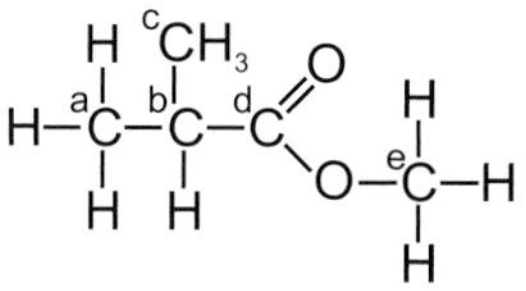

The ^{1}H NMR spectrum of this ester has three peaks. Describe how the peaks will
be split. State which hydrogen atoms are responsible for each splitting pattern.

(3 marks)

4   A student is given samples of two unknown chemicals. She is asked to use analysis techniques to identify the chemicals.

(a)   The student is told that the first chemical has the molecular formula $C_3H_6Cl_2$.

She produces a ^1H NMR spectrum of this chemical, which is shown below.

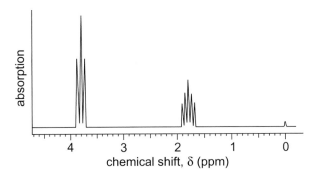

Use the chemical shift values and splitting patterns to identify the chemical. Explain your reasoning.
You may use the table on page 91 to help with this question.

In your answer, you should use appropriate technical terms, spelled correctly.

(6 marks)

(b)   The chemical in the second sample contains only carbon, hydrogen and oxygen. The mass spectrum and the ^{13}C NMR spectrum of this compound are shown below.

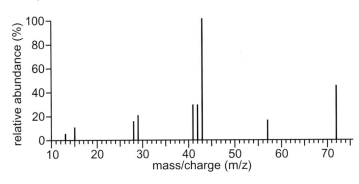

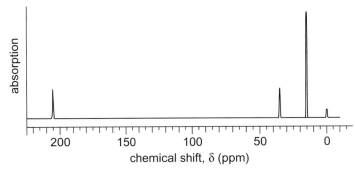

Use these spectra to identify the molecule. Explain your reasoning.
You may use the table on page 87 to help with this question.

(5 marks)

1. Reaction Rates

Learning Objectives:
- Be able to explain and use the term rate of reaction.
- Be able to deduce the rate of a reaction from a concentration–time graph.

Specification Reference 5.1.1

Understanding all about the rates of chemical reactions is a really important part of A2 Chemistry. You've already learnt a bit about reaction rates at AS-level, but now it's time to cover things in a bit more detail.

What are reaction rates?

The **reaction rate** is the change in the amount of reactants or products per unit time (normally per second). If the reactants are in solution, the rate'll be the change in concentration per second and the units will be $mol\ dm^{-3}\ s^{-1}$.

Measuring the progress of a reaction

If you want to find the rate of a reaction, you need to be able to follow the reaction as it's occurring. Although there are quite a few ways to follow reactions, not every method works for every reaction. You've got to pick a property that changes as the reaction goes on. Here are a few examples:

Gas volume

If a gas is given off, you could collect it in a gas syringe and record how much you've got at regular time intervals.

> **Tip:** Make sure you remember the units of reaction rate ($mol\ dm^{-3}\ s^{-1}$) — you'll need to give them with all your calculations.

--- Example ---

This would work for the reaction between an acid and a carbonate in which carbon dioxide gas is given off.

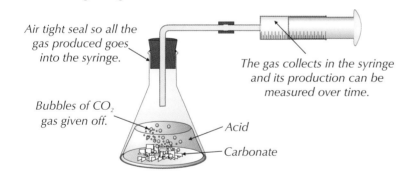

Air tight seal so all the gas produced goes into the syringe.

The gas collects in the syringe and its production can be measured over time.

Bubbles of CO_2 gas given off.

Acid

Carbonate

> **Tip:** You don't always monitor the amount of product produced — sometimes it's easier to monitor the consumption of a reactant instead.

Colour change

Sometimes you can track the colour change of a reaction using a gadget called a colorimeter.

--- Example ---

In the reaction between propanone and iodine, the brown colour fades.

$$CH_3COCH_{3(aq)} + I_{2(aq)} \rightarrow CH_3COCH_2I_{(aq)} + H^+_{(aq)} + I^-_{(aq)}$$

colourless   *brown*   *colourless*

Figure 1: *Measuring the rate of a reaction that involves a colour change.*

Figure 2: *An experiment to measure the electrical conductivity of two different acids.*

Electrical conductivity

If the number of ions changes, so will the electrical conductivity. So if the number of ions changes during a reaction, you can monitor the progress of the reaction by monitoring the electrical conductivity.

┌─ **Example** ─────────────────────

In the reaction between propanone and iodine on the previous page, H^+ and I^- ions are produced, so you can monitor the progress of the reaction by monitoring the electrical conductivity.

Working out reaction rates

You can work out the rate of a reaction using a concentration-time graph. If you draw a graph of the amount of reactant or product against time for a reaction, the rate at any point is given by the gradient at that point on the graph. If the graph's a curve, you have to draw a **tangent** to the curve and find the gradient of that. A tangent is a line that just touches a curve and has the same gradient as the curve does at that point. Figure 3 shows how a graph of the concentration of a reactant against time might look.

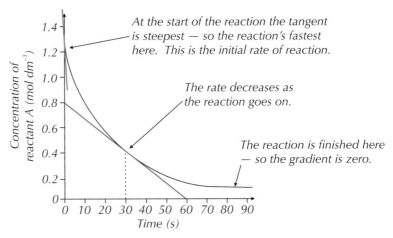

Figure 3: *Graph showing the concentration of a reactant against time.*

Tip: The rate of reaction slows down as time progresses. This is because the reactants get used up, and so collisions between reactant molecules become less likely.

Tip: Don't forget, the x-axis is the horizontal axis and the y-axis is the vertical axis.

The gradient of a tangent is the change in vertical height (Δy) divided by the change in horizontal width (Δx).

┌─ **Example** ─────────────────────

On the concentration-time graph in Figure 3, the gradient of the blue tangent is the rate of reaction at 30 seconds. This tangent makes a triangle with the y-axis and the x-axis. The change in y is –0.8 and the change in x is 60, so:

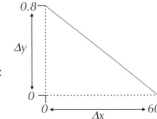

$$\text{Gradient} = \frac{\Delta y}{\Delta x} = \frac{-0.8}{60} = -0.013 \text{ mol dm}^{-3} \text{ s}^{-1}$$

This means that the rate of reaction at 30 seconds is 0.013 mol dm^{-3} s^{-1}.

The sign of the gradient doesn't really matter — it's a negative gradient when you're measuring the reactant concentration because the reactant decreases. If you measured the product concentration, it'd be a positive gradient.

Practice Question — Application

Q1 The concentration-time graph for a reaction is shown below:

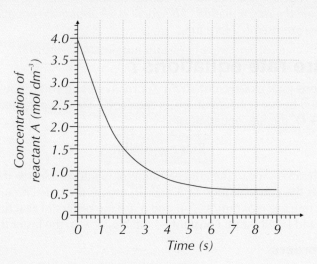

Exam Tip
Don't be afraid to draw on the graphs you're given in the exam — you'll need to draw tangents to find the gradients of curves.

Determine the rate of this reaction after:

a) 1 second.

b) 2 seconds.

c) 4 seconds.

Practice Questions — Fact Recall

Q1 What is a reaction rate?

Q2 What are the units of reaction rate?

Q3 Suggest three ways in which the progress of a reaction could be measured.

Q4 a) Describe how you would produce a concentration-time graph for a reaction.

 b) Explain how you could determine the rate of reaction at a particular time using a concentration-time graph.

- Be able to deduce, from orders, a rate equation of the form: rate = $k[A]^m[B]^n$, for which m and n are 0, 1 or 2.
- Be able to explain and use the terms rate constant and order.
- Be able to calculate the rate constant, k, from a rate equation.
- Be able to explain qualitatively the effect of temperature change on a rate constant and hence the rate of a reaction.

  Specification Reference 5.1.1

2. Rate Equations

The rate of a reaction is linked to the concentrations of the reactants by something called a rate equation. This topic is all about rate equations and why they are useful. Have fun...

What are rate equations?

Rate equations look ghastly, but all they're really telling you is how the rate is affected by the concentrations of reactants. For a general reaction: **A + B → C + D**, the rate equation is:

$$\text{Rate} = k[A]^m[B]^n$$

The square brackets mean the concentration of whatever's inside them. So [A] means the concentration of A and [B] means the concentration of B. The units of rate are $mol\ dm^{-3}\ s^{-1}$. *m* and *n* are the **orders of reaction** (more on this below) and k is the **rate constant** — the bigger k is, the faster the reaction.

Reaction orders

m and n are the orders of the reaction with respect to reactant A and reactant B. *m* tells you how the concentration of reactant A affects the rate and *n* tells you the same for reactant B.

- If [A] changes and the rate stays the same, the order of reaction with respect to A is 0. So if [A] doubles, the rate will stay the same. If [A] triples, the rate will stay the same.

- If the rate is proportional to [A], then the order of reaction with respect to A is 1. So if [A] doubles, the rate will double. If [A] triples, the rate will triple.

- If the rate is proportional to $[A]^2$, then the order of reaction with respect to A is 2. So if [A] doubles, the rate will be $2^2 = 4$ times faster. If [A] triples, the rate will be $3^2 = 9$ times faster.

The overall order of the reaction is $m + n$. So, if m was 2 and n was 1 the overall order of the reaction would be $2 + 1 = 3$.

Writing rate equations

You need to know how to write rate equations for reactions. This example shows you how:

┌─ **Example** ─────────────────────────────

The chemical equation below shows the acid–catalysed reaction between propanone and iodine.

$$CH_3COCH_{3(aq)} + I_{2(aq)} \xrightarrow{\quad H^+_{(aq)} \quad} CH_3COCH_2I_{(aq)} + H^+_{(aq)} + I^-_{(aq)}$$

This reaction is first order with respect to propanone, first order with respect to $H^+_{(aq)}$ and zero order with respect to iodine. Write the rate equation for this reaction.

In this example there are three things that you need to think about — the orders of reaction of propanone (CH_3COCH_3), iodine (I_2) and hydrogen ions (H^+). (Even though H^+ is a catalyst, rather than a reactant, it can still be in the rate equation because it affects the rate of reaction.) So the rate equation will be in the form Rate = $k[A]^m[B]^n[C]^x$.

Tip: There are only two reactants in this general reaction, but you can write rate equations for equations with any number of reactants. E.g. if there are three reactants the equation is:

Rate = $k[A]^m[B]^n[C]^x$

You're told the reaction orders with respect to each reactant in the question so just use that information to construct the rate equation:

$$\text{Rate} = k[CH_3COCH_3]^1[H^+]^1[I_2]^0$$

But $[X]^1$ is usually written as $[X]$, and $[X]^0$ equals 1 so is usually left out of the rate equation. So you can simplify the rate equation to:

$$\text{Rate} = k[CH_3COCH_3][H^+]$$

This rate equation shows that the rate of reaction is proportional to the concentrations of propanone and H^+. So doubling the concentration of either propanone or H^+ will double the rate of the reaction.

Tip: When simplifying rate equations think about the indices laws from maths — the same rules apply here. Anything to the power of zero is one (e.g. $[X]^0 = 1$) and anything to the power of one doesn't change (e.g. $[X]^1 = [X]$).

Calculating the rate constant

If you know the orders of a reaction, you can use the rate equation and experimental data to work out the rate constant, k. The units of k vary, so you'll need to work them out too.

Example

The reaction below is second order with respect to NO and zero order with respect to CO and O_2.

$$NO_{(g)} + CO_{(g)} + O_{2(g)} \rightarrow NO_{2(g)} + CO_{2(g)}$$

At a certain temperature, the rate is 1.76×10^{-3} mol dm^{-3} s^{-1}, when $[NO_{(g)}] = [CO_{(g)}] = [O_{2(g)}] = 2.00 \times 10^{-3}$ mol dm^{-3}. Find the value of the rate constant, k, at this temperature.

- To answer this question you first need to write out the rate equation:
$$\text{Rate} = k[NO]^2[CO]^0[O_2]^0$$
$$= k[NO]^2$$

- Next insert the concentration and the rate, which were given to you in the question:
$$\text{Rate} = k[NO]^2$$
$$1.76 \times 10^{-3} = k \times (2.00 \times 10^{-3})^2$$

- Rearrange the equation and calculate the value of k:
$$k = \frac{1.76 \times 10^{-3}}{(2.00 \times 10^{-3})^2} = 440$$

- Find the units of k by putting the other units in the rate equation:
$$\text{Rate} = k[NO]^2 \quad \text{so} \quad \text{mol dm}^{-3}\text{s}^{-1} = k \times (\text{mol dm}^{-3})^2$$

- Rearrange the equation to get k:
$$k = \frac{\text{mol dm}^{-3}\,\text{s}^{-1}}{(\text{mol dm}^{-3})^2}$$

- Cancel out units wherever possible. In this example you can cancel out a mol dm^{-3} from the top and bottom lines of the fraction:
$$k = \frac{\cancel{\text{mol dm}^{-3}}\,\text{s}^{-1}}{(\cancel{\text{mol dm}^{-3}})(\text{mol dm}^{-3})} = \frac{\text{s}^{-1}}{\text{mol dm}^{-3}}$$

Exam Tip
If you're asked to calculate the rate constant in an exam, make sure you show your working out. That way you might get some marks even if your final answer is wrong.

Exam Tip
If you get stuck in a calculation, re-read the question to check that you've not missed any information — it's dead easy to miss stuff the first time round.

Tip: You need to know how to work out what units your answer is in — it crops up a lot in this section so it's important that you understand how to do it. Have a look at page 238 for more on finding units.

Tip: 'Inversing the powers' just means switching the sign. So if you've got a mol^2 dm^{-6} on the bottom of the fraction it becomes mol^{-2} dm^6. If you've got mol^{-3} dm^9 it becomes mol^3 dm^{-9} (and so on).

- Get rid of the fraction by inversing the powers of whatever's on the bottom line:

$$k = \frac{s^{-1}}{mol\,dm^{-3}} = mol^{-1}\,dm^3\,s^{-1}$$

- So the answer is:

$$k = 440\ mol^{-1}\,dm^3\,s^{-1}$$

Predicting the rate of a reaction

If you know the rate constant and the rate equation for a particular reaction, you can use them to predict the rate of reaction under different conditions. All you have to do is substitute values into the rate equation and solve to find the rate.

Exam Tip
In the exam, you might be asked to predict a rate of reaction after having written the rate equation and calculated a value for k — so make sure you know how to do it.

┌─ **Example** ───

On the previous page you saw that the rate equation for the reaction $NO_{(g)} + CO_{(g)} + O_{2(g)} \rightarrow NO_{2(g)} + CO_{2(g)}$ was rate = $k[NO]^2$ and you worked out that the rate constant for the reaction is 440 mol^{-1} dm^3 s^{-1}.

Calculate the rate of reaction if the concentration of NO is 0.00500 mol dm^{-3}.

$$Rate = k[NO]^2$$
$$= 440 \times (0.00500)^2$$
$$= 0.011\ mol\ dm^{-3}\ s^{-1}$$

Rate constants and temperature

Reactions happen when the reactant particles collide and have enough energy to break the existing bonds. Increasing the temperature speeds up the reactant particles, so that they collide more often. It also increases the chances of the particles reacting when they do hit each other, as they have more energy. In other words, increasing temperature increases the reaction rate.

According to the rate equation, reaction rate depends only on the rate constant and reactant concentrations. Since temperature does increase the reaction rate, it must change the rate constant. The rate constant applies to a particular reaction at a certain temperature. At a higher temperature, the reaction will have a higher rate constant.

Tip: Because the value of k depends on the temperature, predicted rates of reaction will only be accurate if the reaction is performed at the <u>same temperature</u> as the reaction used to calculate k.

Figure 1: *The reaction between Na$_2$S$_2$O$_3$ and HCl. The solution turns cloudy as the reaction progresses which allows the rate of reaction to be measured.*

Practice Questions — Application

Q1 The following reaction occurs between sodium thiosulfate (Na$_2$S$_2$O$_3$) and hydrochloric acid:

$$Na_2S_2O_{3(aq)} + 2HCl_{(aq)} \rightarrow 2NaCl_{(aq)} + S_{(s)} + SO_{2(g)} + H_2O_{(l)}$$

This reaction is first order with respect to Na$_2$S$_2$O$_3$ and zero order with respect to HCl.

a) Construct the rate equation for this reaction.

b) How would you expect the rate of reaction to change if the concentration of Na$_2$S$_2$O$_3$ were doubled?

Q2 The reaction below is second order with respect to NO and first order with respect to Cl_2:

$$2NO_{(g)} + Cl_{2(g)} \rightarrow 2NOCl_{(g)}$$

The rate of reaction is 5.85×10^{-6} mol dm^{-3} s^{-1} at 50 °C, when the concentration of both NO and Cl_2 is 0.400 mol dm^{-3}.

a) Write the rate equation for this reaction.

b) Calculate the value of the rate constant (k) for this reaction at 50 °C.

c) How would you expect the value of k to change if the temperature were increased?

d) Calculate the expected rate of reaction if 0.500 mol dm^{-3} NO were mixed with 0.200 mol dm^{-3} Cl_2 at 50 °C.

Q3 The following reaction occurs between hydrogen and nitrogen monoxide:

$$2H_{2(g)} + 2NO_{(g)} \rightarrow 2H_2O_{(g)} + N_{2(g)}$$

This reaction is first order with respect to H_2 and second order with respect to NO. At temperature X, the rate of reaction was found to be 0.0100 mol dm^{-3} s^{-1} when $[H_2]$ and $[NO]$ were both at a concentration of 5.00×10^{-3} mol dm^{-3}.

a) Calculate the rate constant, k, for this reaction at temperature X and give its units.

b) Predict the rate of reaction at temperature X when $[H_2] = 3.60 \times 10^{-3}$ mol dm^{-3} and $[NO] = 6.40 \times 10^{-3}$ mol dm^{-3}.

c) At temperature Y the value of k was calculated to be 5.80×10^3. Is temperature Y higher or lower than temperature X? Explain your answer.

Exam Tip
When answering calculation questions like these always remember to give the units for your answer.

Practice Questions — Fact Recall

Q1 What does the rate equation tell you?

Q2 In the rate equation Rate = $k[A]^m[B]^n$, what do the following represent:

a) k?   b) $[A]$?   c) m?

Q3 Write the general rate equation for a reaction which has 3 reactants.

Q4 Explain what is meant by the term 'reaction order'.

Q5 What are the units of the rate constant?

Q6 What is the relationship between the rate constant and temperature?

Tip: You need to know how changing the temperature will affect <u>both</u> the reaction rate <u>and</u> the rate constant — so make sure you've got to grips with it.

- Be able to deduce
  the order (0, 1 or
  2) with respect to
  a reactant from a
  rate-concentration
  graph.
- Be able to explain and
  use the term half-life.
- Be able to deduce
  the half-life of a first
  order reaction from
  a concentration-time
  graph.
- Know that the half-life
  of a first-order reaction
  is independent of the
  concentration.

**Specification
Reference 5.1.1**

3. Reaction Orders and Half-Life

You can't work out reaction orders from chemical equations — but you can find them using experiments. There's more on how to do this coming up now...

Working out reaction orders

You can work out the reaction order with respect to a particular reactant using a rate-concentration graph. You can make a rate-concentration graph using a concentration-time graph. Here's how:

- Find the gradient (which is the rate) at various points along the concentration-time graph (see page 108 for a reminder of how to do this). This gives you a set of points for the rate-concentration graph.
- Then just plot the points and join them up with a line or smooth curve.

The shape of the rate-concentration graph tells you the order:

Zero order

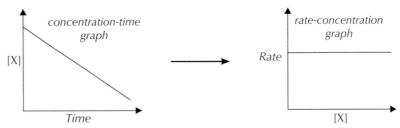

Tip: If something is in [square brackets] it's a concentration. So [X] means the concentration of reactant X.

A horizontal line on a rate-concentration graph means that changing the concentration doesn't change the rate, so the reaction is zero order.

First order

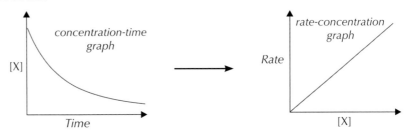

Tip: You can also work out reaction orders using the initial rates method, which will be covered later in this topic.

If the rate-concentration graph is a straight line through the origin, then the reaction is first order. The rate is proportional to [X]. For example, if the concentration of X triples, the rate will triple. If it halves, the rate will halve.

Second order

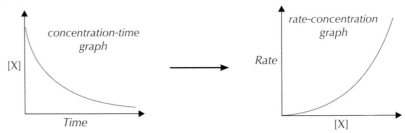

Tip: In theory, a curved rate-concentration graph could mean a higher order than 2. But you won't be asked about any with a higher order than 2 in the exam — so if you see a curve, always say order 2.

A curved rate-concentration graph means that the reaction is second order. The rate is proportional to $[X]^2$. For example, if the concentration of X triples, the rate will be nine times as fast (because $3^2 = 9$).

Half-life

The **half-life** of a reaction is the time it takes for half of the reactant to be used up. You can work out the half-life from a concentration-time graph (see Figure 1). All you have to do is read off the graph how long it takes for the concentration of the reactant to halve.

The half-life of a first order reaction is independent of the concentration. This means that the half life is constant (the same) no matter what the concentration is. This is only true for first order reactions — so if you see a reaction with a constant half-life, you know it must be first order.

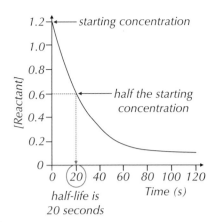

Figure 1: Graph showing how to work out the half-life of a reaction.

Exam Tip
Make sure you learn the definition of half-life — you could be asked for it in the exam.

Tip: Half-life can also be written as $t_{1/2}$.

Tip: Lots of natural processes are first order reactions and so have a constant half-life. E.g. when a radioactive substance decays or a drug is broken down in the body the half-life is usually constant.

Tip: You can measure the half-life between any two concentrations as long as the concentration halves — for example, you could also measure the half-life from 3 to 1.5 mol dm^{-3} and it should be the same.

Example

This graph shows the decomposition of hydrogen peroxide, H_2O_2. Determine the order of reaction with respect to H_2O_2.

To answer this question you have to use the graph to measure the half-life at various points. For example:

$[H_2O_2]$ from 4 to 2 mol dm^{-3} = 200 s,
$[H_2O_2]$ from 2 to 1 mol dm^{-3} = 200 s,
$[H_2O_2]$ from 1 to 0.5 mol dm^{-3} = 200 s.

The half-life is constant, regardless of the concentration, so it's a first order reaction with respect to $[H_2O_2]$.

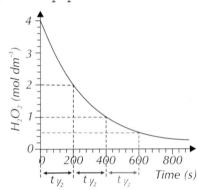

Practice Questions — Application

Q1 Below are the rate-concentration graphs produced as the concentrations of three different reactants (A, B and C) changed during a reaction.

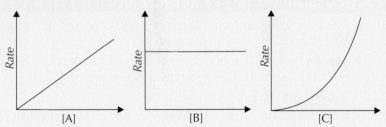

a) Deduce the reaction orders with respect to reactants A, B and C.

b) State how you would expect the rate of reaction to change if the concentration of:

   (i)   reactant A was halved.

   (ii) reactant B was tripled.

   (iii) reactant C was doubled.

Figure 2: Students measuring the rate of a reaction that has a gaseous product.

Q2 The following reaction occurs between nitrogen monoxide (NO) and oxygen (O_2): $2NO_{(g)} + O_{2(g)} \rightarrow 2NO_{2(g)}$

This reaction is second order with respect to NO and first order with respect to O_2.

a) Sketch a graph showing the rate of reaction against the concentration of NO.

b) State how you would expect the rate of reaction to change if the concentration of O_2 was doubled.

Q3 $(CH_3)_3CCl$ will react with hydroxide ions as shown below:

$$(CH_3)_3CCl_{(aq)} + OH^-_{(aq)} \rightarrow (CH_3)_3COH_{(aq)} + Cl^-_{(aq)}$$

The graph below shows how the concentration of $(CH_3)_3CCl$ changes over time:

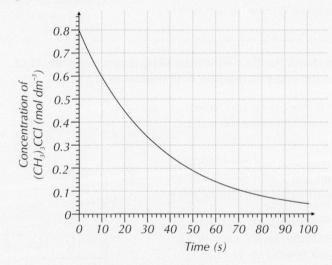

a) Determine the half-life of this reaction.

b) What is the order of reaction with respect to $(CH_3)_3CCl$? Explain your answer.

Exam Tip
Make sure you know how the rate of a reaction is affected when you change the concentration of reactants with different reaction orders (see pages 110 and 114). It's a question that comes up a lot in exams.

Exam Tip
You'll only be asked to find the half-life of reactions that are first order (and so have a constant half-life). This is handy because it means you can double check your answers by finding the half-life at different concentrations and making sure they're the same.

Practice Questions — Fact Recall

Q1 a) Describe how you would produce a rate-concentration graph from a concentration-time graph.

b) Explain how you could determine the order of reaction with respect to a reactant using a rate-concentration graph.

Q2 Define the term half-life.

Q3 How can half-lives be used to determine that a reaction is first order?

4. Initial Rates

Rate-concentration graphs and half-lives aren't the only ways to work out the order of a reaction. Prepare yourself for an exciting (or at least equally usable) alternative — the initial rates method. Cue fanfare...

The initial rates method

On page 114, you found the reaction order by turning a concentration-time graph into a rate-concentration graph and looking at its shape. Another way to find reaction orders is by looking at initial reaction rates. The initial rate of a reaction is the rate right at the start of the reaction. You can find this from a concentration-time graph by calculating the gradient of the tangent at time = 0 (see Figure 1).

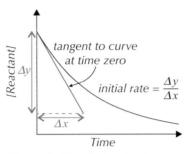

Figure 1: *Graph showing how to calculate the initial rate of reaction.*

Here's how the **initial rates method** works:

- Carry out the reaction, continuously monitoring one reactant. Use this to draw a concentration-time graph.

- Repeat the experiment using a different initial concentration of the reactant. Keep the concentrations of other reactants the same. Draw another concentration-time graph.

- Use your graphs to calculate the initial rate for each experiment using the method above.

- Now look at how the different initial concentrations affect the initial rate — use this to work out the order for that reactant.

- Repeat the process for each reactant (different reactants may have different orders).

The example below shows you how to do this:

Tip: See page 108 for a recap on how to calculate gradients.

Tip: Don't forget — if doubling the concentration doesn't affect the rate it's zero order, if doubling the concentration doubles the rate it's first order and if doubling the concentration quadruples the rate it's second order.

┌─ **Example** ─────────────────────

The table below shows the results of a series of initial rate experiments for the reaction $2NO_{(g)} + Cl_{2(g)} \rightarrow 2NOCl_{(g)}$. Determine the orders of reaction with respect to NO and Cl_2.

Experiment number	[NO] (mol dm⁻³)	[Cl₂] (mol dm⁻³)	Initial rate (mol dm⁻³ s⁻¹)
1	0.125	0.125	1.79×10^{-7}
2	0.250	0.125	7.16×10^{-7}
3	0.250	0.250	1.43×10^{-6}

- Look at experiments 1 and 2 — when [NO] doubles (and [Cl₂] stays constant) the rate is four times faster (it's quadrupled). So the reaction must be second order with respect to NO.

- Look at experiments 2 and 3 — when [Cl₂] doubles (and [NO] stays constant), the rate is two times faster (it's doubled). So the reaction must be first order with respect to Cl₂.

The reaction is second order with respect to NO and first order with respect to Cl_2.

Exam Tip
In questions like this, keep an eye on the powers — 1.43×10^{-6} looks smaller than 7.16×10^{-7} at first glance but it's actually bigger because it has a smaller negative power.

In the exam you could get a question where more than one concentration changes. These are a bit trickier but don't worry, the example below shows you what to do:

Example

The table below shows the results of a series of initial rate experiments for the reaction $NO_{(g)} + CO_{(g)} + O_{2(g)} \rightarrow NO_{2(g)} + CO_{2(g)}$. Work out the reaction orders with respect to each reactant.

Experiment number	[NO] (mol dm^{-3})	[CO] (mol dm^{-3})	[O$_2$] (mol dm^{-3})	Initial rate (mol dm^{-3} s^{-1})
1	2.0×10^{-2}	1.0×10^{-2}	1.0×10^{-2}	0.16
2	1.0×10^{-2}	1.0×10^{-2}	1.0×10^{-2}	0.04
3	2.0×10^{-2}	2.0×10^{-2}	1.0×10^{-2}	0.16
4	4.0×10^{-2}	1.0×10^{-2}	2.0×10^{-2}	0.68

- Look at experiments 1 and 2 — when [NO] doubles (and all the other concentrations stay constant) the rate is four times faster. So the reaction is second order with respect to NO.

- Look at experiments 1 and 3 — when [CO] doubles (but all the other concentrations stay constant), the rate stays the same. So the reaction is zero order with respect to CO.

- Look at experiments 1 and 4 — the rate of experiment 4 is four times faster than experiment 1. The reaction is second order with respect to NO, so the rate will quadruple when you double [NO]. But in experiment 4, [O$_2$] has also been doubled. As doubling [O$_2$] hasn't had any additional effect on the rate, the reaction must be zero order with respect to O$_2$.

So, this reaction is second order with respect to NO, zero order with respect to CO and zero order with respect to O$_2$.

Clock reactions

The method described above is a bit faffy — lots of measuring and drawing graphs. **Clock reactions** can be used to simplify the initial rates method. In a clock reaction, you can easily measure the time it takes for a given amount of product to form — usually there's a sudden colour change. The shorter the time, the faster the initial rate. It's a much easier way to find initial rates than drawing lots of concentration-time graphs.

Example

The most famous clock reaction is the iodine-clock reaction:

- Sodium thiosulfate solution and starch are added to hydrogen peroxide and iodide ions in acid solution.

- The important product is iodine — after a certain amount of time, the solution suddenly turns dark blue.

- Varying iodide or hydrogen peroxide concentration while keeping the others constant will give different times for the colour change. These can be used to work out the reaction order.

Figure 2: *A solution containing starch turns dark blue when iodine is present.*

Practice Questions — Application

Q1 The results of a series of initial rate experiments for the following reaction are shown below:

$$O_3 + C_2H_4 \rightarrow 2CH_2O + \frac{1}{2}O_2$$

Experiment number	$[O_3]$ (mol dm^{-3})	$[C_2H_4]$ (mol dm^{-3})	Initial rate (mol dm^{-3} s^{-1})
1	8.0×10^{-4}	8.0×10^{-4}	0.053
2	1.6×10^{-3}	8.0×10^{-4}	0.106
3	1.6×10^{-3}	2.4×10^{-3}	0.318

Determine the orders of reaction with respect to O_3 and C_2H_4.

Q2 The table below shows the results of a series of initial rate experiments for the reaction:

$$2A + B + C \rightarrow AB + AC$$

Experiment number	[A] (mol dm^{-3})	[B] (mol dm^{-3})	[C] (mol dm^{-3})	Initial rate (mol dm^{-3} s^{-1})
1	1.2	1.2	1.2	0.25
2	1.2	2.4	1.2	1.00
3	1.2	2.4	3.6	3.00
4	0.6	2.4	2.4	1.00

Determine the orders of reaction with respect to reactants A, B and C.

Practice Questions — Fact Recall

Q1 Describe how to determine the initial rate of a reaction from a concentration-time graph.

Q2 a) What is a clock reaction used to find?

b) Give an example of a clock reaction.

Exam Tip
Make sure you get as much practice as you can with the initial rates method — it comes up a lot in exams and you need to be confident with it.

5. The Rate-Determining Step

Reaction mechanisms show step by step how a chemical reaction takes place. The most important step is the rate-determining step — that's what these pages are all about.

What is the rate-determining step?

Mechanisms can have one step or a series of steps. In a series of steps, each step can have a different rate. The overall rate is decided by the step with the slowest rate — the **rate-determining step**.

The rate equation is handy for working out the mechanism of a chemical reaction. You need to be able to pick out which reactants from the chemical equation are involved in the rate-determining step. Here's how:

- If a reactant appears in the rate equation, it must affect the rate. So this reactant, or something derived from it, must be in the rate-determining step.

- If a reactant doesn't appear in the rate equation, then it won't be involved in the rate-determining step and neither will anything derived from it.

An important point to remember about rate-determining steps and mechanisms is that the rate-determining step doesn't have to be the first step in a mechanism. Also, the reaction mechanism can't usually be predicted from just the chemical equation.

Predicting rate equations

The order of a reaction with respect to a reactant shows the number of molecules of that reactant that are involved in the rate-determining step. So, if a reaction's second order with respect to X, there'll be two molecules of X in the rate-determining step. This link means that if you know the rate determining step of a reaction, you can predict the rate equation.

┌─ **Example** ─────────────────────────────

The mechanism for the reaction between chlorine free radicals ($Cl\bullet$) and ozone (O_3) consists of two steps:

$$Cl\bullet_{(g)} + O_{3(g)} \rightarrow ClO\bullet + O_{2(g)} \qquad \text{\textit{This step is slow — it's the rate determining step.}}$$
$$ClO\bullet_{(g)} + O\bullet_{(g)} \rightarrow Cl\bullet + O_{2(g)} \qquad \text{\textit{This step is fast.}}$$

$Cl\bullet$ and O_3 are both in the rate determining step so must both be in the rate equation. So, the rate equation will be:

$$\text{Rate} = k[Cl\bullet]^m[O_3]^n$$

There's only one $Cl\bullet$ and one O_3 molecule in the rate-determining step, so the orders, m and n, are both 1. So the rate equation is:

$$\text{Rate} = k[Cl\bullet][O_3]$$

Predicting reaction mechanisms

It works the other way round too. If you know the rate equation you can predict which reactants are in the rate-determining step and if you know which reactants are in the rate-determining step, you can work out the reaction mechanism. There's an example coming up on the next page to show you how.

Example

2-bromo-2-methylpropane can react with the nucleophile OH^- to give 2-methylpropan-2-ol and bromide ions (Br^-).

There are two possible mechanisms for this reaction. Here's one...

$$H_3C-\underset{\underset{CH_3}{|}}{\overset{\overset{CH_3}{|}}{C}}-Br \quad + \quad OH^- \quad \longrightarrow \quad H_3C-\underset{\underset{CH_3}{|}}{\overset{\overset{CH_3}{|}}{C}}-OH \quad + \quad Br^-$$

Tip: You need to be sure that you understand rate equations before tackling this, or it won't make sense. If you need a reminder, flip back to page 110 and have a quick glance over the relevant bits.

... and here's the other one:

$$H_3C-\underset{\underset{CH_3}{|}}{\overset{\overset{CH_3}{|}}{C}}-Br \quad \longrightarrow \quad H_3C-\underset{\underset{CH_3}{|}}{\overset{\overset{CH_3}{|}}{C^+}} \quad + \quad Br^-$$

This step is slow — it's the rate-determining step.

$$H_3C-\underset{\underset{CH_3}{|}}{\overset{\overset{CH_3}{|}}{C^+}} \quad + \quad OH^- \quad \longrightarrow \quad H_3C-\underset{\underset{CH_3}{|}}{\overset{\overset{CH_3}{|}}{C}}-OH$$

This step is fast.

The actual rate equation was worked out using rate experiments. It is:

$$\text{Rate} = k[(CH_3)_3CBr]$$

OH^- isn't in the rate equation, so it can't be involved in the rate-determining step. The second mechanism is correct because OH^- isn't in the rate-determining step.

If you're suggesting a mechanism, watch out — the most obvious answer might not always be the right one.

Tip: This reaction is zero order with respect to OH^-. Changing the concentration of OH^- ions won't change the reaction rate.

Example

When nitrogen(V) oxide, N_2O_5, decomposes, it forms nitrogen(IV) oxide and oxygen:

$$2N_2O_{5(g)} \rightarrow 4NO_{2(g)} + O_{2(g)}$$

From the chemical equation, it looks like two N_2O_5 molecules react with each other. So that might be your first idea — a simple one-step mechanism. The rate equation for this mechanism would be: rate = $k[N_2O_5]^2$.

But, experimentally, it's been found that the reaction is first order with respect to N_2O_5 — the rate equation is: rate = $k[N_2O_5]$.

This shows that there's only one molecule of N_2O_5 in the rate-determining step. So a one-step mechanism can't be right (a one-step mechanism would have two molecules of N_2O_5 in the rate-determining step).

One possible mechanism that fits the rate equation is:

$$N_2O_{5(g)} \rightarrow NO_{2(g)} + NO_{3(g)} \qquad \textit{slow (rate-determining step)}$$
$$NO_{3(g)} + N_2O_{5(g)} \rightarrow 3NO_{2(g)} + O_{2(g)} \qquad \textit{fast}$$

In this mechanism, only one molecule of N_2O_5 is in the rate-determining step — this fits in with the rate equation.

Tip: When you've come up with a mechanism, don't forget to double check that the steps add up to give you the overall equation. If they don't, it can't be right. (The steps add up fine in this example — I've just checked. Phew.)

Suggesting a mechanism

In the exam, you won't always be given a selection of possible mechanisms and asked to pick the right one. You could be given the overall equation and rate equation for a reaction and be asked to suggest a mechanism yourself. If this happens there are three rules you have to stick to:

- The rate-determining step of the reaction must fit with the rate equation.
- All of the equations in the mechanism must balance.
- The different steps of the reaction must add up to the overall equation.

Often there is more than one correct answer you could give, but as long as you stick to the rules above you should get the marks in the exam.

Example

Nitrogen dioxide can react with fluorine to produce nitryl fluoride (NO_2F):

$$2NO_{2\,(g)} + F_{2\,(g)} \rightarrow 2NO_2F_{(g)}$$

The rate equation for this reaction is rate = $k[NO_2][F_2]$. Suggest a possible two-step mechanism for this reaction. The first step is the slowest step.

The first step is the slowest step so this must be the rate-determining step. From the rate equation you can see that the rate determining step involves one molecule of NO_2 and one molecule of F_2. So the first step in the reaction must be:

$$NO_{2\,(g)} + F_{2\,(g)} \rightarrow \text{ ???}$$

The second molecule of NO_2 isn't involved in the rate-determining step so it must be involved in the second step. This means that the second step in the reaction mechanism must be:

$$NO_{2\,(g)} + \text{ ???} \rightarrow \text{ ???}$$

After that it's just a case of filling in the blanks, making sure that both equations balance and that you only end up with two molecules of NO_2F at the end. One possible solution is shown below:

$$NO_{2\,(g)} + F_{2\,(g)} \rightarrow NO_2F_{(g)} + F\bullet_{(g)}$$
$$NO_{2\,(g)} + F\bullet_{(g)} \rightarrow NO_2F_{(g)}$$

In this example, the F• is an intermediate species — it is generated in the first step and consumed in the second step to leave you with the overall products of the reaction.

Another possible mechanism would be:

$$NO_{2\,(g)} + F_{2\,(g)} \rightarrow NO_2F_{2\,(g)}$$
$$NO_{2\,(g)} + NO_2F_{2\,(g)} \rightarrow 2NO_2F_{(g)}$$

This time NO_2F_2 is the intermediate species.

The correct mechanism is the first one, but in the exam you would get the marks for either answer because either answer fits the information that is given in the question.

Don't panic if you're asked to propose a mechanism in the exam. It sounds hard but as long as you follow the rules above you'll be just fine.

Exam Tip
If the reaction you're given involves a catalyst, you need to make sure that the catalyst is regenerated at the end.

Exam Tip
The rate-determining step won't necessarily be the first step in the reaction — but don't worry, you should be told which one is the slowest step.

Tip: F• is a fluorine radical. See your AS notes for more on free radicals.

Exam Tip
You could have suggested a mechanism like this:
$$NO_2 + F_2 \rightarrow NO + F_2O$$
$$NO_2 + NO + F_2O \rightarrow 2NO_2F$$
But reactions happens when molecules collide and it's very unlikely that 3 molecules would collide simultaneously. So, try and avoid reaction mechanisms which involve more than two molecules reacting at a time.

Practice Questions — Application

Q1 The rate-determining step for a reaction between two reactants (A and B) is $2A + B \rightarrow X + Y$. Predict the rate equation for this reaction.

Q2 The reaction $Br_{2\,(g)} + 2NO_{(g)} \rightarrow 2BrNO_{(g)}$ has a two step mechanism:

Step 1: $Br_{2\,(g)} + NO_{(g)} \rightarrow Br_2NO_{(g)}$

Step 2: $Br_2NO_{(g)} + NO_{(g)} \rightarrow 2BrNO_{(g)}$

Step 1 is the rate-determining step. Write down the rate equation for this reaction.

Q3 The reaction $NO_{2\,(g)} + CO_{(g)} \rightarrow NO_{(g)} + CO_{2\,(g)}$ has a two-step mechanism:

Step 1: $2NO_{2\,(g)} \rightarrow NO_{(g)} + NO_{3\,(g)}$

Step 2: $NO_{3\,(g)} + CO_{(g)} \rightarrow NO_{2\,(g)} + CO_{2\,(g)}$

The rate equation for this reaction is rate = $k[NO_2]^2$.

a) What is the rate-determining step of this reaction? Explain your answer.

b) A one-step mechanism was also proposed for this reaction. How can you tell that this reaction isn't a one-step mechanism?

Q4 Under certain conditions, two molecules of ozone gas (O_3) will decompose to give oxygen gas (O_2):

$$2O_{3\,(g)} \rightarrow 3O_{2\,(g)}$$

The rate equation for this reaction was found to be rate = $k[O_3]$. Suggest a possible two-step mechanism for this reaction, given that the first step is the rate-determining step.

Q5 In the presence of an iodide (I^-) catalyst, hydrogen peroxide decomposes to give oxygen and water, as shown below:

$$2H_2O_{2\,(aq)} \rightarrow 2H_2O_{(l)} + O_{2\,(g)}$$

The rate equation for this reaction is rate = $k[H_2O_2][I^-]$. The first step is the rate-determining step. Suggest a possible two-step mechanism for this reaction.

Practice Questions — Fact Recall

Q1 What is the rate-determining step of a chemical reaction?

Q2 A reaction is second order with respect to oxygen. How many molecules of oxygen are involved in the rate-determining step?

Q3 One molecule of a particular reactant is involved in the rate-determining step of a reaction. What is the order of reaction with respect to that reactant?

Exam Tip
These mechanism questions can feel quite tricky, but don't despair — once you've had a go at all these practice questions you'll feel a lot more confident tackling the ones that come up in the exam.

Tip: Remember that you can use free radicals in possible reaction mechanisms.

Tip: Don't forget — catalysts affect the rate of a reaction so they can be included in the rate equations too.

Figure 1: *Hydrogen peroxide decomposing in the presence of an iodide ion catalyst. The bubbles are oxygen gas forming.*

- Be able to deduce expressions for the equilibrium constant K_c, for homogeneous reactions.

- Be able to calculate the values of the equilibrium constant K_c including determination of units.

- Be able to calculate, the concentration or quantities present at equilibrium, given appropriate data.

Specification Reference 5.1.2

Figure 1: *A flask containing bromine at equilibrium.*

Tip: Most organic reactions are reversible but sometimes the reverse reaction is so slow that the reaction is thought of as going one way.

Tip: The superscript numbers look like the orders of reaction that you saw in rate equations. But they're not — they're the numbers of moles in the equation.

6. The Equilibrium Constant

Hopefully you should remember a bit about reversible reactions and equilibria from AS-level. For A2 you also need to know about the equilibrium constant.

Reactions at equilibrium

Lots of changes are reversible — they can go both ways. To show a change is reversible, you stick in a $\rightleftharpoons$. As the reactants get used up, the forward reaction slows down — and as more product is formed, the reverse reaction speeds up. After a while, the forward reaction will be going at exactly the same rate as the backward reaction. The amounts of reactants and products won't be changing any more, so it'll seem like nothing's happening. It's a bit like you're digging a hole while someone else is filling it in at exactly the same speed. This is called a **dynamic equilibrium**. Equilibria can be set up in physical systems and chemical systems:

Examples

Physical Systems
When liquid bromine is shaken in a closed flask, some of it changes to orange bromine gas. After a while, equilibrium is reached — bromine liquid is still changing to bromine gas and bromine gas is still changing to bromine liquid, but they are changing at the same rate.

$$Br_{2(l)} \rightleftharpoons Br_{2(g)}$$

Chemical Systems
If hydrogen gas and iodine gas are mixed together in a closed flask, hydrogen iodide is formed.

$$H_{2(g)} + I_{2(g)} \rightleftharpoons 2HI_{(g)}$$

Imagine that 1.0 mole of hydrogen gas is mixed with 1.0 mole of iodine gas at a constant temperature of 640 K. When this mixture reaches equilibrium, there will be 1.6 moles of hydrogen iodide and 0.2 moles of both hydrogen gas and iodine gas. No matter how long you leave them at this temperature, the equilibrium amounts never change. As with the physical system, it's all a matter of the forward and backward rates being equal.

A dynamic equilibrium can only happen in a **closed system** (a system where nothing can get in or out) at a constant temperature.

The equilibrium constant, K_c

If you know the molar concentration of each substance at equilibrium, you can work out the **equilibrium constant, K_c**. This is a ratio worked out from the concentrations of the products and reactants after equilibrium is reached. Your value of K_c will only be true for that particular temperature. Before you can calculate K_c, you have to write an expression for it. Here's how:

The lower-case letters a, b, d and e are the number of moles of each substance in the equation.

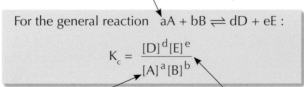

For the general reaction $aA + bB \rightleftharpoons dD + eE$:

$$K_c = \frac{[D]^d[E]^e}{[A]^a[B]^b}$$

The square brackets, [ ], mean concentration in mol dm^{-3}.

The products go on the top line and the reactants go on the bottom line.

Example

For the reaction $H_{2(g)} + I_{2(g)} \rightleftharpoons 2HI_{(g)}$ there are two reactants (H_2 and I_2) and one product (HI). There's one mole of each of the reactants and two moles of the product so the expression for K_c is:

$$K_c = \frac{[HI]^2}{[H_2]^1[I_2]^1} = \frac{[HI]^2}{[H_2][I_2]}$$

Calculating K_c

If you know the equilibrium concentrations, just bung them in your expression. Then with a bit of help from the old calculator, you can work out the value for K_c. The units are a bit trickier though — they vary, so you have to work them out after each calculation.

Example

For the hydrogen iodide example above, the equilibrium concentrations are: [HI] = 0.80 mol dm^{-3}, [H_2] = 0.10 mol dm^{-3} and [I_2] = 0.10 mol dm^{-3} at 640 K. What is the equilibrium constant for this reaction at 640 K?

Just stick the concentrations into the expression for K_c:

$$K_c = \frac{[HI]^2}{[H_2][I_2]} = \frac{0.8^2}{0.1 \times 0.1} = 64$$

To work out the units of K_c put the units in the expression instead of the numbers:

$$K_c = \frac{(mol\,dm^{-3})^2}{(mol\,dm^{-3})(mol\,dm^{-3})} = \frac{\cancel{(mol\,dm^{-3})}\cancel{(mol\,dm^{-3})}}{\cancel{(mol\,dm^{-3})}\cancel{(mol\,dm^{-3})}}$$

The concentration units cancel, so there are no units and K_c is just **64**.

You might have to figure out some of the equilibrium concentrations before you can find K_c. To do this follow these steps:

Step 1: Find out how many moles of each reactant and product there are at equilibrium.

(You'll usually be given the number of moles at equilibrium for one of the reactants. You can then use the balanced reaction equation to work out the number of moles of all the others.)

Step 2: Calculate the molar concentrations of each reactant and product by dividing each number of moles by the volume of the reaction.

(You'll be told the volume in the question but you may have to convert it into different units. To work out molar concentrations you need the volume to be in dm^3.)

Once you've done this you're ready to substitute your values into the expression for K_c and calculate it.

Example

0.20 moles of phosphorus(V) chloride decomposes at 600 K in a vessel of 5.00 dm^3. The equilibrium mixture is found to contain 0.080 moles of chlorine. Write the expression for K_c and calculate its value, including units.

$$PCl_{5(g)} \rightleftharpoons PCl_{3(g)} + Cl_{2(g)}$$

Exam Tip
You may be asked to calculate the molar amounts of some substances in an earlier part of the question — if this happens you can reuse your answers to find K_c. Handy.

1. Find out how many moles of PCl_5 and PCl_3 there are at equilibrium:
   - The equation tells you that when 1 mole of PCl_5 decomposes, 1 mole of PCl_3 and 1 mole of Cl_2 are formed.
   - So if 0.080 moles of chlorine are produced at equilibrium, then there will be 0.080 moles of PCl_3 as well.
   - 0.080 mol of PCl_5 must have decomposed to form 0.080 moles of Cl_2 and PCl_3, so there will be 0.12 moles of PCl_5 left at equilibrium (0.20 − 0.080 = 0.12).

2. Divide each number of moles by the volume of the flask to give the molar concentrations:

$$[PCl_3] = [Cl_2] = \frac{0.080}{5.00} = 0.016 \text{ mol dm}^{-3}$$

$$[PCl_5] = \frac{0.12}{5.00} = 0.024 \text{ mol dm}^{-3}$$

Put the concentrations in the expression for K_c and calculate it:

$$K_c = \frac{[PCl_3][Cl_2]}{[PCl_5]} = \frac{[0.016][0.016]}{[0.024]} = 0.011$$

Exam Tip
When you're writing expressions for K_c make sure you use [square brackets]. If you use (rounded brackets) you won't get the marks.

Now find the units of K_c:

$$K_c = \frac{(\text{mol dm}^{-3})(\cancel{\text{mol dm}^{-3}})}{\cancel{\text{mol dm}^{-3}}} = \text{mol dm}^{-3}$$

So $K_c = \mathbf{0.011 \text{ mol dm}^{-3}}$

Using K_c

If you know the value of K_c you can use it to find unknown equilibrium concentrations. Here's how you do it:

Step 1: Put all the values you know into the expression for K_c.

Step 2: Rearrange the equation and solve it to find the unknown values.

--- Example ---

When ethanoic acid was allowed to reach equilibrium with ethanol at 25 °C, it was found that the equilibrium mixture contained 2.0 mol dm^{-3} ethanoic acid and 3.5 mol dm^{-3} ethanol. The K_c of the equilibrium is 4.0 at 25 °C. What are the concentrations of the other components?

$$CH_3COOH_{(l)} + C_2H_5OH_{(l)} \rightleftharpoons CH_3COOC_2H_{5(l)} + H_2O_{(l)}$$

1. Put all the values you know in the K_c expression:

$$K_c = \frac{[CH_3COOC_2H_5][H_2O]}{[CH_3COOH][C_2H_5OH]} \quad \text{so} \quad 4.0 = \frac{[CH_3COOC_2H_5][H_2O]}{2.0 \times 3.5}$$

Tip: The units of concentration should always be mol dm^{-3}. If your answer doesn't give you this then go back and check your calculation to see where you've gone wrong.

2. Rearranging this gives:

$$[CH_3COOC_2H_5][H_2O] = 4.0 \times 2.0 \times 3.5 = 28.0$$

From the equation, you know that $[CH_3COOC_2H_5] = [H_2O]$, so:

$$[CH_3COOC_2H_5] = [H_2O] = \sqrt{28} = 5.3 \text{ mol dm}^{-3}$$

The concentration of $CH_3COOC_2H_5$ and H_2O is **5.3 mol dm^{-3}**.

Practice Questions — Application

Q1 The following equilibrium exists under certain conditions:

$$C_2H_4 + H_2O \rightleftharpoons C_2H_5OH$$

a) Write out the expression for the equilibrium constant, K_c, for this reaction.

5.00 moles of C_2H_5OH was placed in a container and allowed to reach equilibrium. At a certain temperature and pressure the equilibrium mixture was found to contain 1.85 moles of C_2H_4, and have a total volume of 15.0 dm³.

b) Determine the number of moles of each substance at equilibrium.

c) Calculate the molar concentrations (in mol dm⁻³) of all the reagents at equilibrium.

d) Calculate K_c for this equilibrium.

At a different temperature and pressure the equilibrium constant (K_c) for this reaction is 3.8 and the equilibrium mixture contained 0.80 mol dm⁻³ C_2H_5OH.

e) Determine the equilibrium concentrations of C_2H_4 and H_2O under these conditions.

> **Tip:** Don't forget — you need to work out the units of K_c too.

Q2 Under certain conditions the following equilibrium is established:

$$2SO_2 + O_2 \rightleftharpoons 2SO_3$$

a) Write out an expression for K_c for this reaction.

At a certain temperature the equilibrium concentrations for the three reagents were found to be:

SO_2 = 0.250 mol dm⁻³ O_2 = 0.180 mol dm⁻³ SO_3 = 0.360 mol dm⁻³

b) Calculate K_c for this equilibrium.

c) If all other conditions (including the concentrations of O_2 and SO_3) were to stay the same, what would the equilibrium concentration of SO_2 have to be for K_c to be 15?

Practice Questions — Fact Recall

Q1 Explain what is meant by the term "dynamic equilibrium".

Q2 Describe the conditions that are needed for a dynamic equilibrium to be established.

Q3 Write out an expression for K_c for the general reaction:

$$aA + bB \rightleftharpoons dD + eE$$

Q4 What are the units of K_c?

7. Changing the Equilibrium

- Be able to explain the effect of changing temperature on the value of K_c for exothermic and endothermic reactions.

- Know that the value of K_c is unaffected by changes in concentration, pressure or by the presence of a catalyst.

Specification Reference 5.1.2

The position of equilibrium for a reaction can change if conditions change, but not all changes in conditions result in a change in the value of K_c.

Changing the position of equilibrium

If you change the concentration, pressure or temperature of a reversible reaction, you're going to alter the position of equilibrium. This just means you'll end up with different amounts of reactants and products at equilibrium.

- If the position of equilibrium moves to the left, you'll get more reactants.

$$H_{2(g)} + I_{2(g)} \rightleftharpoons 2HI_{(g)}$$

- If the position of equilibrium moves to the right, you'll get more products.

$$H_{2(g)} + I_{2(g)} \rightleftharpoons 2HI_{(g)}$$

There's a rule that lets you predict how the position of equilibrium will change if a condition changes. This rule is known as **Le Chatelier's Principle**:

Tip: You've come across Le Chatelier's Principle before — in Unit 2 of AS Chemistry.

> Le Chatelier's Principle: If there's a change in concentration, pressure or temperature, the equilibrium will move to help counteract the change.

So, basically, if you raise the temperature, the position of equilibrium will shift to try to cool things down. And if you raise the pressure or concentration, the position of equilibrium will shift to try to reduce it.

Although changes in temperature and changes in concentration both affect the position of the equilibrium, only changing the temperature affects the value of K_c.

Figure 1: Henri Le Chatelier.

Changing the temperature

If you increase the temperature, you add heat. The equilibrium shifts in the **endothermic** (positive ΔH) direction to absorb the heat. Decreasing the temperature removes heat energy. The equilibrium shifts in the **exothermic** (negative ΔH) direction to try to replace the heat. If the forward reaction's endothermic, the reverse reaction will be exothermic, and vice versa. If the change means more product is formed, K_c will rise. If it means less product is formed, then K_c will decrease.

Tip: The ΔH values given for reversible reactions show the ΔH of the forward reaction.

┌ **Examples** ─────────────────

The reaction below is exothermic in the forward direction:

Exothermic ⟶

$$2SO_{2(g)} + O_{2(g)} \rightleftharpoons 2SO_{3(g)} \qquad \Delta H = -197 \text{ kJ mol}^{-1}$$

⟵ *Endothermic*

If you increase the temperature, the equilibrium shifts to the left (in the endothermic direction) to absorb some of the extra heat energy. This means that less product's formed so the concentration of product ([SO_3]) will be less.

$$K_c = \frac{[SO_3]^2}{[SO_2]^2[O_2]}$$ As [SO_3] will be a smaller value, K_c will also be lower.

The reaction below is endothermic in the forward direction:

$$Endothermic \longrightarrow$$
$$2CH_4 \rightleftharpoons 3H_2 + C_2H_2 \qquad \Delta H = +377 \text{ kJ mol}^{-1}$$
$$\longleftarrow Exothermic$$

This time increasing the temperature shifts the equilibrium to the right. This means more product's formed, so K_c increases.

Tip: If the temperature <u>decreases</u> the opposite happens — for reactions that are exothermic in the forward direction K_c will increase and for reactions that are endothermic in the forward direction K_c will decrease.

Changing the concentration

The value of the equilibrium constant, K_c, is fixed at a given temperature. So if the concentration of one thing in the equilibrium mixture changes then the concentrations of the others must change to keep the value of K_c the same.

Tip: Don't get confused — the position of the equilibrium can change without affecting the value of K_c.

Example

$$CH_3COOH_{(l)} + C_2H_5OH_{(l)} \rightleftharpoons CH_3COOC_2H_{5(l)} + H_2O_{(l)}$$

If you increase the concentration of CH_3COOH then the equilibrium will move to the right to get rid of some of the extra CH_3COOH — so more $CH_3COOC_2H_5$ and H_2O are produced. This keeps the equilibrium constant the same.

Changing the pressure

Changing the pressure only really affects equilibria involving gases. Increasing the pressure shifts the equilibrium to the side with fewer gas molecules — this reduces the pressure. Decreasing the pressure shifts the equilibrium to the side with more gas molecules. This raises the pressure again. K_c stays the same, no matter what you do to the pressure.

Example

The following equilibrium exists between nitrogen dioxide (NO_2) and nitrogen tetroxide (N_2O_4):

$$2NO_{2(g)} \rightleftharpoons N_2O_{4(g)}$$

There are 2 moles of gas on the left, but only 1 mole of gas on the right. So an increase in pressure would shift the equilibrium to the right.

This shift in equilibrium can be seen because NO_2 is a brown gas (see Figure 2a). If pressure is applied to the gas (e.g. in a syringe), the colour becomes paler (see Figure 2b). This is because the equilibrium has shifted to the right and some of the brown NO_2 has been converted to N_2O_4 which is colourless.

So, the equilibrium shifts and the value of K_c stays the same.

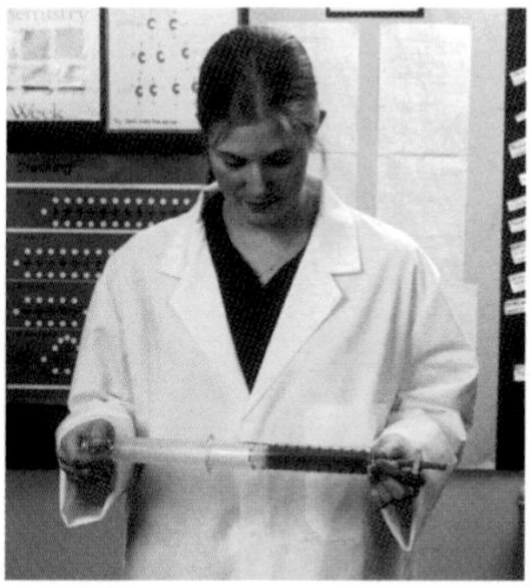

Figure 2a: Equilibrium between $NO_{2(g)}$ (brown) and $N_2O_{4(l)}$ (colourless).

Figure 2b: When pressure is applied the colour changes because the equilibrium shifts in favour of $N_2O_{4(l)}$.

Adding a catalyst

Catalysts have no effect on the position of equilibrium or on the value of K_c. This is because a catalyst will increase the rate of both the forward and backward reactions by the same amount. As a result, the equilibrium position will be the same as the uncatalysed reaction, but equilibrium will be reached faster. So catalysts can't increase yield (the amount of product produced) — but they do decrease the time taken to reach equilibrium.

Exam Tip
Don't be thrown if a reaction you're given in the exam has a catalyst. Catalysts don't affect K_c.

Example

The Haber process is used to synthesise ammonia:

$$N_{2(g)} + 3H_{2(g)} \rightleftharpoons 2NH_{3(g)}$$

This reaction uses an iron catalyst. Adding the iron catalyst decreases the amount of time taken for this reaction to reach equilibrium, but it has no effect on the equilibrium position or on the value of K_c.

Practice Questions — Application

Q1 The following equilibrium is established under certain conditions:

$$2CHClF_2 \rightleftharpoons C_2F_4 + 2HCl \qquad \Delta H = +128 \text{ kJ mol}^{-1}$$

State and explain how you would expect the following to affect the value of K_c for this equilibrium:

a) Increasing the concentration of C_2F_4.

b) Increasing the temperature.

c) Adding a catalyst

Q2 The value of K_c for the following equilibrium increases if the temperature is decreased:

$$2SO_{2(g)} + O_{2(g)} \rightleftharpoons 2SO_{3(g)}$$

a) Is the forward reaction endothermic or exothermic? Explain your answer.

b) How would decreasing the pressure of this reaction affect:

(i) the position of equilibrium?

(ii) the value of K_c?

Q3 The reaction below occurs between methane and steam:

$$CH_{4(g)} + H_2O_{(g)} \rightleftharpoons CO_{(g)} + 3H_{2(g)}$$

The forward reaction is endothermic.

a) How could you increase the value of K_c for this equilibrium?

b) How could you increase production of $H_{2(g)}$ without affecting the value of K_c?

Exam Tip
In the exam, make sure you read the question really carefully and pay attention to whether concentrations and temperatures are increasing or decreasing — one slip up could cause you trouble...

Practice Questions — Fact Recall

Q1 State Le Chatelier's principle.

Q2 How will increasing the temperature affect K_c if:

a) the forward reaction is endothermic?

b) the forward reaction is exothermic?

Q3 Explain why changing the concentration of a reagent does not affect K_c.

Q4 How does increasing the pressure of a reaction affect the value of K_c?

Q5 How does adding a catalyst affect an equilibrium?

8. Acids and Bases

There are a few different theories that describe acids and bases.
One of those theories is the Brønsted–Lowry theory. Here it is...

Brønsted–Lowry acids and bases

Brønsted–Lowry acids are proton donors — they release hydrogen ions (H^+) when they're mixed with water. For example, for the general acid HA:

$$HA_{(aq)} \rightleftharpoons H^+_{(aq)} + A^-_{(aq)}$$

Brønsted–Lowry bases do the opposite — they're proton acceptors.
When they're in solution, they grab hydrogen ions from water molecules.
For example, for the general base B:

$$B_{(aq)} + H_2O_{(l)} \rightleftharpoons BH^+_{(aq)} + OH^-_{(aq)}$$

Reactions of acids

There are a few reactions of acids that you need to know about.

Reactions with metals

Reactive metals react with acids forming a salt and releasing hydrogen gas.
The metal atoms donate electrons to the H^+ ions in the acid solution. The metal atoms are oxidised and the H^+ ions are reduced.

--- Example ---

Magnesium reacts with hydrochloric acid to produce magnesium chloride and hydrogen:

Full equation: $Mg_{(s)} + 2HCl_{(aq)} \rightarrow MgCl_{2(aq)} + H_{2(g)}$

Ionic equation: $Mg_{(s)} + 2H^+_{(aq)} \rightarrow Mg^{2+}_{(aq)} + H_{2(g)}$

Oxidation states: $0 \qquad +1 \qquad +2 \qquad 0$

Oxidation   Reduction

Reactions with carbonates

Carbonates react with acids to produce carbon dioxide, water and a salt.

--- Example ---

Sodium carbonate reacts with sulfuric acid to produce carbon dioxide, water and sodium sulfate:

Full equation: $Na_2CO_{3(s)} + H_2SO_{4(aq)} \rightarrow Na_2SO_{4(aq)} + CO_{2(g)} + H_2O_{(l)}$

Ionic equation: $CO_3^{2-}{}_{(aq)} + 2H^+_{(aq)} \rightarrow H_2O_{(l)} + CO_{2(g)}$

Reactions with bases and alkalis

Acids produce H^+ ions when dissolved in water and alkalis produce OH^- ions.
Acids and alkalis neutralise each other to form water. The other ions present form a salt. The ionic equation for the reaction of an acid with an alkali is:

$$H^+_{(aq)} + OH^-_{(aq)} \rightarrow H_2O_{(l)}$$

--- Example ---

Hydrochloric acid reacts with potassium hydroxide to produce potassium chloride and water:

Full equation: $HCl_{(aq)} + KOH_{(aq)} \rightarrow KCl_{(aq)} + H_2O_{(l)}$

Ionic equation: $H^+_{(aq)} + OH^-_{(aq)} \rightarrow H_2O_{(l)}$

Learning Objectives:
- Be able to describe an acid as a species that can donate a proton and a base as a species that can accept a proton.
- Be able to illustrate, using ionic equations, the role of H^+ in the reactions of acids with metals, carbonates, bases and alkalis.
- Be able to explain qualitatively, in terms of dissociation, the differences between strong and weak acids.
- Be able to describe and use the term conjugate acid-base pairs.

Specification Reference 5.1.3

Tip: Don't forget — oxidation is the loss of electrons, reduction is the gain of electrons. You've seen this at AS so have a skim over your notes if you've forgotten.

Figure 1: *Sodium carbonate reacting with acid. The bubbles are the CO_2 gas that's being given off.*

Tip: Alkalis are bases that dissolve in water.

Acids can react with insoluble bases in a similar way. Here's how an acid neutralises an insoluble base:

$$2H^+_{(aq)} + O^{2-}_{(s)} \rightarrow H_2O_{(l)}$$

Example

Hydrochloric acid reacts with solid copper oxide to produce copper chloride and water:

Full equation: $2HCl_{(aq)} + CuO_{(s)} \rightarrow CuCl_{2(aq)} + H_2O_{(l)}$

Ionic equation: $H^+_{(aq)} + O^{2-}_{(s)} \rightarrow H_2O_{(l)}$

Dissociation in water

Acids and bases dissociate in water. This just means they break up into positively and negatively charged ions. The amount of dissociation depends on how weak or strong the acid or base is. **Strong acids** dissociate (or ionise) almost completely in water — nearly all the H^+ ions will be released. **Strong bases** (like sodium hydroxide) ionise almost completely in water too.

Examples

Hydrochloric acid is a strong acid: $HCl_{(g)} \rightarrow H^+_{(aq)} + Cl^-_{(aq)}$

Sodium hydroxide is a strong base: $NaOH_{(s)} \rightarrow Na^+_{(aq)} + OH^-_{(aq)}$

These reactions are really reversible reactions but the equilibrium lies extremely far to the right, so only the forward reaction is shown in the equation.

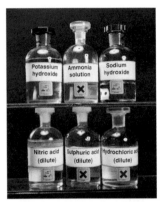

Weak acids (e.g. ethanoic or citric) dissociate only very slightly in water — so only small numbers of H^+ ions are formed. An equilibrium is set up which lies well over to the left. **Weak bases** (such as ammonia) only slightly dissociate in water too. Just like with weak acids, the equilibrium lies well over to the left.

Examples

Ethanoic acid is a weak acid: $CH_3COOH_{(aq)} + H_2O_{(l)} \rightleftharpoons CH_3COO^-_{(aq)} + H_3O^+_{(aq)}$

Ammonia is a weak base: $NH_{3(aq)} + H_2O_{(l)} \rightleftharpoons NH_4^+_{(aq)} + OH^-_{(aq)}$

Conjugate pairs

When an acid reacts with a base, conjugate pairs are formed. A **conjugate pair** is a set of two species that can be transformed into each other by gaining or losing a proton. The species that loses the proton is called the conjugate acid and the species that gains the proton is called the conjugate base.

Conjugate pairs when acids dissolve in water

When an acid is added to water, the equilibrium below is set up:

$$HA_{(aq)} + H_2O_{(l)} \rightleftharpoons H_3O^+_{(aq)} + A^-_{(aq)}$$

When HA loses a proton it forms A^- and when A^- gains a proton it forms HA — HA and A^- are linked by proton transfer so are a conjugate pair. HA loses a proton so is the conjugate acid and A^- gains a proton so is the conjugate base.

conjugate acid $\longrightarrow$ HA $\rightleftharpoons$ H⁺ + A⁻ $\longleftarrow$ *conjugate base*

linked by proton transfer

H_2O and H_3O^+ are also a conjugate pair. H_2O forms H_3O^+ when it gains a proton so it's the conjugate base and H_3O^+ forms H_2O when it loses a proton so it's the conjugate acid.

$$H^+ + H_2O \rightleftharpoons H_3O^+$$

linked by proton transfer — *conjugate acid*

conjugate base

Tip: H_3O^+ is also known as the hydroxonium ion.

So you get two conjugate pairs when an acid dissolves in water:

conjugate pair 2

$$HA + H_2O \rightleftharpoons H_3O^+ + A^-$$

acid 1   base 2   acid 2   base 1

conjugate pair 1

Example

Here's the equilibrium for aqueous HCl. Cl^- is the conjugate base of HCl.

conjugate pair 2

$$HCl + H_2O \rightleftharpoons H_3O^+ + Cl^-$$

acid 1   base 2   acid 2   base 1

conjugate pair 1

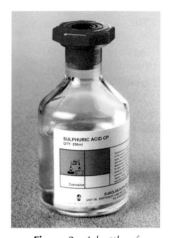

Figure 3: *A bottle of aqueous sulfuric acid. In this bottle the following equilibrium is established:*

$$H_2SO_4 + H_2O \rightleftharpoons H_3O^+ + HSO_4^-$$

H_2SO_4 and HSO_4^- are a conjugate pair — H_2SO_4 is an acid and HSO_4^- is a base.

Conjugate pairs when bases dissolve in water

An equilibrium with conjugate pairs is also set up when a base (B) dissolves in water. Here's the equilibrium:

$$B + H_2O \rightleftharpoons BH^+ + OH^-$$

The base, B, takes a proton from the water to form BH^+ — so B is the conjugate base of BH^+, and BH^+ is the conjugate acid of B. H_2O and OH^- also form a conjugate pair. H_2O is the conjugate acid and OH^- is the conjugate base.

conjugate pair 2

$$B + H_2O \rightleftharpoons BH^+ + OH^-$$

base 1   acid 2   acid 1   base 2

conjugate pair 1

Example

Here's the equilibrium when NH_3 is dissolved in water. NH_4^+ is the conjugate acid of NH_3.

conjugate pair 2

$$NH_3 + H_2O \rightleftharpoons NH_4^+ + OH^-$$

base 1   acid 2   acid 1   base 2

conjugate pair 1

Tip: Alkalis like NaOH and KOH produce hydroxide ions (OH^-). The conjugate acid of hydroxide ions is water.

Identifying conjugate pairs

In the exam you need to be able to identify the conjugate pairs formed in a reaction. It's easy enough to do — just find the species that are linked by proton transfer and work out which one is the acid and which one is the base.

Tip: Two species can't be a conjugate pair if they are on the same side of the equation — they have to be on opposite sides.

┌─ **Example** ─────────────────────────────

When ammonium nitrate, NH_4NO_3 is dissolved in water the following equilibrium is set up: $NH_4^+ + NO_3^- \rightleftharpoons HNO_3 + NH_3$

Identify the conjugate pairs in this reaction.

NH_4^+ and NH_3 are linked by proton transfer so they must form one conjugate pair.

NO_3^- and HNO_3 are also linked by proton transfer so they must be the other conjugate pair.

In the NH_4^+/NH_3 conjugate pair, NH_4^+ donates a proton so must be the conjugate acid — NH_3 accepts a proton so must be the conjugate base.

In the NO_3^-/HNO_3 pair, NO_3^- accepts a proton so must be the conjugate base — HNO_3 donates a proton so must be the conjugate acid.

So the conjugate pairs in this reaction are:

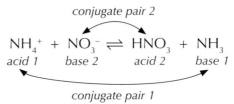

conjugate pair 2

$$NH_4^+ + NO_3^- \rightleftharpoons HNO_3 + NH_3$$
acid 1   base 2   acid 2   base 1

conjugate pair 1

Exam Tip
Always check your answer in the exam — you should end up with an acid and a base from different conjugate pairs on each side of the equation.

Practice Questions — Application

Q1 Write full and ionic equations for the reaction of:
  a) Hydrochloric acid (HCl) with sodium metal (Na).
  b) Sulfuric acid (H_2SO_4) with solid calcium carbonate ($CaCO_3$).
  c) Nitric acid (HNO_3) with potassium hydroxide solution (KOH).
  d) Hydrocyanic acid (HCN) with solid sodium oxide (Na_2O).

Q2 Identify the conjugate acid-base pairs in the following reactions by labelling them 'acid 1' and 'base 1' and 'acid 2' and 'base 2':
  a) $H_2CO_{3(aq)} + H_2O_{(l)} \rightleftharpoons H_3O^+_{(aq)} + HCO_3^-_{(aq)}$
  b) $CH_3NH_{2(aq)} + H_2O_{(l)} \rightleftharpoons CH_3NH_3^+_{(aq)} + OH^-_{(aq)}$
  c) $CH_3COO^-_{(aq)} + NH_4^+_{(aq)} \rightleftharpoons CH_3COOH_{(aq)} + NH_{3(aq)}$
  d) $HCl_{(aq)} + OH^-_{(aq)} \rightleftharpoons Cl^-_{(aq)} + H_2O_{(l)}$

Practice Questions — Fact Recall

Q1 What is the definition of:
  a) a Brønsted–Lowry acid?   b) a Brønsted–Lowry base?

Q2 What products are formed when an acid reacts with:
  a) a metal?   b) a carbonate?   c) a base?

Q3 a) What type of acid dissociates almost completely in water?
  b) What type of base dissociates only slightly in water?

Q4 What is a conjugate pair?

Figure 4: *J.N. Brønsted — co-author of the Brønsted–Lowry theory.*

9. pH Calculations

There are lots of pH calculations that you need to know how to do for your exam. The next few pages tell you everything you need to know to get started.

The pH scale

The **pH** scale is a measure of the hydrogen ion concentration in a solution. The concentration of hydrogen ions in a solution can vary enormously, so those wise chemists of old decided to express the concentration on a logarithmic scale. pH can be calculated using the following equation:

$$pH = -\log_{10}[H^+]$$

$[H^+]$ is the concentration of hydrogen ions in a solution, measured in mol dm⁻³. So, if you know the hydrogen ion concentration of a solution, you can calculate its pH by sticking the numbers into the formula.

Example

A solution of hydrochloric acid has a hydrogen ion concentration of 0.01 mol dm⁻³. What is the pH of the solution?

$pH = -\log_{10}[H^+]$
$= -\log_{10} 0.01$
$= 2.00$

Just substitute the [H⁺] value into the pH formula and solve.

The pH scale normally goes from 0 (very acidic) to 14 (very alkaline). pH 7 is regarded as being neutral. Solutions that have a very low pH include strong acids such as HCl and H_2SO_4. Strong bases such as NaOH and KOH have a very high pH. Pure water has a pH of 7 and is neutral.

Calculating [H⁺] from pH

If you've got the pH of a solution, and you want to know its hydrogen ion concentration, then you need the inverse of the pH formula:

$$[H^+] = 10^{-pH}$$

Now you can use this formula to find $[H^+]$.

Example

A solution of nitric acid has a pH of 1.52. What is the hydrogen ion concentration of this solution?

$[H^+] = 10^{-pH}$
$= 10^{-1.52}$
$= 0.030$ mol dm⁻³
$= 3.0 \times 10^{-2}$ mol dm⁻³

Just substitute the pH value into the inverse pH formula and solve.

Figure 1: pH can be measured using a pH meter like this one.

Practice Questions — Application

Q1 A solution of hydrochloric acid (HCl) has a hydrogen ion concentration of 0.05 mol dm⁻³. Calculate the pH of this solution.

Q2 A solution of nitric acid (HNO_3) has a pH of 2.86. Calculate the concentration of hydrogen ions in this solution.

Q3 Calculate the pH of a solution of hydrochloric acid (HCl) with a hydrogen ion concentration of 0.02 mol dm⁻³.

Monobasic means that each molecule of an acid will release one proton when it dissociates. Hydrochloric acid (HCl) and nitric acid (HNO_3) are strong acids so they ionise fully:

$$HCl_{(aq)} \rightarrow H^+_{(aq)} + Cl^-_{(aq)}$$

HCl and HNO_3 are also monobasic, so each mole of acid produces one mole of hydrogen ions. This means the H^+ concentration is the same as the acid concentration. So, if you know the concentration of the acid you know the H^+ concentration and you can calculate the pH.

Exam Tip
Acids like H_2SO_4 are dibasic — they release two protons when they dissociate. Don't worry though, you won't have to do pH calculations for dibasic acids in the exam.

Examples

Calculate the pH of 0.100 mol dm⁻³ hydrochloric acid:

$$[HCl] = [H^+] = 0.100 \text{ mol dm}^{-3}. \text{ So:}$$
$$pH = -\log_{10}[H^+]$$
$$= -\log_{10} 0.100$$
$$= 1.00$$

Calculate the pH of 0.050 mol dm⁻³ nitric acid:

$$[HNO_3] = [H^+] = 0.050 \text{ mol dm}^{-3}. \text{ So:}$$
$$pH = -\log_{10} 0.050$$
$$= 1.30$$

If a solution of hydrochloric acid has a pH of 2.45, what is the concentration of the acid?

$$[HCl] = [H^+] = 10^{-pH}. \text{ So:}$$
$$[HCl] = 10^{-2.45}$$
$$= 3.55 \times 10^{-3} \text{ mol dm}^{-3}$$

Figure 2: *Hydrochloric acid is a strong acid.*

Practice Questions — Application

Q1 Hydrochloric acid (HCl) is a strong monobasic acid.
Calculate the pH of a 0.080 mol dm⁻³ solution of HCl.

Q2 Nitric acid (HNO_3) is a strong monobasic acid.
Calculate the pH of a 0.12 mol dm⁻³ solution of HNO_3.

Q3 A solution of hydrochloric acid has a pH of 0.96.
Calculate the concentration of this hydrochloric acid solution.

Q4 A solution of nitric acid has a pH of 1.28.
Calculate the concentration of this nitric acid solution.

Exam Tip
Calculating the pH of acids from their concentrations comes up in loads of calculations so you need to be really confident that you know how to do it.

Practice Questions — Fact Recall

Q1 Write out the expression that defines pH.

Q2 Write out the equation that you would need to calculate the hydrogen ion concentration of an acid, given its pH.

Q3 Explain what is meant by the term monobasic.

Q4 What is the relationship between the concentration of H^+ ions and the acid concentration in strong monobasic acids?

10. The Ionic Product of Water

Learning Objectives:

- Be able to state and use the expression for the ionic product of water, K_w.
- Be able to calculate pH from $[H^+_{(aq)}]$ and $[H^+_{(aq)}]$ from pH for strong bases, using K_w.

Specification Reference 5.1.3

The ionic product of water (also known as K_w) is really just another equilibrium constant. "So why do I need to know about it?", I hear you cry. Well, mainly because it comes in handy for calculating the pH of strong bases. Read on...

What is K_w?

Water dissociates into hydroxonium ions and hydroxide ions. So this equilibrium exists in water:

$$H_2O_{(l)} + H_2O_{(l)} \rightleftharpoons H_3O^+_{(aq)} + OH^-_{(aq)}$$

If you remove an H_2O from both sides, this simplifies to:

$$H_2O_{(l)} \rightleftharpoons H^+_{(aq)} + OH^-_{(aq)}$$

And, just like for any other equilibrium reaction, you can apply the equilibrium law and write an expression for the equilibrium constant:

$$K_c = \frac{[H^+][OH^-]}{[H_2O]}$$

Water only dissociates a tiny amount, so the equilibrium lies well over to the left. There's so much water compared to the amounts of H^+ and OH^- ions that the concentration of water is considered to have a constant value. So if you multiply the expression you wrote for K_c (which is a constant) by $[H_2O]$ (another constant), you get a constant. This new constant is called the **ionic product of water** and it is given the symbol K_w.

$$K_w = K_c \times [H_2O] = \frac{[H^+][OH^-]}{\cancel{[H_2O]}} \times \cancel{[H_2O]}$$

So... $\boxed{K_w = [H^+][OH^-]}$

Tip: See page 124 for more on the equilibrium constant K_c.

K_w always has the same value for an aqueous solution at a given temperature. For example, at 298 K (25 °C), K_w has a value of 1.00×10^{-14} mol^2 dm^{-6}.

Tip: The units of K_w are <u>always</u> mol^2 dm^{-6} because mol dm^{-3} × mol dm^{-3} = mol^2 dm^{-6}.

Finding the pH of strong bases

Sodium hydroxide (NaOH) and potassium hydroxide (KOH) are strong bases that fully ionise in water — they donate one mole of OH^- ions per mole of base. This means that the concentration of OH^- ions is the same as the concentration of the base. So for 0.02 mol dm^{-3} sodium hydroxide solution, $[OH^-]$ is also 0.02 mol dm^{-3}. But to work out the pH you need to know $[H^+]$ — luckily this is linked to $[OH^-]$ through the ionic product of water, K_w:

$$K_w = [H^+][OH^-]$$

So if you know $[OH^-]$ for a strong aqueous base and K_w at a certain temperature, you can work out $[H^+]$ and then the pH. Just follow these steps:

Step 1:   Find the values of K_w and $[OH^-]$. You may be told these in the question or you may have to work them out.

Step 2:   Rearrange the equation, substitute the values for K_w and $[OH^-]$ into the equation, and solve it to find $[H^+]$.

Step 3:   Once you know $[H^+]$, substitute this into the pH equation ($pH = -\log_{10}[H^+]$) and solve it to find out the pH.

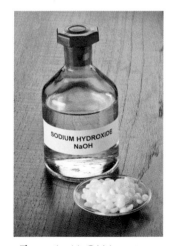

***Figure 1:** NaOH is a strong base. It can be a solid or an aqueous solution.*

Figure 2: *Sodium hydroxide turns this universal indicator paper dark blue, which shows that it has a high pH.*

Example

The value of K_w at 298 K is 1.0×10^{-14} mol^2 dm^{-6}.
Find the pH of 0.100 mol dm^{-3} NaOH at 298 K.

1. Find the values of K_w and [OH$^-$]:
   - The value of K_w is given in the question as 1.0×10^{-14} mol^2 dm^{-6}
   - NaOH is a strong base so will donate one mole of OH$^-$ ions per mole of base. The concentration of NaOH is 0.100 mol dm^{-3} so [OH$^-$] must be 0.100 mol dm^{-3}.

2. Substitute the values of K_w and [OH$^-$] into the K_w equation:

$$K_w = [H^+][OH^-] \text{ so } [H^+] = \frac{K_w}{[OH^-]} = \frac{1.0 \times 10^{-14}}{0.100} = 1.0 \times 10^{-13} \text{ mol dm}^{-3}$$

3. Substitute the value of [H$^+$] into the pH equation:
$$pH = -\log_{10}(1.0 \times 10^{-13}) = 13.00$$

Practice Questions — Application

Q1 Calculate the pH of a 0.200 mol dm^{-3} solution of KOH at 50 °C. The value of K_w at 50 °C is 5.48×10^{-14} mol^2 dm^{-6}.

Q2 Calculate the pH of a 0.155 mol dm^{-3} solution of NaOH at 20 °C. The value of K_w at 20 °C is 6.8×10^{-15} mol^2 dm^{-6}.

Q3 Calculate the pH of a 0.084 mol dm^{-3} solution of KOH at 10 °C. The value of K_w at 10 °C is 2.9×10^{-15} mol^2 dm^{-6}.

Exam Tip
Don't worry — you don't have to memorise any values of K_w. You'll always be told K_w in the question if you need to use it.

Tip: This is very similar to finding the pH of strong bases — you just have to do the steps in reverse.

Exam Tip
Make sure you know how to find the pH and the concentration of a strong base — you could be asked to do either in the exam.

Finding the concentration of strong bases

If you know the pH of a strong base you can use K_w to find its concentration. Here's what you have to do:

Step 1: Use the equation [H$^+$] = 10^{-pH} to find the value of [H$^+$] in the solution.

Step 2: Substitute your value for [H$^+$] along with the value of K_w into the K_w equation and solve it to find [OH$^-$].

Step 3: Because strong bases fully dissociate, [OH$^-$] is the same as the concentration of the base.

Example

A solution of NaOH has a pH of 12.50 at 30 °C. The value of K_w at 30 °C is 1.47×10^{-14} mol^2 dm^{-6}. Calculate the concentration of this NaOH solution.

1. Find [H$^+$]:
$$[H^+] = 10^{-pH} = 10^{-12.50} = 3.16 \times 10^{-13}$$

2. Substitute [H$^+$] and the value for K_w into the K_w equation:
$$K_w = [H^+][OH^-] \text{ so } [OH^-] = \frac{K_w}{[H^+]} = \frac{1.47 \times 10^{-14}}{3.16 \times 10^{-13}} = 0.0465 \text{ mol dm}^{-3}$$

3. Because NaOH is a strong base [NaOH] = [OH$^-$] so the concentration of the NaOH solution is 0.0465 mol dm^{-3}.

Q1 Find the concentration of a solution of KOH that has a pH of 12.40 at 20 °C. The value of K_w at 20 °C is 6.8×10^{-15} mol^2 dm^{-6}.

Q2 Find the concentration of a solution of NaOH that has a pH of 13.98 at 40 °C. The value of K_w at 40 °C is 2.92×10^{-14} mol^2 dm^{-6}.

Q3 Find the concentration of a solution of KOH that has a pH of 13.25 at 30 °C. The value of K_w at 30 °C is 1.47×10^{-14} mol^2 dm^{-6}.

Tip: The temperature at which measurements are taken and the temperature of K_w have to match — otherwise the calculation won't be valid. See page 229 for more on valid results.

Finding the pH of water

The pH of water is not always exactly 7 — it actually varies depending on the temperature. You can calculate the pH of water using K_w. The expression for K_w is $K_w = [H^+][OH^-]$. But in pure water, there is always one H^+ ion for each OH^- ion. So $[H^+] = [OH^-]$. That means if you are dealing with pure water, you can say that:

$$K_w = [H^+]^2$$

If you want to find the pH of water at a particular temperature, substitute the value for K_w at that temperature into the equation above, solve it to find $[H^+]$ by taking the square root of both sides, then use pH = $-\log[H^+]$ to find the pH.

Exam Tip
Remember — K_w only equals $[H^+]^2$ in <u>pure water</u>. If you're asked to write an expression for K_w, always give $K_w = [H^+][OH^-]$.

Example

At 50 °C, the value of K_w is 5.48×10^{-14} mol^2 dm^{-6}.
Calculate the pH of pure water at this temperature.

- Substituting in K_w gives $5.48 \times 10^{-14} = [H^+]^2$

- So $[H^+] = \sqrt{5.48 \times 10^{-14}} = 2.341 \times 10^{-7}$

- pH = $-\log[H^+] = -\log(2.341 \times 10^{-7}) = 6.63$

So the pH of pure water at 50 °C is 6.63.

Tip: Although the pH of water changes with temperature, water is always described as neutral (not acidic or alkaline) because $[H^+]$ always equals $[OH^-]$.

Q4 Calculate the pH of pure water at 30 °C. The value of K_w at 30 °C is 1.47×10^{-14} mol^2 dm^{-6}.

Q5 Calculate the pH of pure water at 40 °C. The value of K_w at 40 °C is 2.92×10^{-14} mol^2 dm^{-6}.

Q6 Calculate the pH of pure water at 100 °C. The value of K_w at 100 °C is 5.13×10^{-13} mol^2 dm^{-6}.

Figure 3: *Measuring the pH of pure water. Water only has a pH of 7 at a temperature of 25 °C.*

Q1 Write an expression for K_w.

Q2 What are the units of K_w?

Q3 Explain why $K_w = [H^+]^2$ for pure water.

Tip: K_a is a type of equilibrium constant, so the formula for K_a is based on the one for K_c.

Figure 1: *Lemon juice contains citric acid. It turns this universal indicator paper orange, which shows that it's a weak acid.*

Exam Tip
It's really important to show all the steps of your working in exam questions — that way the examiner can give you some marks for your method even if your final answer is wrong.

11. The Acid Dissociation Constant

You've already seen how to calculate the pH of strong acids and strong bases. Now get ready for part three: calculating the pH of weak acids.

What is the acid dissociation constant?

Weak acids don't ionise fully in solution, so the $[H^+]$ isn't the same as the acid concentration. This makes it a bit trickier to find their pH. You have to use yet another equilibrium constant — the **acid dissociation constant**, K_a. The units of K_a are mol dm^{-3} and the equation for K_a is derived as follows:

For a weak aqueous acid, HA, you get the equilibrium $HA_{(aq)} \rightleftharpoons H^+_{(aq)} + A^-_{(aq)}$. As only a tiny amount of HA dissociates, you can assume that [HA] at the start of the reaction is the same as [HA] at equilibrium. So if you apply the equilibrium law, you get:

$$K_a = \frac{[H^+][A^-]}{[HA]}$$

When dealing with weak acids, you can assume that all the H$^+$ ions come from the acid, so $[H^+] = [A^-]$. So the formula for K_a can be simplified to:

$$K_a = \frac{[H^+]^2}{[HA]}$$

Finding the pH of weak acids

You can use K_a to find the pH of a weak acid. Just follow these steps.

Step 1: Write an expression for K_a for the weak acid. (You can write out the equilibrium equation first if it helps you write this expression.)

Step 2: Rearrange the equation and substitute in the values for K_a and [HA] to find $[H^+]^2$.

Step 3: Take the square root of the number to find $[H^+]$.

Step 4: Substitute $[H^+]$ into the pH equation to find the pH.

--- Example ---

Find the pH of a 0.020 mol dm^{-3} solution of propanoic acid (CH_3CH_2COOH) at 298 K. K_a for propanoic acid at this temperature is 1.30×10^{-5} mol dm^{-3}.

1. First write an expression for K_a for the weak acid.

   Propanoic acid equilibrium: $CH_3CH_2COOH \rightleftharpoons H^+ + CH_3CH_2COO^-$

   So, $K_a = \dfrac{[H^+][CH_3CH_2COO^-]}{[CH_3CH_2COOH]} = \dfrac{[H^+]^2}{[CH_3CH_2COOH]}$

2. Rearrange the equation to find $[H^+]^2$:

   $$[H^+]^2 = K_a[CH_3CH_2COOH]$$
   $$= (1.30 \times 10^{-5}) \times 0.020 = 2.60 \times 10^{-7}$$

3. Take the square root of this number to find $[H^+]$:

   $$[H^+] = \sqrt{2.60 \times 10^{-7}}$$
   $$= 5.10 \times 10^{-4} \text{ mol dm}^{-3}$$

4. Use $[H^+]$ to find the pH of the acid:

   $$pH = -\log_{10}[H^+]$$
   $$= -\log_{10} 5.10 \times 10^{-4} = \textbf{3.29}$$

Finding the concentration of weak acids

If you already know the pH you can use K_a to find the concentration of the acid. You don't need to know anything new for this type of calculation — you use the same formulas you used to find the pH.

Step 1: Substitute the pH into the inverse pH equation to calculate $[H^+]$.

Step 2: Write an expression for K_a.

Step 3: Rearrange the equation to give the concentration of the acid.

Step 4: Substitute the values for K_a and $[H^+]$ into the equation and solve it.

Figure 2: *Ethanoic acid is a weak acid.*

┌─ **Example** ─────────────

The pH of an ethanoic acid (CH_3COOH) solution is 3.02 at 298 K. Calculate the molar concentration of this solution. The K_a of ethanoic acid is 1.75×10^{-5} mol dm^{-3} at 298 K.

1. Use the pH of the acid to find $[H^+]$:
$$[H^+] = 10^{-pH}$$
$$= 10^{-3.02}$$
$$= 9.55 \times 10^{-4} \text{ mol dm}^{-3}$$

2. Write an expression for K_a:
$$K_a = \frac{[H^+][CH_3COO^-]}{[CH_3COOH]} = \frac{[H^+]^2}{[CH_3COOH]}$$

3. Rearrange it to give $[CH_3COOH]$:
$$[CH_3COOH] = \frac{[H^+]^2}{K_a}$$

4. Substitute in K_a and $[H^+]$ and solve the equation to find $[CH_3COOH]$:
$$[CH_3COOH] = \frac{(9.55 \times 10^{-4})^2}{1.75 \times 10^{-5}} = \textbf{0.0521 mol dm}^{-3}$$

> **Tip:** Remember, you can write out the equilibrium equation to help with Step 2 if you like.

Finding the K_a of weak acids

If you know both the concentration and the pH, you can use them to find the K_a of the weak acid. Just find $[H^+]$ (as shown in the example above), substitute the values you know into the expression for K_a and solve.

> **Exam Tip**
> If you can't work out the chemical formula of an acid, just use HA instead and you might still get the marks.

┌─ **Example** ─────────────

A solution of 0.162 mol dm^{-3} HCN has a pH of 5.05 at 298 K. What is the value of K_a for HCN at 298 K?

1. Use the pH of the acid to find $[H^+]$:
$$[H^+] = 10^{-pH}$$
$$= 10^{-5.05}$$
$$= 8.91 \times 10^{-6} \text{ mol dm}^{-3}$$

2. Write an expression for K_a:
$$K_a = \frac{[H^+][CN^-]}{[HCN]} = \frac{[H^+]^2}{[HCN]}$$

3. Substitute in the values for $[H^+]$ and $[HCN]$:
$$K_a = \frac{[H^+]^2}{[HCN]} = \frac{(8.91 \times 10^{-6})^2}{0.162} = \textbf{4.90} \times \textbf{10}^{-10} \textbf{ mol dm}^{-3}$$

> **Exam Tip**
> You need to be able to do all three types of calculation in the exam — any one of them could crop up so make sure you understand these examples.

The logarithmic constant pK_a

The value of K_a varies massively from one acid to the next. This can sometimes make the numbers difficult to manage so to make life easier, scientists often use the pK_a instead. pK_a is calculated from K_a in exactly the same way as pH is calculated from $[H^+]$ — and vice versa:

$$pK_a = -\log_{10}(K_a)$$
$$K_a = 10^{-pKa}$$

Tip: Notice how pK_a values aren't annoyingly tiny like K_a values.

So if an acid has a K_a value of 1.50×10^{-7} mol dm^{-3}, then:

$$pK_a = -\log_{10}(K_a)$$
$$= -\log_{10}(1.50 \times 10^{-7})$$
$$= 6.82.$$

Tip: The larger the pK_a, the weaker the acid. Strong acids have very small pK_a values.

And if an acid has a pK_a value of 4.32, then:

$$K_a = 10^{-pKa}$$
$$= 10^{-4.32}$$
$$= 4.79 \times 10^{-5} \text{ mol dm}^{-3}$$

Just to make things that bit more complicated, there might be a pK_a value in a 'find the pH' type of question. If so, you need to convert it to K_a so that you can use the K_a expression.

Example

Calculate the pH of 0.050 mol dm^{-3} methanoic acid (HCOOH). Methanoic acid has a pK_a of 3.75 at 298 K.

Tip: These are the same steps as you followed on page 140 but with an extra step (converting the pK_a into K_a) at the beginning.

1. Convert the pK_a value to a K_a value:
$$K_a = 10^{-pKa}$$
$$= 10^{-3.75}$$
$$= 1.78 \times 10^{-4} \text{ mol dm}^{-3}$$

2. Write out an expression for K_a:
$$K_a = \frac{[H^+][HCOO^-]}{[HCOOH]} = \frac{[H^+]^2}{[HCOOH]}$$

3. Rearrange it to give $[H^+]^2$:
$$[H^+]^2 = K_a[HCOOH]$$
$$= 1.78 \times 10^{-4} \times 0.050$$
$$= 8.9 \times 10^{-6}$$

4. Take the square root to get $[H^+]$:
$$[H^+] = \sqrt{8.9 \times 10^{-6}}$$
$$= 2.98 \times 10^{-3} \text{ mol dm}^{-3}$$

Exam Tip
pH values for weak acids are usually between 2 and 5. If you get an answer much bigger or smaller than this in your exam, double-check your calculation — you may have gone wrong somewhere.

5. Substitute $[H^+]$ into the pH equation and solve:
$$pH = -\log(2.98 \times 10^{-3})$$
$$= \textbf{2.53}$$

It works the other way round too. Sometimes you are asked to calculate K_a but have to give your answer as a pK_a value. In this case, you just work out the K_a value as usual and then convert it to pK_a — and Bob's your pet hamster.

Calculating percentage dissociation

Once you've calculated the concentration of H^+ ions in an acid solution, you can calculate the percentage molar dissociation of the acid. You just need to use this equation:

$$\text{Percentage dissociation} = \frac{[H^+]}{[HA]} \times 100$$

Example

In the example on the previous page you saw that a 0.050 mol dm^{-3} solution of methanoic acid has an H^+ ion concentration of 2.98×10^{-3} mol dm^{-3}.

$$\text{Percentage dissociation} = \frac{[H^+]}{[HA]} \times 100 = \frac{2.98 \times 10^{-3}}{0.050} \times 100 = 6.0\%$$

This means that 6% of the methanoic acid molecules have dissociated into H^+ ions and $HCOO^-$ ions.

Tip: The higher the percentage dissociation the lower the pH and the stronger the acid.

Tip: Strong acids fully dissociate — they have a percentage dissociation of 100%.

Practice Questions — Application

Q1 A solution of hydrocyanic acid (HCN) has a concentration of 2.0 mol dm^{-3}. The K_a of this acid at 25 °C is 4.9×10^{-10} mol dm^{-3}.
   a) Write down an expression for the K_a of this acid.
   b) Calculate the pH of this solution at 25 °C

Q2 Some nitrous acid (HNO$_2$) has a pH of 3.8 in solution at 25 °C. The K_a of this acid at 25 °C is 4.0×10^{-4} mol dm^{-3}. Determine the concentration of this solution at 25 °C.

Q3 The K_a of lactic acid at 25 °C is 1.38×10^{-4} mol dm^{-3}. Calculate the pH of a 0.480 mol dm^{-3} solution of lactic acid at 25 °C.

Q4 A 0.280 mol dm^{-3} solution of a weak acid (HA) has a pH of 4.11 at 25 °C. Calculate the K_a of this acid at 25 °C.

Q5 Methanoic acid (HCOOH) has a K_a of 1.8×10^{-4} mol dm^{-3} at 298 K. The pH of a solution of methanoic acid was measured to be 3.67 at 298 K. Determine the concentration of this solution of HCOOH.

Q6 Ethanoic acid has a pK$_a$ of 4.78 at 298 K. A 0.250 mol dm^{-3} solution of ethanoic acid was prepared.
   a) Determine the K_a of ethanoic acid at 298 K.
   b) Calculate the percentage molar dissociation of this acid.

Q7 A 0.154 mol dm^{-3} weak acid solution has a pH of 4.5 at 45 °C. Calculate the pK$_a$ of this acid at 45 °C.

Q8 The pK$_a$ of hydrofluoric acid (HF) is 3.14 at a certain temperature. Calculate the concentration of a solution of hydrofluoric acid that has a pH of 3.2 at this temperature.

Q9 A weak acid (HX) has a pK$_a$ of 4.5 at 25 °C. Calculate the pH of a 0.60 mol dm^{-3} solution of this acid at 25 °C.

Exam Tip
You'll almost certainly have to use expressions for terms like pH and pK$_a$ in the exam so you really, really need to make sure that you know the formulas. Have a look at page 235 for a summary of all the formulas in this section.

Practice Questions — Fact Recall

Q1 What are the units for K_a?
Q2 a) Write an expression for the K_a of a general weak acid (HA).
   b) Rearrange this equation to give an expression for calculating [HA].
Q3 Give two things that K_a can be used for.
Q4 a) Write out the expression that defines pK$_a$.
   b) Rearrange this equation to give an expression for K_a.

Learning Objectives:

Learning Objectives:

- Be able to describe a buffer solution as a system that minimises pH changes on addition of small amounts of an acid or a base.

- Know that a buffer solution can be made from a weak acid and a salt of the weak acid, e.g. CH_3COOH/ CH_3COONa.

- Be able to explain the role of the conjugate acid–base pair in an acid buffer solution, e.g. CH_3COOH/ CH_3COO^-, in the control of pH.

- Be able to explain the role of carbonic acid/ hydrogencarbonate as a buffer in the control of blood pH.

Specification Reference 5.1.3

Tip: The acid has to be a weak acid — you can't make an acidic buffer with a strong acid.

Tip: CH_3COOH and CH_3COO^- are a conjugate pair. See page 132 for more on conjugate pairs.

Figure 1: *An acidic buffer solution.*

12. Buffer Action

Sometimes, it's useful to have a solution that doesn't change pH when small amounts of acid or alkali are added to it. That's where buffers come in handy.

What is a buffer?

A **buffer** is a solution that resists changes in pH when small amounts of acid or alkali are added. A buffer doesn't stop the pH from changing completely — it does make the changes very slight though. Buffers only work for small amounts of acid or alkali — put too much in and they won't be able to cope. You get acidic buffers and basic buffers — but you only need to know about acidic ones.

Acidic buffers

Acidic buffers have a pH of less than 7 — they're made by mixing a weak acid with one of its salts. They can resist a change in pH when either an acid or a base is added to the solution.

--- **Example** ---

A mixture of ethanoic acid (CH_3COOH) and sodium ethanoate ($CH_3COO^-Na^+$) is an **acidic buffer**. Ethanoic acid is a weak acid, so it only slightly dissociates:

$$CH_3COOH_{(aq)} \rightleftharpoons H^+_{(aq)} + CH_3COO^-_{(aq)}$$

But the salt fully dissociates into its ions when it dissolves:

$$CH_3COONa_{(s)} \xrightarrow{water} CH_3COO^-_{(aq)} + Na^+_{(aq)}$$

So in the solution you've got heaps of undissociated ethanoic acid molecules ($CH_3COOH_{(aq)}$), and heaps of ethanoate ions ($CH_3COO^-_{(aq)}$) from the salt.

When you alter the concentration of H^+ or OH^- ions in the buffer solution the equilibrium position moves to counteract the change (this is down to Le Chatelier's principle — see page 128). Here's how it all works:

Resisting an acid

The large number of CH_3COO^- ions from the salt make the buffer able to cope with the addition of acid. If you add a small amount of acid (e.g. $HCl_{(aq)}$) the H^+ concentration increases. Most of the extra H^+ ions join with CH_3COO^- ions to form CH_3COOH. This shifts the equilibrium to the left, reducing the H^+ concentration to almost its original value. So the pH doesn't change much.

$$\overset{\textstyle\text{Addition of } H^+ \text{ (acid)}}{\xleftarrow{\hspace{3cm}}}$$
$$CH_3COOH_{(aq)} \rightleftharpoons H^+_{(aq)} + CH_3COO^-_{(aq)}$$

Resisting a base

If a small amount of base (e.g. NaOH) is added, the OH^- concentration increases. Most of the extra OH^- ions react with H^+ ions to form water — removing H^+ ions from the solution. This causes more CH_3COOH to dissociate to form H^+ ions — shifting the equilibrium to the right. There's no problem doing this as there's loads of spare undissociated CH_3COOH molecules. The H^+ concentration increases until it's close to its original value, so the pH doesn't change much.

$$\overset{\textstyle\text{Addition of } OH^- \text{ (base)}}{\xrightarrow{\hspace{3cm}}}$$
$$CH_3COOH_{(aq)} \rightleftharpoons H^+_{(aq)} + CH_3COO^-_{(aq)}$$

Preparing buffer solutions

Mixing a weak acid with its salt is not the only way to make an acidic buffer — you could also take a weak acid and add a small amount of alkali. In this buffer solution, some of the acid is neutralised to make a salt, but some is left un-neutralised. The reaction mixture would then contain a weak acid and its salt, and so would act as an acidic buffer.

Tip: When preparing buffer solutions in this way, you have to make sure the acid is in excess. If the alkali is in excess, all the acid will react and there will be no acid left to buffer changes in pH.

Example

You could make an acidic buffer by mixing an excess of propanoic acid (CH_3CH_2COOH) with ammonia (NH_3). Some of the propanoic acid would react with the ammonia to form an ammonium salt:

$$CH_3CH_2COOH + NH_3 \rightleftharpoons CH_3CH_2COO^-NH_4^+$$

But because the acid is in excess, some of the propanoic acid will remain un-neutralised. This means the solution contains some propanoic acid (which can donate protons to remove any added base) and some ammonium salt (which can remove any added protons), so is an acidic buffer.

Tip: You could also make a buffer by mixing propanoic acid with NaOH to form a sodium salt.

The biological importance of buffers

Buffer solutions are important in biological environments. For example:

Cells

Cells need a constant pH to allow biochemical reactions to take place. The pH is controlled by a buffer based on the equilibrium between dihydrogen phosphate ions and hydrogen phosphate ions.

Here's the equilibrium: $H_2PO_4^- \rightleftharpoons H^+ + HPO_4^{2-}$

Blood

Blood needs to be kept at pH 7.4. It is buffered using carbonic acid. Carbonic acid dissociates into H^+ ions and HCO_3^- ions as shown below:

$$H_2CO_{3(aq)} \rightleftharpoons H^+_{(aq)} + HCO_{3\ (aq)}^-$$

The levels of H_2CO_3 are controlled by respiration. By breathing out CO_2 the level of H_2CO_3 is reduced as it moves this equilibrium to the right:

$$H_2CO_{3(aq)} \rightleftharpoons H_2O_{(l)} + CO_{2(aq)}$$

The levels of HCO_3^- are controlled by the kidneys with excess being excreted in the urine.

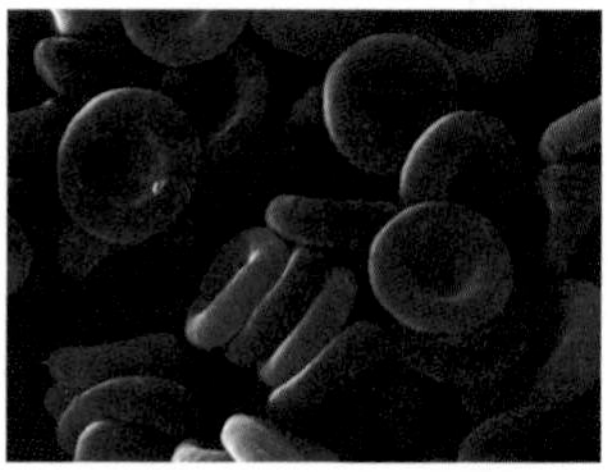

Figure 2: Red blood cells. Blood has to be kept at a pH of 7.4 so is buffered by carbonic acid.

Food Production

Buffers are also used in food products to control the pH. Changes in pH can be caused by bacteria and fungi and cause food to deteriorate. A common buffer is citric acid and sodium citrate. Phosphoric acid/phosphate ions and benzoic acid/benzoate ions are also used as buffers.

Tip: The HCO_3^- ion is called the hydrogencarbonate ion. So this buffer is sometimes known as a 'carbonic acid/hydrogencarbonate buffer'. Snappy name...

Practice Questions — Fact Recall

Q1 What is a buffer?

Q2 Explain how an acidic buffer resists changes in pH when:
a) a small amount of acid is added.
b) a small amount of base is added.

Q3 Describe two ways of making an acidic buffer.

Q4 How is blood kept at a pH of 7.4?

Q5 Explain why buffers are sometimes used in food production.

- Be able to calculate the pH of a buffer solution, from the K_a value of a weak acid and the equilibrium concentrations of the conjugate acid–base pair.

Specification Reference 5.1.3

13. Calculating the pH of Buffers

You need to be able to calculate the pH of buffer solutions. These calculations look scary, but don't worry — they're not nearly as bad as they look.

Calculations using known concentrations

If you know the K_a of the weak acid and the equilibrium concentrations of the weak acid and its salt, calculating the pH of an **acidic buffer** isn't too tricky. Here's how to go about it:

Step 1: Write out the expression for the K_a of the weak acid.

Step 2: Rearrange the equation to give an expression for $[H^+]$.

Step 3: Substitute the value for K_a and the equilibrium concentrations of the acid and salt into the equation.

Step 4: Solve the equation to find a value for $[H^+]$.

Step 5: Substitute your value for $[H^+]$ into the pH equation $(pH = -\log[H^+])$ and solve it to calculate the pH.

--- Example ---

A buffer solution contains 0.400 mol dm^{-3} methanoic acid, HCOOH, and 0.600 mol dm^{-3} sodium methanoate, HCOO$^-$Na$^+$. For methanoic acid, $K_a = 1.6 \times 10^{-4}$ mol dm^{-3}. What is the pH of this buffer?

Tip: Writing expressions for K_a was covered on page 140. Have a look back if you need a recap.

1. Write the expression for K_a of the weak acid:

$$HCOOH_{(aq)} \rightleftharpoons H^+_{(aq)} + HCOO^-_{(aq)} \quad \text{so} \quad K_a = \frac{[H^+][HCOO^-]}{[HCOOH]}$$

2. Rearrange the equation to get $[H^+]$:

$$[H^+] = \frac{K_a \times [HCOOH]}{[HCOO^-]}$$

Tip: Remember — the concentrations in the expression for K_a all have to be equilibrium concentrations.

3. Substitute in the value of K_a and the concentrations given in the question: You have to make a few assumptions here:
   - HCOO$^-$ Na$^+$ is fully dissociated, so assume that the equilibrium concentration of HCOO$^-$ is the same as the initial concentration of HCOO$^-$ Na$^+$.
   - HCOOH is only slightly dissociated, so assume that its equilibrium concentration is the same as its initial concentration.

$$[H^+] = \frac{K_a \times [HCOOH]}{[HCOO^-]} = \frac{(1.6 \times 10^{-4}) \times 0.400}{0.600}$$

4. Solve to find H$^+$:

$$[H^+] = \frac{(1.6 \times 10^{-4}) \times 0.400}{0.600} = 1.07 \times 10^{-4} \text{ mol dm}^{-3}$$

Tip: See page 135 for a reminder on how to calculate pH.

5. Use your value of $[H^+]$ to calculate the pH:

$$pH = -\log[H^+]$$
$$= -\log(1.07 \times 10^{-4})$$
$$= \textbf{3.97}$$

Finding the equilibrium concentrations

If a buffer has been prepared by mixing an acid with a base, you might have to work out the equilibrium concentrations of the acid and its salt before you can calculate the pH. Here's what to do:

Tip: See page 145 for more on how a buffer can be prepared by mixing an acid and a base.

Step 1: Write out the equation for the neutralisation reaction — remember acid + base → salt + water.

Step 2: Calculate the number of moles of acid and base at the start of the reaction using the volumes and concentrations given in the question.

Step 3: Use the molar ratios in the equation to work out the moles of acid and salt left at the end of the reaction.

Step 4: Calculate the concentration of the acid and salt in the buffer solution by dividing by the volume of the solution — this is the volume of the acid and the base added together.

Tip: The <u>molar ratios</u> tell you how many moles of acid will react with a certain number of moles of base, and how many moles of salt are produced. These numbers will <u>always</u> be in the same ratio for a given reaction.

Step 5: Then you're ready to calculate the pH.

Example

A buffer is formed by mixing 15 cm³ of 0.10 mol dm⁻³ sodium hydroxide (NaOH) and 30 cm³ of 0.60 mol dm⁻³ propanoic acid (CH_3CH_2COOH). Calculate the pH of this buffer solution ($K_a = 1.35 \times 10^{-5}$ mol dm⁻³).

1. Write out the equation for the reaction:

$$CH_3CH_2COOH + NaOH \rightarrow CH_3CH_2COO^-Na^+ + H_2O$$

2. Calculate the number of moles of acid and base:

$$\text{Moles } CH_3CH_2COOH = \frac{\text{Conc.} \times \text{Vol.}}{1000} = \frac{0.60 \times 30}{1000} = 0.018 \text{ moles}$$

$$\text{Moles } NaOH = \frac{\text{Conc.} \times \text{Vol.}}{1000} = \frac{0.10 \times 15}{1000} = 0.0015 \text{ moles}$$

Tip: It's really important that you know formulas like:

$$\text{moles} = \frac{\text{conc.} \times \text{vol.}}{1000}$$

You won't be able to do the harder calculations if you haven't got your head around the basics. Check out pages 235-236 for a summary of the formulas that you need to know for your A2 Chemistry exams.

3. The acid is in excess, so all the base reacts. There's 0.0015 moles of NaOH at the start of the reaction. If it all reacts there will be 0.0015 moles of salt at the end of the reaction.

   The equation shows us that 1 mole of base will react with 1 mole of acid to give 1 mole of salt. So if there are 0.0015 moles of salt, 0.0015 moles of acid must have been used up.
   This leaves 0.018 – 0.0015 = 0.0165 moles of acid.

   So, the buffer solution contains 0.0015 moles of $CH_3CH_2COO^-Na^+$ and 0.0165 moles of CH_3CH_2COOH.

4. Calculate the concentration of acid and salt in the buffer solution:

   The total volume of the solution is 15 + 30 = 45 cm³

$$\text{Conc. } CH_3CH_2COOH = \frac{\text{moles} \times 1000}{\text{volume}} = \frac{0.0165 \times 1000}{45}$$
$$= 0.37 \text{ mol dm}^{-3}$$

$$\text{Conc. } CH_3CH_2COO^-Na^+ = \frac{\text{moles} \times 1000}{\text{volume}} = \frac{0.0015 \times 1000}{45}$$
$$= 0.033 \text{ mol dm}^{-3}$$

Tip: This bit was covered in much more detail on page 140 — have a look back if you need a quick reminder of what's going on.

5. Work out the pH as before:

$$CH_3CH_2COOH \rightleftharpoons H^+ + CH_3CH_2COO^- \quad so \quad K_a = \frac{[H^+][CH_3CH_2COO^-]}{[CH_3CH_2COOH]}$$

$$[H^+] = \frac{K_a \times [CH_3CH_2COOH]}{[CH_3CH_2COO^-]} = \frac{(1.35 \times 10^{-5}) \times 0.37}{0.033} = 1.5 \times 10^{-4} \text{ mol dm}^{-3}$$

$$pH = -\log[H^+] = -\log(1.5 \times 10^{-4}) = 3.8$$

Practice Questions — Application

Q1 An acidic buffer solution contains 0.200 mol dm^{-3} propanoic acid (CH_3CH_2COOH) and 0.350 mol dm^{-3} potassium propanoate. For propanoic acid, $K_a = 1.35 \times 10^{-5}$ mol dm^{-3}.

    a) Write an expression for the K_a of propanoic acid.

    b) Calculate the concentration of H$^+$ ions in this buffer solution.

    c) Calculate the pH of this buffer solution.

Q2 A buffer solution contains 0.150 mol dm^{-3} ethanoic acid and 0.250 mol dm^{-3} potassium ethanoate. For ethanoic acid $K_a = 1.74 \times 10^{-5}$ mol dm^{-3}. Calculate the pH of this buffer.

Q3 A buffer is made by mixing 30.0 cm^3 of 0.500 mol dm^{-3} propanoic acid (CH_3CH_2COOH) with 20.0 cm^3 of 0.250 mol dm^{-3} potassium hydroxide (KOH). For propanoic acid, $K_a = 1.35 \times 10^{-5}$ mol dm^{-3}.

    a) Write an equation to show the reaction of propanoic acid with potassium hydroxide.

    b) Calculate the number of moles of propanoic acid and potassium hydroxide at the beginning of the reaction.

    c) Calculate the concentration of propanoic acid and potassium propanoate in the buffer solution.

    d) Calculate the concentration of H$^+$ ions in this buffer solution.

    e) Calculate the pH of the buffer solution.

Q4 A buffer is formed by mixing together 25.0 cm^3 of 0.200 mol dm^{-3} methanoic acid (HCOOH) and 15.0 cm^3 of 0.100 mol dm^{-3} sodium hydroxide (NaOH). For methanoic acid, $K_a = 1.60 \times 10^{-4}$ mol dm^{-3}. Calculate the pH of this buffer.

14. Titrations and pH Curves

When acids and bases are mixed together a neutralisation reaction occurs — *H⁺ ions from the acid join with OH⁻ ions from the base to create water. If there are equal numbers of H⁺ and OH⁻ ions the mixture will be neutral (pH 7). What do titrations and pH curves have to do with this? Read on...*

Learning Objectives:

- Be able to interpret, or sketch, the shapes of acid–base titration pH curves for strong and weak acids and bases.

- Be able to explain the choice of suitable indicators for acid-base titrations, given the pH range of the indicator.

Specification Reference 5.1.3

Titrations

Titrations allow you to find out exactly how much alkali is needed to neutralise a quantity of acid. Here's how you do one...

Step 1: You measure out some acid of known concentration using a pipette and put it in a flask, along with some appropriate **indicator** (indicators change colour at a certain pH — see page 151 for more).

Step 2: Do a rough titration — add the alkali to the acid using a burette fairly quickly to get an approximate idea where the solution changes colour. This is the **end point** — the point at which all of the acid is just neutralised. Give the flask a regular swirl to make sure the acid and alkali are mixed properly.

Step 3: Repeat step one and then do an accurate titration. Run the alkali in, to within 2 cm³ of the end point, then add it drop by drop. If you don't notice exactly when the solution changes colour you've overshot and your result won't be accurate.

Step 4: Record the amount of alkali needed to neutralise the acid.

It's best to repeat this process a few times, making sure you get very similar answers each time (within about 0.1 cm³ of each other).

You can also find out how much acid is needed to neutralise a quantity of alkali. It's exactly the same process as above, but you add acid to alkali instead. The equipment you'll need to do a titration is illustrated in Figure 2.

Tip: Sometimes you'll hear about alkalis being used in titrations, sometimes bases. Don't get yourself in a muddle over it — an alkali is just a type of base, it's a base that's <u>soluble in water</u>.

Pipette: *Pipettes measure only one volume of solution. Fill the pipette to just above the line, then drop the level down carefully to the line.*

Burette: *Burettes measure different volumes and let you add the solution drop by drop.*

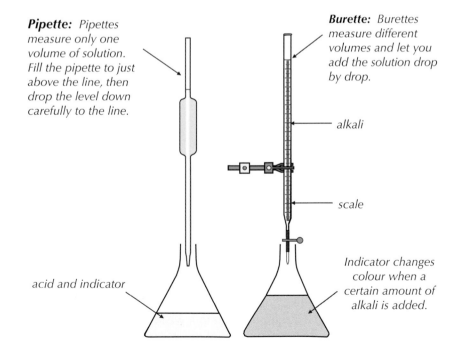

alkali

scale

acid and indicator

Indicator changes colour when a certain amount of alkali is added.

Figure 2: *Equipment needed to perform a titration.*

Figure 1: *An acid–base titration experiment.*

Tip: This equipment should look familiar to you. You've probably used it in a practical lesson at some point.

pH curves

pH curves show the results of titration experiments. They can be made by plotting the pH of the titration mixture against the amount of base added as the titration goes on. The pH of the mixture can be measured using a pH meter and the scale on the burette can be used to see how much base has been added.

The shape of the curve looks a bit different depending on the strengths of the acid and base that are used. The graphs below show the pH curves for the different combinations of strong and weak monobasic acids and bases:

Figure 3: A student using a pH meter to measure pH during an acid–base titration.

Tip: If you titrate a base with an acid instead, the shapes of the curves stay the same, but they're reversed. For example:

Strong base/strong acid

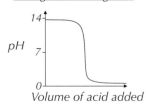

Strong base/weak acid

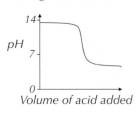

Weak base/strong acid

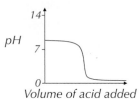

Weak base/weak acid

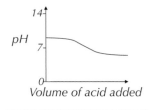

Strong acid/strong base

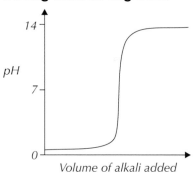

The pH starts around 1, as there's an excess of strong acid.
It finishes up around pH 13, when you have an excess of strong base.

Strong acid/weak base

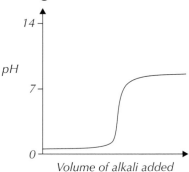

The pH starts around 1, as there's an excess of strong acid.
It finishes up around pH 9, when you have an excess of weak base.

Weak acid/strong base

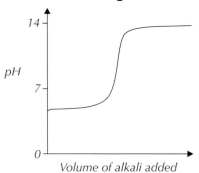

The pH starts around 5, as there's an excess of weak acid.
It finishes up around pH 13, when you have an excess of strong base.

Weak acid/weak base

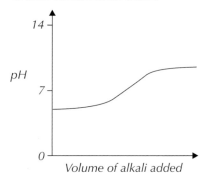

The pH starts around 5, as there's an excess of weak acid.
It finishes up around pH 9, when you have an excess of weak base.

All the graphs apart from the weak acid/weak base graph have a bit that's almost vertical — the mid-point of this vertical section is the equivalence point or end point. At this point, a tiny amount of base causes a sudden, big change in pH — it's here that all the acid is just neutralised.

You don't get such a sharp change in a weak acid/weak base titration. If you used an indicator for this type of titration, its colour would change very gradually, and it would be very tricky to see the exact end point. So you're usually better using a pH meter to find the end point for this type of titration.

Indicators

When you use an indicator, you need it to change colour exactly at the end point of your titration. So you need to pick one that changes colour over a narrow pH range that lies entirely on the vertical part of the pH curve.

So for the titration shown in Figure 4 (below) you'd want an indicator that changed colour somewhere between pH 8 and pH 11:

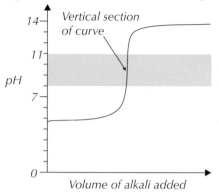

Vertical section of curve

The curve is vertical between pH 8 and pH 11— so a very small amount of alkali will cause the pH to change from 8 to 11.

So, an indicator that changes colour between pH 8 and pH 11 is needed.

Figure 4: *Graph showing how to select an indicator.*

Figure 5: *The red to yellow colour change of methyl orange.*

Methyl orange and **phenolphthalein** are indicators that are often used for acid-base titrations. They each change colour over a different pH range:

Name of indicator	Colour at low pH	Approx. pH of colour change	Colour at high pH
Methyl orange	red	3.1 – 4.4	yellow
Phenolphthalein	colourless	8.3 – 10	pink

▪ For a strong acid/strong alkali titration, you can use either of these indicators — there's a rapid pH change over the range for both indicators.

▪ For a strong acid/weak alkali only methyl orange will do. The pH changes rapidly across the range for methyl orange, but not for phenolphthalein.

▪ For a weak acid/strong alkali, phenolphthalein is the stuff to use. The pH changes rapidly over phenolphthalein's range, but not over methyl orange's.

▪ For weak acid/weak alkali titrations there's no sharp pH change, so no indicator will work.

Figure 6: *The colourless to pink colour change of phenolphthalein.*

You need to be able to use a pH curve to explain a choice of indicator:

--- Example ---

The graph to the right shows the pH curve produced when a strong acid is added to a weak base. Bromophenol blue, which has a pH range of 3.0 – 4.6, was used as an indicator. Explain why bromophenol blue is a suitable indicator to use.

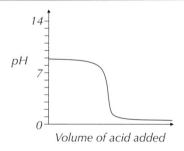

Volume of acid added

Exam Tip
Don't worry, you don't have to learn the pH ranges of any indicators. You'll always be told them in the question if you need to use them.

The graph shows that the vertical part of the pH curve is between about pH 2 and pH 6. So you need an indicator with a pH range between 2 and 6. Bromophenol blue changes colour within this range so bromophenol blue is a suitable indicator to choose.

Practice Questions — Application

Q1 The graphs below show the pH curves for four different acid–base titrations. For each reaction state what type of acid and base were used and select an appropriate indicator from the table below.

Indicator	pH range
Thymol blue	1.2 – 2.8
Methyl orange	3.1 – 4.4
Litmus	5.0 – 8.0
Cresol purple	7.6 – 9.2
Phenolphthalein	8.3 – 10

a)

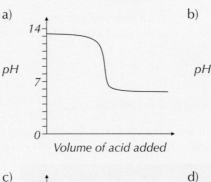

b)

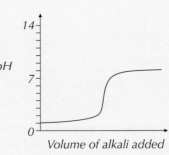

c)

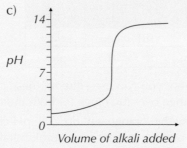

d)

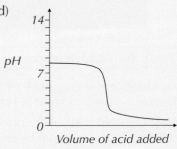

Tip: You need to look at where the curves start and finish to work out if you've got an acid neutralising a base or a base neutralising an acid.

Q2 Neutral red changes colour from red to yellow between pH 6.8 and pH 8.0. Sketch the pH curve for a titration reaction that this indicator could be used for.

Practice Questions — Fact Recall

Q1 Sketch the pH curve produced when:
a) A strong acid neutralises a weak base.
b) A strong base neutralises a strong acid.
c) A weak acid neutralises a strong base.

Tip: Don't forget — acids have low pHs and bases have high pHs.

Q2 a) What happens at the end point of a titration reaction?
b) How can you see that the end point has been reached when you're carrying out a titration?
c) How can you tell the end point has been reached using a pH curve?

Q3 How would you know if an indicator is suitable for a particular titration reaction?

15. Titration Calculations

Now that you've learnt all about titrations it's time to find out what you can do with the results. At A2 there are a few titration calculations you'll need to be able to do — the next few pages tell you how.

Learning Objective:

▪ Be able to perform non-structured titration calculations, based on experimental results.

Specification Reference 5.3.1

Titration results

When you've done a titration you can use your results to calculate the concentration of your acid or base.

If you're doing an acid-base titration using an indicator, you can use the volume of acid added when the indicator changes colour to calculate how much acid is needed to neutralise the alkali (or vice versa). Once you know this, you can use it to work out the concentration of the alkali.

If you use a pH meter rather than an indicator, you can draw a pH curve of the titration and use it to work out how much acid or base is needed for neutralisation. You do this by finding the equivalence point (the mid–point of the line of rapid pH change) and drawing a vertical line downwards until it meets the x-axis. The value at this point on the x-axis is the volume of acid or base needed — see Figure 1.

Tip: When you do an experiment (like a titration) in the lab, you should plan it and carry it out carefully to make sure that your results are <u>accurate</u> and <u>reliable</u> (see page 229 for more).

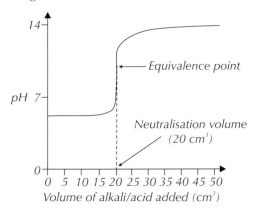

Figure 1: Finding how much base is needed for neutralisation.

Calculating concentrations

Once you know the neutralisation volume you can use it to calculate the concentration of the acid or base. To do this:

Step 1: Write out a balanced equation for the titration reaction.

Step 2: Decide what you know already and what you need to know — usually you'll be given the two volumes and a concentration and you'll have to work out the other concentration.

Step 3: For one reagent you'll know both the concentration and the volume. Calculate the number of moles of this reagent using the equation:

$$\text{moles} = \frac{\text{concentration} (\text{mol dm}^{-3}) \times \text{volume} (\text{cm}^3)}{1000}$$

Step 4: Use the molar ratios in the balanced equation to find out how many moles of the other reagent reacted.

Step 5: Calculate the unknown concentration using the equation:

$$\text{concentration} = \frac{\text{moles} \times 1000}{\text{volume}}$$

in mol dm^{-3} → concentration ← *in cm^3*

Figure 2: A pH meter being used to monitor the pH during a titration.

Tip: You came across the formula:

moles = $\dfrac{\text{conc.} \times \text{vol.}}{1000}$

in AS, but you need to know it for A2 as well. The dividing by 1000 bit is to get the volume from cm^3 to dm^3 — if your volume is already in dm^3 then it's just:

moles = conc. × vol.

Example

The graph on the right shows the results when 0.500 mol dm⁻³ HCl was titrated against 35.0 cm³ of NaOH. Calculate the concentration of the NaOH solution.

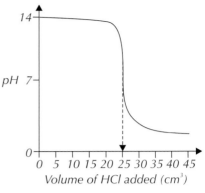

From the graph you can see that 25 cm³ of HCl was required to neutralise the NaOH. You can use this information to work out the concentration of the NaOH solution by following the steps on the previous page.

1. The balanced equation for this titration reaction is:
$$HCl \ + \ NaOH \ \rightarrow \ NaCl + H_2O$$

2. You know the concentration of HCl (0.500 mol dm⁻³), the volume of HCl (25.0 cm³) and the volume of NaOH (35.0 cm³). You need to know the concentration of NaOH.

3. Calculate the moles of HCl:

$$\text{moles HCl} = \frac{\text{concentration} \times \text{volume}}{1000} = \frac{0.500 \times 25.0}{1000} = 0.0125 \text{ moles}$$

4. From the equation, you know 1 mole of HCl neutralises 1 mole of NaOH. So 0.0125 moles of HCl must neutralise 0.0125 moles of NaOH.

5. Calculate the concentration of NaOH:

$$\text{Conc. NaOH} = \frac{\text{moles} \times 1000}{\text{volume}} = \frac{0.0125 \times 1000}{35.0} = 0.357 \text{ mol dm}^{-3}$$

Practice Questions — Application

Q1 In a titration, the equivalence point was reached after 13.8 cm³ of a 1.50 mol dm⁻³ solution of HCl had been added to 20.0 cm³ of NaOH. Calculate the concentration of the NaOH solution.

Q2 Nitric acid (HNO_3) was added to 30.0 cm³ of a 0.250 mol dm⁻³ solution of NaOH in the presence of methyl orange. A colour change was observed after 17.8 cm³ of the acid had been added. Calculate the concentration of the nitric acid solution.

Q3 The graph on the right shows the pH curve produced when 0.850 mol dm⁻³ HCl was titrated against 30.0 cm³ of an NaOH solution of unknown concentration. Calculate the concentration of the NaOH solution.

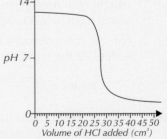

Q4 32.0 cm³ of an NaOH solution is fully neutralised when 18.0 cm³ of a 0.400 mol dm⁻³ solution of HCl is added to it. Calculate the concentration of the NaOH solution.

Section Summary

Make sure you know...

- That reaction rate is the change in the amount of reactants or products per unit time.
- How to work out reaction rates from concentration–time graphs.
- That the rate equation for the reaction $A + B \rightarrow C + D$ is rate $= k[A]^m[B]^n$.
- What each of the terms in the rate equation means.
- That reaction orders tell you how a reactant's concentration affects the rate of reaction.
- How to calculate the rate constant and its units, using the rate equation and experimental data.
- That the rate constant, k, is always the same for a certain reaction at a particular temperature.
- That increasing the temperature increases the rate constant.
- How to deduce reaction orders from rate-concentration graphs.
- That the half-life of a reaction is the time taken for the amount of reactant to halve.
- How to deduce half-lives from concentration-time graphs.
- That the half-lives of first order reactions don't vary with concentration (the half-life is constant).
- How to use the initial rates method to work out reaction orders.
- That the rate-determining step is the slowest step in a reaction mechanism.
- How to use the rate equation to determine which step in a reaction is the rate-determining step.
- How to propose a reaction mechanism from the rate equation and the overall equation for a reaction.
- That K_c is the equilibrium constant and how to derive expressions for the equilibrium constant, K_c.
- How to calculate K_c and its units from the equilibrium concentrations and molar ratios for a reaction.
- How to use K_c to find unknown equilibrium concentrations for a reaction.
- How changing the temperature will affect the value of K_c for endothermic and exothermic reactions.
- That changing the concentration or pressure of reactants or adding a catalyst has no effect on K_c.
- That an acid is a species that can donate a proton and a base is a species that can accept a proton.
- How acids react with metals, carbonates, bases and alkalis.
- That strong acids/bases dissociate fully in water while weak acids/bases only partially dissociate.
- What conjugate acid/base pairs are and how to identify them.
- That pH $= -\log[H^+]$ where $[H^+]$ is the concentration of H^+ ions in mol dm^{-3}.
- How to convert pH into $[H^+]$ and vice versa.
- How to calculate the pH of a strong acid from its concentration.
- That water is weakly dissociated and the ionic product of water is $K_w = [H^+][OH^-]$.
- How to calculate the pH of a strong base from its concentration and vice versa, using K_w.
- That K_a is the dissociation constant for a weak acid, and how to write expressions for K_a.
- How to calculate the pH of a weak acid from its concentration and K_a.
- How to calculate the concentration of a weak acid from its pH and K_a.
- How to calculate K_a for a weak acid from its pH and concentration.
- That $pK_a = -\log(K_a)$ and how to convert K_a to pK_a and vice versa.
- What a buffer is, how to make one and how an acidic buffer can resist changes in pH.
- The role of buffers in biological systems (e.g. carbonic acid in maintaining blood pH at 7.4).
- How to calculate the pH of an acidic buffer.
- What the pH curves for all the different combinations of weak and strong acids and bases look like.
- How to use pH curves to select an appropriate pH indicator to use in a titration.
- How to calculate the concentration of monobasic acids and bases using the results of a titration.

Exam-style Questions

1   Under certain conditions the following reaction occurs between nitrogen monoxide (NO) and hydrogen (H_2):

$$2NO_{(g)} + 2H_{2(g)} \rightarrow N_{2(g)} + 2H_2O_{(g)}$$

The table below shows the results of a series of initial rate experiments for this reaction.

Experiment number	[NO] (mol dm^{-3})	[H$_2$] (mol dm^{-3})	Initial rate (mol dm^{-3} s^{-1})
1	3.0×10^{-3}	6.0×10^{-3}	4.50×10^{-3}
2	3.0×10^{-3}	3.0×10^{-3}	2.25×10^{-3}
3	6.0×10^{-3}	1.5×10^{-3}	4.50×10^{-3}

(a)   Determine the orders of reaction with respect to NO and H_2.

(2 marks)

(b)   Write out the rate equation for this reaction.

(1 mark)

(c)   Using the data above, calculate the rate constant (k) for this reaction and give its units.

(3 marks)

(d)   What would the rate of reaction be if 4.5×10^{-3} mol dm^{-3} NO were mixed with 2.5×10^{-3} mol dm^{-3} H_2 under the same conditions as the experiment above?

(If you were unable to answer 1 (c), use $k = 6.5 \times 10^5$.)

(2 marks)

(e) (i)   Using the rate equation, explain why a one-step mechanism is not possible for this reaction.

(2 marks)

    (ii)   Suggest a possible two step mechanism for this reaction. The first step is the slowest step.

(2 marks)

2   The following equilibrium establishes at temperature X:

$$CH_{4(g)} + 2H_2O_{(g)} \rightleftharpoons CO_{2(g)} + 4H_{2(g)} \qquad \Delta H = +165 \text{ kJ mol}^{-1}$$

At equilibrium the mixture was found to contain 0.080 mol dm^{-3} CH_4, 0.320 mol dm^{-3} H_2O, 0.200 mol dm^{-3} CO_2 and 0.280 mol dm^{-3} H_2.

(a) (i)   Write an expression for K_c for this equilibrium.

(1 mark)

    (ii)   Calculate the value of K_c at temperature X, and give its units.

(3 marks)

(b) At a different temperature, Y, the value of K_c was found to be 0.0800 and the equilibrium concentrations were as follows:

Gas	CH_4	H_2O	CO_2	H_2
Concentration (mol dm^{-3})	?	0.560	0.420	0.480

(i) Calculate the equilibrium concentration of CH_4 at this temperature.

(2 marks)

(ii) At another temperature, Z, the value of K_c was found to be 1.20×10^{-3}. Suggest whether temperature Z is higher or lower than temperature Y. Explain your answer.

(3 marks)

(c) State how the value of K_c would change if a catalyst was added to the reaction. Explain your answer.

(2 marks)

3 The concentrations of strong acids and strong bases can be found by carrying out titrations. Titrations are usually done at room temperature (25.0 °C). The value of K_w at 25.0 °C is 1.00×10^{-14} mol dm^{-3}.

(a) (i) Give the expression for K_w.

(1 mark)

(ii) Give the expression for pH.

(1 mark)

(b) Calculate the pH of a 0.150 mol dm^{-3} solution of NaOH at 25.0 °C.

(3 marks)

(c) In a titration reaction at 25.0 °C, 25.0 cm^3 of this 0.150 mol dm^{-3} solution of NaOH was neutralised by 18.5 cm^3 of a HCl solution of unknown concentration.

(i) Which of the graphs below (A, B and C) shows the pH curve for this reaction?

A
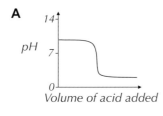

B
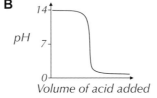

C
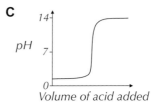

(1 mark)

(ii) Calculate the concentration of the unknown HCl solution.

(3 marks)

(iii) Calculate the pH of the HCl solution.

(2 marks)

(d) The pH curve for another titration is shown below.

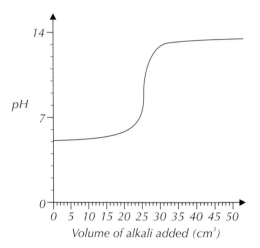

Indicator	pH range
Thymol blue	1.2 – 2.8
Bromophenol blue	3.0 – 4.6
Litmus	5.0 – 8.0
Phenolphthalein	8.3 – 10

(i) Suggest an acid and a base that could have been used in this titration.

(2 marks)

(ii) From the table above, suggest an indicator that would be suitable for this titration.

(1 mark)

4 Methanoic acid (HCOOH) is a weak acid. A 0.240 mol dm^{-3} solution of HCOOH has a pH of 2.2 at 25 °C.

(a) (i) Write out the equation for the dissociation of CHOOH.

(1 mark)

(ii) Write out an expression for K_a for this acid.

(1 mark)

(iii) Calculate the pK_a of methanoic acid at 25 °C.

(3 marks)

(b) A buffer solution contains 0.0840 mol dm^{-3} methanoic acid (HCOOH) and 0.0600 mol dm^{-3} ammonium methanoate (HCOONH$_4$)

(i) Calculate the pH of this buffer.

(2 marks)

(ii) This buffer can be prepared by reacting methanoic acid with ammonia.
- Write an equation for the reaction of methanoic acid with ammonia.
- Label one conjugate acid/base pair 'Acid 1' and 'Base 1'.
- Label the other conjugate acid/base pair 'Acid 2' and 'Base 2'.

(3 marks)

(iii) Explain how this buffer resists changes in pH when an acid is added.

(3 marks)

1. Neutralisation and Enthalpy

Learning Objectives:
- Be able to define and use the term enthalpy change of neutralisation.
- Be able to calculate enthalpy changes from appropriate experimental results.

   Specification Reference 5.1.3

Some of this stuff may ring a few bells from your AS course. Make sure that you understand all the definitions in this topic because they're really important for the rest of the section.

The basics
Enthalpy notation

Enthalpy change, ΔH (delta H), is the heat energy transferred in a reaction at constant pressure. The units of ΔH are kJ mol^{-1}. You write $\Delta H^{\ominus}$ to show that the substances were in their standard states and that the measurements were made under **standard conditions**. Standard conditions are 100 kPa (about 1 atm) pressure and a stated temperature (e.g. $\Delta H^{\ominus}_{298}$). In this book, all the enthalpy changes are measured at 298 K (25 °C). Sometimes the notation will also include a letter to signify whether the enthalpy change is for a reaction (r), for combustion (c), or for the formation of a new compound (f).

Tip: You studied enthalpy at AS level so if you need a reminder, get your old AS notes out.

Exothermic and endothermic reactions

Exothermic reactions have a negative ΔH value, because heat energy is given out (the chemicals lose energy). **Endothermic reactions** have a positive ΔH value, because heat energy is absorbed (the chemicals gain energy).

Calculating enthalpy changes

You can work out ΔH from a calorimeter experiment. This involves measuring the temperature change of some water as a result of a reaction. If a reaction is exothermic, the heat given out by the reaction will cause the temperature of the water to rise. If a reaction is endothermic, it will absorb heat and the temperature of the water will fall. Once you've measured the temperature change, you can calculate the enthalpy change of the water (q) in J using this equation:

$$q = mc\Delta T$$

m = mass of the water (in g)
c = specific heat capacity (for water it's 4.18 J g^{-1} K^{-1})
ΔT = the change in temperature of the water (K)

Figure 1: *Parts of a calorimeter used to measure enthalpy changes.*

Enthalpy change of neutralisation

When an acid reacts with a base a neutralisation reaction occurs. Neutralisation always involves the reaction of hydrogen ions (H^+) with hydroxide ions (OH^-) to make water (H_2O).

$$H^+ + OH^- \rightarrow H_2O$$

The change in energy when this happens is called the enthalpy change of neutralisation ($\Delta H^{\ominus}_{neutralisation}$). Here's the definition:

The **enthalpy change of neutralisation**, $\Delta H^{\ominus}_{neutralisation}$, is the enthalpy change when 1 mole of water is formed by the reaction between an acid and a base under standard conditions.

Calculating enthalpy change of neutralisation

You can calculate the enthalpy change of neutralisation from the results of a calorimeter experiment. All you have to do is mix together known quantities of acid and alkali and measure the temperature change of the reaction. Then you can calculate the enthalpy change of neutralisation by following the steps below:

1. Calculate the amount of heat lost or gained during the reaction using $q = mc\Delta T$ and the measured values of m and ΔT.

2. Divide by 1000 to change the units of q from joules to kilojoules.

3. Write out a balanced chemical equation for the neutralisation reaction Use this to determine how many moles of water have been produced.

Calculate the standard enthalpy change of neutralisation, $\Delta H^{\ominus}_{neutralisation}$ (in kJ mol^{-1}), using the heat change for the reaction, q (in kJ), and the number of moles of water produced, n, using the equation:

$$\Delta H^{\ominus} = \frac{q}{n}$$

If the reaction is exothermic you'll need to change the sign of ΔH to get your final answer. Here's an example of how it all works:

Figure 2: A computer monitoring the temperature change during an exothermic reaction.

Tip: Neutralisation reactions are usually exothermic — they give out heat, so $\Delta H^{\ominus}_{neutralisation}$ is usually negative.

Tip: Temperature changes are the same in °C and K. This is because the size of one K is the same as the size of one °C. So a change in temperature of one K is the same as a change in temperature of one °C.

Tip: If the equation showed that two moles of H_2O were formed per mole of acid, you would multiply the moles of acid by two to find the moles of H_2O produced.

Example

150 ml of hydrochloric acid (concentration 0.25 mol dm^{-3}) was neutralised by 150 ml of potassium hydroxide. The temperature increased by 1.71 °C. Calculate $\Delta H^{\ominus}_{neutralisation}$.

1. First calculate the heat change (q) during the neutralisation reaction:
   - The final volume of the solution is $150 + 150 = 300$ cm^3. Assuming the acid/base mixture has the same density as water (1 g/cm^3) this is equivalent to 300 g, so $m = 300$.
   - The specific heat capacity of water is 4.18 J g^{-1} K^{-1} so $c = 4.18$
   - From the question we can see that $\Delta T = 1.71$ °C $= 1.71$ K.

   So: $\quad q = mc\Delta T = 300 \times 4.18 \times 1.71 = 2144$ J

2. Divide q by 1000 to change it into kJ:
   2144 J $\div 1000 = 2.144$ kJ

3. The balanced equation for this reaction is:

   $$HCl + KOH \rightarrow KCl + H_2O$$

   From the equation you can see that the number of moles of H_2O made is equal to the number of moles of acid used. To work that out you can use the information in the question:

   Moles of acid $=$ concentration (mol dm^{-3}) $\times$ volume (dm)
   $= 0.25 \times (150 \div 1000) = 0.0375$

   So 0.0375 moles of water are produced.

4. Now calculate the enthalpy change of neutralisation for the reaction:

   $$\frac{q}{n} = 2.144 \div 0.0375 = 57.2 \text{ kJ mol}^{-1}$$

   But the reaction is exothermic — it gives out heat to the surroundings.
   So: $\Delta H^{\ominus}_{neutralisation} = -57.2$ kJ mol^{-1}

Weirdly, the value for any strong acid is about -57 kJ mol^{-1}. This is because all strong acids and bases completely ionise in water so essentially the reaction for each of them is the same ($H^+ + OH^- \rightarrow H_2O$).

For weaker acids and alkalis the value is less negative because energy is used to fully dissociate the acid or alkali meaning there's less energy released.

Tip: See page 132 for more on weak and strong acids and bases.

Other types of enthalpy change

The enthalpy change of neutralisation isn't the only type of enthalpy change you need to know about. There are lots of different enthalpy terms you need to know on the next few pages. So spend some time looking at them now and it'll make everything coming up a bit easier. Unfortunately, each specific type of enthalpy change has its own definition and you need to learn them all.

- **Enthalpy change of formation**, $\Delta H^{\ominus}_f$ is the enthalpy change when 1 mole of a compound is formed from its elements in their standard states under standard conditions, e.g. $Ca_{(s)} + Cl_{2(g)} \rightarrow CaCl_{2(s)}$

- **Enthalpy change of atomisation of an element**, $\Delta H^{\ominus}_{at}$, is the enthalpy change when 1 mole of gaseous atoms is formed from an element in its standard state, e.g. $\frac{1}{2}Cl_{2(g)} \rightarrow Cl_{(g)}$

- **Enthalpy change of atomisation of a compound**, $\Delta H^{\ominus}_{at}$, is the enthalpy change when 1 mole of a compound in its standard state is converted to gaseous atoms, e.g. $NaCl_{(s)} \rightarrow Na_{(g)} + Cl_{(g)}$

- The **first ionisation enthalpy**, $\Delta H^{\ominus}_{ie1}$, is the enthalpy change when 1 mole of gaseous 1+ ions is formed from 1 mole of gaseous atoms, e.g. $Mg_{(g)} \rightarrow Mg^+_{(g)} + e^-$

- The **second ionisation enthalpy**, $\Delta H^{\ominus}_{ie2}$, is the enthalpy change when 1 mole of gaseous 2+ ions is formed from 1 mole of gaseous 1+ ions, e.g. $Mg^+_{(g)} \rightarrow Mg^{2+}_{(g)} + e^-$

- **First electron affinity**, $\Delta H^{\ominus}_{ea1}$, is the enthalpy change when 1 mole of gaseous 1− ions is made from 1 mole of gaseous atoms, e.g. $O_{(g)} + e^- \rightarrow O^-_{(g)}$

- **Second electron affinity**, $\Delta H^{\ominus}_{ea2}$, is the enthalpy change when 1 mole of gaseous 2− ions is made from 1 mole of gaseous 1− ions, e.g. $O^-_{(g)} + e^- \rightarrow O^{2-}_{(g)}$

- The **enthalpy change of hydration**, $\Delta H^{\ominus}_{hyd}$, is the enthalpy change when 1 mole of aqueous ions is formed from gaseous ions, e.g. $Na^+_{(g)} \rightarrow Na^+_{(aq)}$

- The **enthalpy change of solution**, $\Delta H^{\ominus}_{solution}$, is the enthalpy change when 1 mole of solute is dissolved in sufficient solvent that no further enthalpy change occurs on further dilution, e.g. $NaCl_{(s)} \rightarrow NaCl_{(aq)}$

Exam Tip
You could be asked to give any of these definitions in the exam, so make sure you've learned them all word for word.

Tip: These terms will crop up a lot in this section so don't move on until you understand what each one means — you might want to fold this page over so you can find it again if you need to.

Tip: There's lots more on enthalpy change of hydration and enthalpy change of solution on page 169.

Practice Questions — Application

For all of these questions, assume that the density and the specific heat capacity of the acid/base solutions are the same as those of water.

Q1 25.0 cm^3 of a $0.500 \text{ mol dm}^{-3}$ solution of hydrochloric acid (HCl) was neutralised by 25.0 cm^3 of sodium hydroxide (NaOH). The temperature increased by $3.45 \,°C$. Calculate $\Delta H^{\ominus}_{neutralisation}$.

Tip: The specific heat capacity of water is $4.18 \text{ kJ kg}^{-1} \text{K}^{-1}$.

Tip: Remember that the value of $\Delta H^{\ominus}_{neutralisation}$ for a strong acid should be about −57 kJ mol^{-1} — if your answer's way off this, then you know that something's gone wrong with your calculation.

Q2 250 ml of a 0.150 mol dm^{-3} solution of nitric acid (HNO$_3$) was neutralised by 150 ml of potassium hydroxide (KOH). The temperature increased by 1.26 °C. Calculate $\Delta H^{\ominus}_{neutralisation}$.

Q3 32.0 cm^3 of a 0.500 mol dm^{-3} solution of hydrochloric acid (HCl) was neutralised by 28.0 cm^3 of lithium hydroxide (LiOH). The temperature increased by 3.65 °C. Calculate $\Delta H^{\ominus}_{neutralisation}$.

Q4 125 ml of a 0.240 mol dm^{-3} solution of hydrobromic acid (HBr) was neutralised by 75 ml of sodium hydroxide (NaOH). The temperature increased by 2.07 °C. Calculate $\Delta H^{\ominus}_{neutralisation}$.

Practice Questions — Fact Recall

Q1 What is meant by the term enthalpy change?

Q2 Give the symbol for enthalpy change.

Q3 a) Define the term enthalpy of neutralisation.

b) Describe an experiment you could use to determine the enthalpy change of neutralisation of a reaction.

Q4 Define the following:

a) enthalpy change of formation.

b) second electron affinity.

c) enthalpy change of solution.

Q5 Name the changes in enthalpy defined below:

a) The enthalpy change when 1 mole of gaseous atoms is formed from an element in its standard state.

b) The enthalpy change when 1 mole of gaseous 1+ ions is formed from 1 mole of gaseous atoms.

Q6 Write the symbol for the following enthalpy changes:

a) The enthalpy change of hydration.

b) The second ionisation enthalpy.

2. Lattice Enthalpy

As you might have guessed from the title, this topic is all about lattice enthalpies. Read on to find out what lattice enthalpies are, why they are useful and what affects the lattice enthalpy of an ionic compound.

What is lattice enthalpy?

Remember how ionic compounds form regular structures called giant ionic lattices — and how the positive and negative ions are held together by electrostatic attraction. Well, when gaseous ions combine to make a solid lattice, energy is given out — this is called the lattice enthalpy. Here's the definition of standard lattice enthalpy that you need to know:

> The **standard lattice enthalpy**, $\Delta H^{\ominus}_{latt}$, is the enthalpy change when 1 mole of a solid ionic compound is formed from its gaseous ions under standard conditions.

Learning Objectives:

- Be able to explain and use the term lattice enthalpy as a measure of ionic bond strength.
- Be able to explain, in qualitative terms, the effect of ionic charge and ionic radius on the exothermic value of a lattice enthalpy.

Specification Reference 5.2.1

--- Example ---

Sodium chloride (NaCl) is an example of an ionic lattice. The diagram below shows how NaCl is formed from gaseous Na^+ and Cl^- ions.

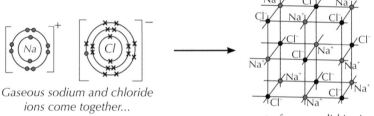

Gaseous sodium and chloride ions come together...

... to form a solid ionic lattice of sodium chloride.

Lattice formation enthalpy, $\Delta H^{\ominus}_{latt}$, for this reaction is -787 kJ mol^{-1}. The negative ΔH value shows that lattice formation is an exothermic process.

Figure 1: A 3D model of a sodium chloride lattice.

Lattice enthalpies are quite handy because they tell you how strong the ionic bonding is. The more negative the lattice enthalpy, the stronger the bonding.

--- Example ---

The lattice enthalpies of NaCl and MgO are:

$$Na^+_{(g)} + Cl^-_{(g)} \rightarrow NaCl_{(s)} \qquad \Delta H^{\ominus}_{latt} = -787 \text{ kJ mol}^{-1}$$
$$Mg^{2+}_{(g)} + O^{2-}_{(g)} \rightarrow MgO_{(s)} \qquad \Delta H^{\ominus}_{latt} = -3791 \text{ kJ mol}^{-1}$$

Out of NaCl and MgO, MgO has the more negative lattice enthalpy so the MgO lattice is held together by stronger ionic bonds.

Factors affecting lattice enthalpy

Lattice enthalpies have specific values that differ depending on the ions involved. There are two main factors which influence the lattice enthalpy:

1. Ionic charge

The higher the charge on the ions, the more energy is released when an ionic lattice forms. More energy released means that the lattice enthalpy will be more negative. So the lattice enthalpies for compounds with 2+ or 2− ions (e.g. Mg^{2+} or S^{2-}) are more negative than those with 1+ or 1− ions (e.g. Na^+ or Cl^-).

Tip: Ionic compounds with two 1+ (or 1−) ions and one 2− (or 2+) ion, like Na_2O, have intermediate lattice enthalpies.

Examples

The lattice enthalpy of NaCl is only -787 kJ mol^{-1}, but the lattice enthalpy of MgCl$_2$ is -2526 kJ mol^{-1}.

MgS has an even higher lattice enthalpy (-3299 kJ mol^{-1}) because both magnesium and sulfur ions have double charges.

Magnesium oxide has a very exothermic lattice enthalpy too, which means it is very resistant to heat. This makes it great as a lining in furnaces.

2. Ionic radius

The smaller the ionic radii of the ions involved, the more exothermic (more negative) the lattice enthalpy. Smaller ions attract more strongly because their charge density is higher.

Examples

Here are the standard lattice enthalpies of some chloride compounds:

Compound	Standard lattice enthalpy (kJ mol^{-1})
LiCl	−826
NaCl	−787
KCl	−701
RbCl	−692

Of all the positive ions, Li$^+$ has the smallest ionic radius. This means that LiCl has the most exothermic lattice enthalpy because the smaller Li$^+$ ions are more strongly attracted to the Cl$^-$ ions than larger ions like Rb$^+$.

You should remember from AS that ionic radius increases down a group — so have a look at the periodic table if you're unsure about which ions have the largest ionic radii.

Practice Questions — Application

Q1 The table below shows the standard lattice enthalpies of some sodium containing compounds.

Compound	Standard lattice enthalpy (kJ mol^{-1})
NaCl	−787
NaBr	−747
NaI	−704

a) Explain why the standard lattice enthalpy becomes less exothermic from NaCl to NaI.
b) Which of these compounds contains the strongest ionic bonds?

Q2 The standard lattice enthalpy of Na$_2$O is -2481 kJ mol^{-1}. Would you expect the lattice enthalpy of MgO to be more or less negative than this? Explain your answer.

Practice Questions — Fact Recall

Q1 a) Define the term 'standard lattice enthalpy'.
   b) What is the symbol for standard lattice enthalpy?

Q2 What is the relationship between the lattice enthalpy of an ionic compound and the ionic bond strength?

Q3 What two factors affect the lattice enthalpy of an ionic compound?

3. Calculating Lattice Enthalpies

Get those rulers and pencils out — it's time to draw some Born-Haber cycles.

Forming ionic lattices

The lattice enthalpy is the enthalpy change when an ionic lattice is formed from its gaseous ions. But when an ionic lattice forms, you won't usually start with gaseous ions — you'll probably start with atoms in their standard states. There are two routes you can follow to get from the elements in their standard states to an ionic lattice:

- A direct route, which involves converting the elements in their standard states directly into an ionic lattice. The enthalpy change for this reaction is given by the enthalpy of formation ($\Delta H^{\ominus}_f$) of the lattice.

- An indirect route, which involves forming gaseous atoms, converting these into gaseous ions and then forming the ionic lattice. Each of the steps in this route has its own enthalpy change — see Figure 1.

Learning Objective:

- Be able to use the lattice enthalpy of a simple ionic solid (i.e. NaCl, MgCl$_2$) and relevant energy terms to construct Born–Haber cycles and carry out related calculations.

Specification Reference 5.2.1

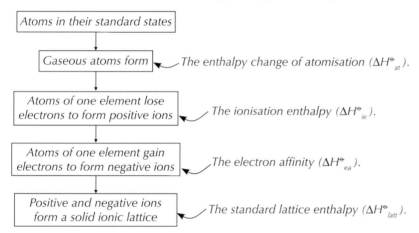

Figure 1: The indirect route for forming an ionic lattice.

The boxes in Figure 1 read:
- Atoms in their standard states
- Gaseous atoms form — The enthalpy change of atomisation ($\Delta H^{\ominus}_{at}$).
- Atoms of one element lose electrons to form positive ions — The ionisation enthalpy ($\Delta H^{\ominus}_{ie}$).
- Atoms of one element gain electrons to form negative ions — The electron affinity ($\Delta H^{\ominus}_{ea}$).
- Positive and negative ions form a solid ionic lattice — The standard lattice enthalpy ($\Delta H^{\ominus}_{latt}$).

Tip: See page 161 for a recap on the definitions of all these different enthalpy changes.

Born-Haber cycles

The two different routes for forming an ionic lattice and the enthalpy changes involved can be illustrated using a **Born-Haber cycle**. Here's how to draw a Born-Haber cycle:

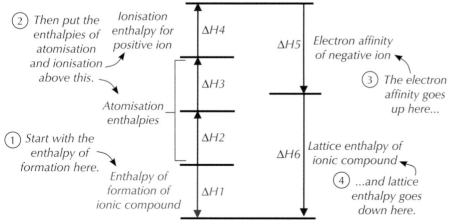

① Start with the enthalpy of formation here.

② Then put the enthalpies of atomisation and ionisation above this.

Ionisation enthalpy for positive ion — $\Delta H4$

$\Delta H5$ Electron affinity of negative ion

③ The electron affinity goes up here...

$\Delta H3$

Atomisation enthalpies

$\Delta H2$

$\Delta H6$ Lattice enthalpy of ionic compound

④ ...and lattice enthalpy goes down here.

Enthalpy of formation of ionic compound — $\Delta H1$

Figure 2: German physicist Max Born who, along with Fritz Haber, developed Born-Haber cycles.

Tip: The Haber who helped develop Born-Haber cycles is the same Haber who invented the Haber process for synthesising ammonia.

On the diagram above, the blue arrow shows the direct route and the red arrows show the indirect route.

Calculating lattice enthalpies using Born-Haber cycles

Lattice enthalpies can't be measured directly, but **Hess's law** states that:

> The total enthalpy change of a reaction is always the same, no matter which route is taken.

This means that if you know all the other enthalpy changes, you can use a Born-Haber cycle to calculate the lattice enthalpy via an indirect route. All you have to do is use an alternative route around the diagram — for example, route 2 on the diagram below:

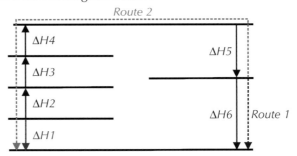

According to Hess's law, the enthalpy change of route 1 (the standard lattice enthalpy) is the same as the enthalpy change of route 2.

You can find the ΔH of route 2 by adding all the enthalpy changes in this route together and adding in a minus sign whenever you go the wrong way along an arrow. So...

$$\Delta H_{route\ 2} = (-\Delta H5) + (-\Delta H4) + (-\Delta H3) + (-\Delta H2) + \Delta H1$$

Add all the enthalpy changes in route 2 together.   *Add a minus sign if you go the wrong way along an arrow.*

$$\Delta H_{route\ 2} = \Delta H_{route\ 1} = \Delta H6 \quad so...$$

$$\boxed{\Delta H6 = -\Delta H5 - \Delta H4 - \Delta H3 - \Delta H2 + \Delta H1}$$

Example

This is the Born-Haber cycle for the formation of sodium chloride:

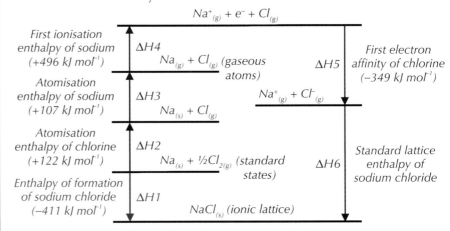

Hess's law says that the total enthalpy change of a reaction is always the same, no matter which route is taken. So ...

$$\Delta H^{\ominus}_{latt} = \Delta H6 = -\Delta H5 - \Delta H4 - \Delta H3 - \Delta H2 + \Delta H1$$
$$= -(-349) - (+496) - (+107) - (+122) + (-411) = \mathbf{-787\ kJ\ mol^{-1}}$$

Figure 3: *Victor Franz Hess — the scientist who proposed Hess's law.*

Tip: If you already know $\Delta H^{\ominus}_{latt}$ you can use this technique to calculate any of the enthalpy changes in the Born-Haber cycle — just use an alternative route round the diagram.

Tip: Don't forget — ΔH is the symbol for enthalpy change. See page 159 for more.

Tip: You can also get the equation above by re-arranging this equation:
$\Delta H1 = \Delta H2 + \Delta H3 + \Delta H4 + \Delta H5 + \Delta H6$.

Tip: Be really careful with your + and − signs in these calculations. You could end up minusing a minus number which is the same as adding it.

Born-Haber cycles for compounds containing Group 2 elements have a few changes from the ones on the previous page. Here's a Born-Haber cycle for a compound containing a Group 2 element:

Group 2 elements form 2+ ions — so you've got to include the second ionisation enthalpy.

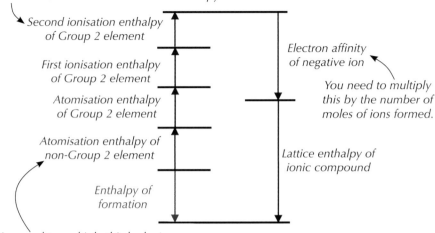

You need to multiply this by the number of moles of ions formed.

You need to multiply this by however many moles of the element there are in one mole of the ionic lattice.

Tip: Remember, enthalpy change of formation, $\Delta H^{\ominus}_{f}$, is the enthalpy change when <u>one mole of a compound</u> is formed from its elements in their standard states under standard conditions.

Example

Magnesium can react with chlorine to form magnesium chloride. Here's how you calculate the lattice enthalpy of magnesium chloride ($MgCl_2$).

Magnesium forms 2+ ions — so you've got to include the second ionisation enthalpy.

$$Mg_{(g)} + Cl_{2(g)} \rightarrow MgCl_{2(s)}$$

You need to multiply the atomisation energy of chlorine by 2 because there are two moles of Cl in one mole of $MgCl_2$.

You need to multiply the electron affinity of chlorine by 2 because two moles of ions form.

Here's the Born-Haber cycle:

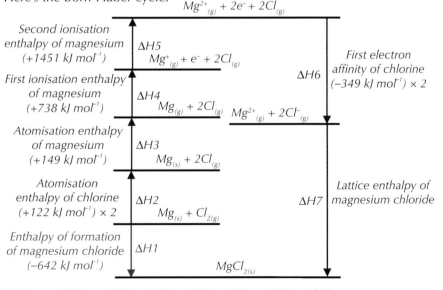

Figure 4: Dry magnesium chloride.

Tip: State symbols are really important here. If you're not sure of which state symbols go with which steps, check the definitions on page 161.

$$\Delta H^{\ominus}_{latt} = \Delta H7 = -\Delta H6 - \Delta H5 - \Delta H4 - \Delta H3 - \Delta H2 + \Delta H1$$
$$= -(-349 \times 2) - (+1451) - (+738) - (+149) - (+122 \times 2) + (-642)$$
$$= \textbf{-2526 kJ mol}^{-1}$$

Practice Questions — Application

Q1 Look at the following Born-Haber cycle.

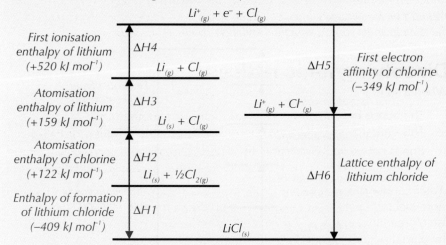

Use Hess's law to calculate the standard lattice enthalpy of lithium chloride.

Q2 Complete the following Born-Haber cycle for the formation of $CaBr_2$.

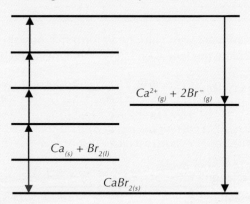

Q3 Look at the table below.

Enthalpy change	$\Delta H^\ominus$ / kJ mol^{-1}
Enthalpy change of atomisation of potassium	+89
Enthalpy change of atomisation of fluorine	+79
First ionisation enthalpy of potassium	+419
Electron affinity of fluorine	−328
Enthalpy of formation of potassium fluoride	−563

a) Draw the Born-Haber cycle for the formation of KF.

b) Use Hess's law to calculate the standard lattice enthalpy of KF.

Practice Questions — Fact Recall

Q1 Name 4 different types of enthalpy that you could combine to work out the standard lattice enthalpy of an ionic compound.

Q2 What does Hess's law state?

4. Enthalpies of Solution

Lattice enthalpies aren't the only enthalpies you can calculate using Hess's law. You can work out enthalpies of solution too. You'll need to remind yourself of the definition of standard lattice enthalpy (page 163) before you start.

Dissolving ionic lattices

When a solid ionic lattice dissolves in water these two things happen:

- The bonds between the ions break — this is endothermic. This enthalpy change is the opposite of the **standard lattice enthalpy**.

- Bonds between the ions and the water are made — this is exothermic. The enthalpy change here is called the **enthalpy change of hydration**.

Water can form bonds with the ions because it is a polar molecule. Oxygen is more electronegative than hydrogen, so it draws the bonding electrons toward itself, creating a dipole. Consequently, positive ions form weak bonds with the partial negative charge on the oxygen atom and negative ions form weak bonds with the partial positive charge on the hydrogen atoms (see Figure 1).

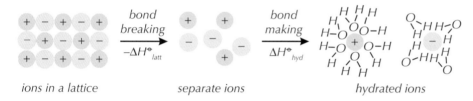

ions in a lattice   *separate ions*   *hydrated ions*

Figure 1: *A solid ionic lattice dissolving in water.*

The **enthalpy change of solution** is the overall effect on the enthalpy of bond breaking and bond making. Here are the definitions you need to know:

> The **enthalpy change of hydration**, $\Delta H^{\ominus}_{hyd}$, is the enthalpy change when 1 mole of aqueous ions is formed from gaseous ions, e.g. $Na^{+}_{(g)} \rightarrow Na^{+}_{(aq)}$

> The **enthalpy change of solution**, $\Delta H^{\ominus}_{solution}$, is the enthalpy change when 1 mole of solute is dissolved in sufficient solvent that no further enthalpy change occurs on further dilution, e.g. $NaCl_{(s)} \rightarrow NaCl_{(aq)}$

Entropy and dissolving ionic lattices

Substances generally only dissolve if the energy released is roughly the same, or greater than the energy taken in. But enthalpy change isn't the only thing that decides if something will dissolve — **entropy** change is important too.

    A reaction or state change is more likely when there is a positive entropy change. Dissolving normally causes an increase in entropy. But for small, highly charged ions there may be a decrease because when water molecules surround the ions, it makes things more orderly. The entropy changes are usually pretty small but they can sometimes make the difference between something being soluble or insoluble.

Learning Objectives:

- Be able to explain and use the terms enthalpy change of solution and enthalpy change of hydration.

- Be able to use the enthalpy change of solution of a simple ionic solid (i.e. NaCl, $MgCl_2$) and relevant energy terms (enthalpy change of hydration, and lattice enthalpy) to construct Born–Haber cycles and carry out related calculations.

- Be able to explain, in qualitative terms, the effect of ionic charge and ionic radius on the exothermic value of an enthalpy change of hydration.

Specification Reference 5.2.1

Tip: Take a look back at your AS notes if you need a reminder about electronegativity and the δ^+ and δ^- charges on polar molecules such as water:

$$\delta^- \overset{H\delta^+}{\underset{}{\overset{|}{O}}-H\delta^+}$$

Tip: These definitions should look familiar — you've seen them before on page 161.

Tip: Entropy is a measure of the disorder of a system. It's covered in loads of detail on pages 173-175 so don't worry about it too much just yet.

Calculating enthalpy change of solution

You can work out the enthalpy change of solution using an enthalpy cycle. You just need to know the lattice enthalpy of the compound and the enthalpies of hydration of the ions. Here's how to draw an enthalpy cycle for calculating the enthalpy change of solution:

Figure 2: *Copper(II) sulfate ($CuSO_4$) dissolved in water.*

Tip: You don't have to draw your enthalpy cycles in this triangular shape — you could use a square shape, like the Born-Haber cycles on pages 165-167.

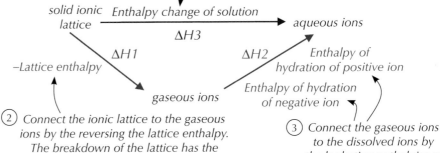

① *Put the ionic lattice and the dissolved ions on the top — connect them by the enthalpy change of solution. This is the direct route.*

② *Connect the ionic lattice to the gaseous ions by the reversing the lattice enthalpy. The breakdown of the lattice has the opposite enthalpy change to the formation of the lattice.*

③ *Connect the gaseous ions to the dissolved ions by the hydration enthalpies of each ion. This completes the indirect route.*

Examples

Here's the enthalpy cycle for working out the enthalpy change of solution for sodium chloride.

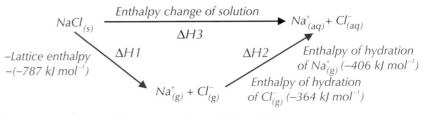

From Hess's law: $\Delta H^{\ominus}_{solution} = \Delta H3 = \Delta H1 + \Delta H2$
$= -(-787) + (-406 + -364) = $ **+17 kJ mol⁻¹**

Tip: For this enthalpy cycle, $\Delta H2$ is equal to the two enthalpies of hydration added together.

The enthalpy change of solution is slightly endothermic, but this is compensated for by a small increase in entropy, so sodium chloride still dissolves in water.

Tip: Take a look back at page 166 for more on Hess's law.

And here's another example. This enthalpy cycle is for working out the enthalpy change of solution for silver chloride.

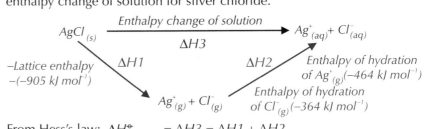

From Hess's law: $\Delta H^{\ominus}_{solution} = \Delta H3 = \Delta H1 + \Delta H2$
$= -(-905) + (-464 + -364) = $ **+77 kJ mol⁻¹**

Tip: A positive enthalpy value means that a reaction is endothermic.

This is much more endothermic than the enthalpy change of solution for sodium chloride. There is an increase in entropy, but it's pretty small and not enough to make a difference — so silver chloride is insoluble in water.

If 2+ or 2– ions are involved, you need to multiply the enthalpies of hydration by the number of moles of the ion that are reacting.

┌─ **Example** ──────────────────────────────────

Here's the enthalpy cycle for working out the enthalpy change of solution for magnesium chloride ($MgCl_2$).

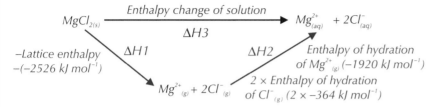

Enthalpy change of solution

$MgCl_{2(s)}$ $\xrightarrow{\hspace{2cm}}$ $Mg^{2+}_{(aq)} + 2Cl^-_{(aq)}$

$\Delta H3$

$\Delta H1$ $\Delta H2$

–Lattice enthalpy   *Enthalpy of hydration*
–(–2526 kJ mol⁻¹)   *of $Mg^{2+}_{(g)}$ (–1920 kJ mol⁻¹)*

$Mg^{2+}_{(g)} + 2Cl^-_{(g)}$ *2 × Enthalpy of hydration*
    of $Cl^-_{(g)}$ (2 × –364 kJ mol⁻¹)

In this example, there are two moles of Cl^- ions in the ionic lattice, so you have to multiply the enthalpy of hydration of Cl^- by two when you're calculating the enthalpy change of solution. So...

From Hess's law: $\Delta H^{\ominus}_{solution} = \Delta H3 = \Delta H1 + \Delta H2$

$= -(-2526) + [-1920 + (2 \times -364)] = $ **–122 kJ mol⁻¹**

$\Delta H^{\ominus}_{solution}$ is negative, so $MgCl_2$ dissolving in water is an exothermic processes and $MgCl_2$ is soluble.

└──────────────────────────────────

Tip: If there were three moles of an ion present in an ionic lattice you'd have to multiply the enthalpy of hydration for that ion by three to calculate the enthalpy of solution.

Tip: If you know the enthalpy of solution you can calculate the lattice enthalpy or an enthalpy of hydration — you just have to rearrange the equation.

Factors affecting the enthalpy of hydration

The two things that can affect the lattice enthalpy (see pages 163-164) can also affect the enthalpy of hydration. They are the charge and the size of the ions.

Tip: Remember — more exothermic processes have more negative enthalpy changes, more endothermic processes have more positive enthalpy changes.

1. Ionic charge

Ions with a greater charge have a greater enthalpy of hydration. This is because ions with a higher charge are better at attracting water molecules than those with lower charges. More energy is released when the bonds are made giving them a more exothermic enthalpy of hydration.

2. Ionic radius

Smaller ions have a greater enthalpy of hydration. This is because smaller ions have a higher charge density than bigger ions. They attract the water molecules better and have a more exothermic enthalpy of hydration.

┌─ **Example** ──────────────────────────────────

The diagram below shows aqueous Na^+ and Mg^{2+} ions:

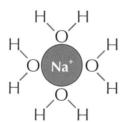 

The magnesium ion is smaller and has a higher charge than the sodium ion. The higher charge and smaller size create a higher charge density. This creates a stronger attraction for the water molecules and gives it a much more negative enthalpy of hydration. The enthalpies of hydration of Mg^{2+} and Na^+ ions are: $Mg^{2+} = -1927$ kJ mol⁻¹, $Na^+ = -406$ kJ mol⁻¹

└──────────────────────────────────

Figure 3: *Hydration of copper(II) sulfate. Because the Cu^{2+} ions are small and highly charged, this reaction is exothermic enough to produce steam.*

Practice Questions — Application

Q1 The cycle below shows the enthalpy change of solution for LiCl.

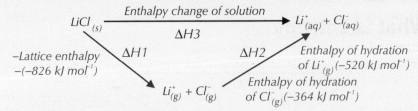

Calculate the enthalpy change of solution for LiCl.

Q2 a) Draw a cycle to show the enthalpy change of solution for sodium bromide. Use the following values:

Lattice enthalpy of NaBr = –747 kJ mol^{-1}
Enthalpy of hydration of Na^+ = –406 kJ mol^{-1}
Enthalpy of hydration of Br^- = –336 kJ mol^{-1}

b) Calculate the enthalpy change of solution for sodium bromide.

Q3 Use the data given in Q1 and Q2 a) and the data below to calculate enthalpy changes of solution for the following compounds:

a) lithium bromide.

b) potassium chloride.

c) magnesium bromide.

Lattice enthalpy of LiBr = –807 kJ mol^{-1}
Lattice enthalpy of KCl = –701 kJ mol^{-1}
Lattice enthalpy of $MgBr_2$ = –2440 kJ mol^{-1}
Enthalpy of hydration of K^+ = –322 kJ mol^{-1}
Enthalpy of hydration of Mg^{2+} = –1921 kJ mol^{-1}

Q4 Explain why the enthalpy of hydration of Mg^{2+} is more negative than the enthalpy of hydration of K^+.

Exam Tip
Don't be afraid to draw out an enthalpy cycle in the exam if you think it will help you answer the question.

Practice Questions — Fact Recall

Q1 a) What two things happen when a solid ionic lattice dissolves in water?

b) State whether each of these things is exothermic or endothermic.

Q2 The enthalpy change of solution is the combined effect of two enthalpy changes. Name them.

Q3 Explain why some ionic compounds dissolve even though their enthalpy of solution is endothermic.

Q4 Give two factors which influence the enthalpy of hydration of an ion.

5. Entropy

Some reactions can happen spontaneously — that's where entropy comes in.

What is entropy?

Entropy tells you how much disorder there is. It's a measure of the number of ways that particles can be arranged and the number of ways that the energy can be shared out between the particles. Substances really like disorder — they're actually more energetically stable when there's more disorder. So the particles move to try to increase the entropy. Entropy is represented by the symbol S. There are a few things that affect entropy, such as:

Physical state

Physical state affects entropy. You have to go back to the old 'solid-liquid-gas particle explanation thingy' to understand this. Solid particles just wobble about a fixed point — there's hardly any randomness, so they have the lowest entropy. Gas particles whizz around wherever they like. They've got the most random arrangements of particles, so they have the highest entropy.

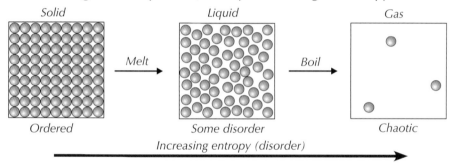

Increasing entropy (disorder)

Dissolution

Dissolving a solid also increases its entropy — dissolved particles can move freely as they're no longer held in one place:

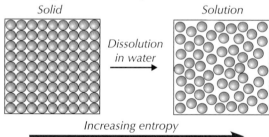

Increasing entropy

Number of particles

More particles means more entropy. It makes sense — the more particles you've got, the more ways they and their energy can be arranged. So in a reaction like $N_2O_{4(g)} \rightarrow 2NO_{2(g)}$, entropy increases because the number of moles increases:

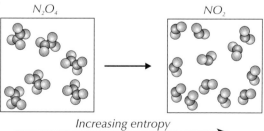

Increasing entropy

Figure 1: *Melting ice. When ice melts its entropy increases.*

Spontaneous endothermic reactions

A **spontaneous** (or **feasible**) change is one that'll just happen by itself — you don't need to give it energy. You might think that only exothermic reactions could be spontaneous because you need to supply energy to endothermic reactions. But the weird thing is, some endothermic reactions are spontaneous. You normally do have to supply energy to make an endothermic reaction happen, but in some reactions the entropy increases such a lot that the reaction will happen by itself, without you supplying any energy.

Figure 2: *Water evaporates spontaneously and then condenses to form clouds even though evaporation is an endothermic process.*

Tip: These reactions are both feasible, even though they are endothermic, because they involve an overall increase in entropy.

┌─ Examples ─────────────────

Evaporation of water
Water evaporates at room temperature. This change needs energy to break the bonds between the molecules (i.e. it's endothermic) — but because it's changing state from a liquid to a gas, the entropy increases.

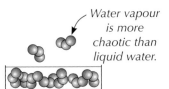

Water vapour is more chaotic than liquid water.

Reaction of $NaHCO_3$ and HCl
The reaction of sodium hydrogen carbonate with hydrochloric acid is a spontaneous endothermic reaction. Again there's an increase in entropy.

$$NaHCO_{3(s)} + H^+_{(aq)} \rightarrow Na^+_{(aq)} + CO_{2(g)} + H_2O_{(l)}$$

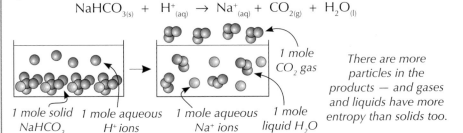

1 mole solid $NaHCO_3$ *1 mole aqueous H^+ ions*   *1 mole aqueous Na^+ ions*   *1 mole CO_2 gas*   *1 mole liquid H_2O*

There are more particles in the products — and gases and liquids have more entropy than solids too.

Effect of entropy change

Reactions won't happen unless the total entropy change is positive. During a reaction, there's an entropy change (ΔS) between the reactants and products — the entropy change of the system. The entropy of the surroundings changes too (because energy is transferred to or from the system). The total entropy change is the sum of the entropy changes of the system and the surroundings.

$$\Delta S_{total} = \Delta S_{system} + \Delta S_{surroundings}$$

The units of entropy are J K^{-1} mol^{-1}

This equation isn't much use unless you know ΔS_{system} and $\Delta S_{surroundings}$. Luckily, there are formulas for them too:

This is just the difference between the entropies of the reactants and products.

$$\Delta S_{system} = S_{products} - S_{reactants}$$

$$\Delta S_{surroundings} = -\frac{\Delta H}{T}$$

enthalpy change (in J mol^{-1})
temperature (in K)

Exam Tip
You need to be able to calculate entropy changes in your exam so make sure you learn these equations.

Exam Tip
If there is more than one mole of a reactant in an equation you need to multiply the S° value by the number of moles.

┌─ Example ─────────────────

Calculate the total entropy change for the reaction of ammonia and hydrogen chloride under standard conditions.

$$NH_{3(g)} + HCl_{(g)} \rightarrow NH_4Cl_{(s)}$$

$$\Delta H^{\circ} = -315 \text{ kJ mol}^{-1}$$

$S^{\circ}[NH_{3(g)}] = 192.3$ J K^{-1} mol^{-1}
$S^{\circ}[HCl_{(g)}] = 186.8$ J K^{-1} mol^{-1}
$S^{\circ}[NH_4Cl_{(s)}] = 94.6$ J K^{-1} mol^{-1}

First find the entropy change of the system:

$$\Delta S_{system} = S_{products} - S_{reactants} = 94.6 - (192.3 + 186.8)$$
$$= -284.5 \text{ J K}^{-1} \text{mol}^{-1}$$

This reaction has a negative change in entropy. It's not surprising, as 2 moles of gas have combined to form 1 mole of solid.

Tip: When you calculate an entropy change, don't forget to give the units — they're always J K⁻¹ mol⁻¹.

Now find the entropy change of the surroundings:

$$\Delta H^{\ominus} = -315 \text{ kJ mol}^{-1} = -315 \times 10^3 \text{ J mol}^{-1}$$

Put $\Delta H^{\ominus}$ in the right units.

$$\Delta S_{surroundings} = -\frac{\Delta H}{T} = \frac{-(-315 \times 10^3)}{298} = +1057.0 \text{ J K}^{-1} \text{mol}^{-1}$$

Tip: The reaction takes place under standard conditions, so $T = 298$ K.

Finally you can find the total entropy change:

$$\Delta S^{\ominus}_{total} = \Delta S^{\ominus}_{system} + \Delta S^{\ominus}_{surroundings} = -284.5 + (+1057.0)$$
$$= +772.5 \text{ J K}^{-1} \text{mol}^{-1}$$

The total entropy has increased so the reaction will happen spontaneously.

Tip: If the total entropy change was negative the reaction wouldn't happen spontaneously.

Practice Questions — Application

Q1 Solid sodium hydroxide is added to aqueous hydrogen chloride. The reaction produces sodium chloride solution. The solution is heated to produce solid sodium chloride and water vapour.

Describe the entropy changes that take place during these processes.

Q2 Using the data from Figure 3 for this reaction under standard conditions: $CH_{4(g)} + 2O_{2(g)} \rightarrow CO_{2(g)} + 2H_2O_{(l)}$ $\Delta H^{\ominus} = -730$ kJ mol⁻¹

a) calculate ΔS_{system}.

b) calculate $\Delta S^{\ominus}_{surroundings}$.

c) calculate $\Delta S^{\ominus}_{total}$.

d) explain whether the reaction will happen spontaneously.

Q3 Using the data in Figure 3 work out the total entropy change for this reaction under standard conditions:

$$SO_{2(g)} + 2H_2S_{(g)} \rightarrow 3S_{(s)} + 2H_2O_{(l)} \qquad \Delta H^{\ominus} = -235 \text{ kJ mol}^{-1}$$

Substance	Standard entropy of substance, $S^{\ominus}$ ($J K^{-1} mol^{-1}$)
$CH_{4(g)}$	186
$O_{2(g)}$	205
$CO_{2(g)}$	214
$H_2O_{(l)}$	69.9
$SO_{2(g)}$	248
$H_2S_{(g)}$	206
$S_{(s)}$	31.6

Figure 3: *Standard entropy values for different substances.*

Practice Questions — Fact Recall

Q1 a) What is entropy?

b) Give the symbol for entropy change.

Q2 Explain how the following affect the entropy of a system:

a) a substance changing from a liquid to a gas.

b) a solid dissolving in water.

c) a reaction that results in an increased number of particles.

Q3 Explain why entropy changes mean that an endothermic reaction can happen spontaneously.

Q4 Give the formulas you'd use to work out the following:

a) total entropy change.

b) entropy change of the system.

c) entropy change of the surroundings.

- Be able to explain that the tendency of a process to take place depends on temperature, T, the entropy change in the system, ΔS, and the enthalpy change, ΔH, with the surroundings.
- Be able to state and use the relationship $\Delta G = \Delta H - T\Delta S$.
- Be able to explain that the balance between entropy and enthalpy changes is the free energy change, ΔG, which determines the feasibility of a reaction.

Specification Reference 5.2.2

Tip: The units of ΔH and ΔS must be the same. So, if you have a value for ΔH in kJ, multiply it by 10^3 to get it in J.

Figure 1: *Calcium carbonate ($CaCO_3$) being heated to produce CaO and CO_2. This reaction isn't feasible at room temperature .*

Tip: You can also re-arrange the free energy equation to find ΔS or ΔH if you know ΔG.

6. Free-Energy Change

Everyone likes free things, so I can almost guarantee you'll like free energy.

What is free-energy?

The tendency of a process to take place is dependent on three things — the entropy, ΔS, the enthalpy, ΔH, and the temperature, T. When you put all these things together you get the **free energy change**, ΔG, and it tells you if a reaction is feasible or not. Of course, there's a formula for it:

Free energy change (in J mol⁻¹) ⟶ $$\Delta G = \Delta H - T\Delta S_{system}$$ ⟵ Entropy change of the system (in J K⁻¹ mol⁻¹)

Enthalpy change (in J mol⁻¹) ⟋   ⟍ Temperature (in K)

For spontaneous reactions, the value of ΔG must be negative or zero. But a negative ΔG doesn't guarantee a reaction will happen or tell you about its rate. Even if ΔG shows that a reaction is theoretically feasible, it might have a really high activation energy or be so slow that you wouldn't notice it happening at all.

Calculating free-energy change

You need to be able to calculate the free-energy change for a reaction and say whether or not a reaction is feasible at a particular temperature. All you have to do is substitute the values for ΔS, ΔH and T into the equation above and solve it to find ΔG. If ΔG is negative or equal to zero the reaction is feasible — if ΔG is positive the reaction is not feasible. Here's an example:

Example

Calculate the free energy change for the following reaction at 298 K.

$$MgCO_{3(s)} \rightarrow MgO_{(s)} + CO_{2(g)}$$ $\Delta H° = +117$ **kJ mol⁻¹**
$\Delta S°_{system} = +175$ **J K⁻¹ mol⁻¹**

$\Delta G = \Delta H - T\Delta S_{system} = (+117 \times 10^3) - [(298 \times (+175)]$
$= +64\ 850$ **J mol⁻¹**

ΔG is positive — so the reaction isn't feasible at this temperature.

Calculating the feasibility of a reaction

If a reaction is exothermic (negative ΔH) and has a positive entropy change, then ΔG is always negative since $\Delta G = \Delta H - T\Delta S_{system}$. These reactions are feasible at any temperature.

If a reaction is endothermic (positive ΔH) and has a negative entropy change, then ΔG is always positive. These reactions are not feasible at any temperature. But for other combinations, temperature has an effect.

For reactions where temperature has an effect, you can use the free energy change equation to calculate the temperature at which the reaction becomes feasible. When ΔG is zero, a reaction is just feasible. You can find the temperature when ΔG is zero by rearranging the free energy equation.

$\Delta G = \Delta H - T\Delta S_{system}$, so when $\Delta G = 0$, $T\Delta S_{system} = \Delta H$. So:

temperature at which a reaction becomes feasible (in K) ⟶ $$T = \frac{\Delta H}{\Delta S_{system}}$$ ⟵ enthalpy change (in J mol⁻¹)

⟵ entropy change of the system (in J K⁻¹ mol⁻¹)

Example

Tungsten, W, can be extracted from its ore, WO$_3$, by reduction using hydrogen.

$$WO_{3(s)} + 3H_{2(g)} \rightarrow W_{(s)} + 3H_2O_{(g)} \qquad \Delta H^{\circ} = +117 \text{ kJ mol}^{-1}$$

Use the data in Figure 2 to find the minimum temperature at which the reaction becomes feasible.

First, convert the enthalpy change, ΔH, to joules per mole:

$\Delta H = 117 \times 10^3 = 117\ 000 \text{ J mol}^{-1}$

Then find the entropy change, ΔS_{system}:

$$\Delta S_{system} = S_{products} - S_{reactants} \quad = [33 + (3 \times 189)] - [76 + (3 \times 65)]$$
$$= +329 \text{ J K}^{-1} \text{mol}^{-1}$$

Then divide ΔH by ΔS_{system} to find the temperature at which the reaction just becomes feasible:

$$T = \frac{\Delta H}{\Delta S_{system}} = \frac{117\ 000}{329} = \textbf{356 K}$$

Tip: In this example you have to calculate the ΔS before you can calculate the free energy change. See page 174 for more on how to calculate ΔS.

Substance	Standard entropy of substance, S° ($J\ K^{-1} mol^{-1}$)
$WO_{3(s)}$	76
$H_{2(g)}$	65
$W_{(s)}$	33
$H_2O_{(g)}$	189
$Al_2O_{3(s)}$	51.0
$Mg_{(s)}$	32.5
$Al_{(s)}$	28.3
$MgO_{(s)}$	27.0

Figure 2: *Standard entropy values for different substances.*

Practice Questions — Application

Q1 Using the data from Figure 2 for this reaction under standard conditions: $Al_2O_{3(s)} + 3Mg_{(s)} \rightarrow 2Al_{(s)} + 3MgO_{(s)}$ $\quad \Delta H^{\circ} = -130 \text{ kJ mol}^{-1}$

  a) calculate ΔS_{system}.

  b) calculate ΔG.

  c) explain whether the reaction is feasible at 298K.

Q2 Consider the reaction below:

$$ZnCO_{3(s)} \rightarrow ZnO_{(s)} + CO_{2(g)}$$
$$\Delta H^{\circ} = +71 \text{ kJ mol}^{-1} \qquad \Delta S_{system} = +176 \text{ J K}^{-1} \text{mol}^{-1}$$

  a) Determine whether or not this reaction is feasible at:

   (i) 298 K   (ii) 600 K

  b) Calculate the temperature at which this reaction becomes feasible.

Q3 Calculate the temperature at which this reaction becomes feasible:

$$CaCO_{3(s)} \rightarrow CaO_{(s)} + CO_{2(g)}$$
$$\Delta H^{\circ} = +178 \text{ kJ mol}^{-1} \qquad \Delta S_{system} = +165 \text{ J K}^{-1} \text{mol}^{-1}$$

Tip: When calculating free-energy changes be really careful with your units. The temperature must be in K (add 273 if it's given in °C) and the enthalpy and entropy values should involve J not kJ.

Practice Questions — Fact Recall

Q1 a) What is free energy change?

  b) Give the symbol for free energy change.

Q2 Give the formula needed to work out free energy.

Q3 A reaction is endothermic, has a negative entropy change and so has a positive value for free energy. Is this reaction feasible?

Q4 Give the formula that you'd use to calculate the temperature at which a reaction becomes feasible.

- Be able to explain the terms redox, oxidation number, half-reaction, oxidising agent and reducing agent for simple redox reactions.
- Be able to construct redox equations using relevant half equations or oxidation numbers.
- Be able to interpret and make predictions for reactions involving electron transfer.

Specification Reference 5.2.3

7. Redox Equations

You did quite a lot about redox reactions and half-equations at AS-level but you need to know it at A2-level as well — so here's a reminder.

What is a redox reaction?

A loss of electrons is called **oxidation**. A gain of electrons is called **reduction**. Reduction and oxidation happen simultaneously — hence the term 'redox' reaction. An **oxidising agent** accepts electrons and gets reduced. A **reducing agent** donates electrons and gets oxidised.

Example

In the reaction between potassium and chlorine:

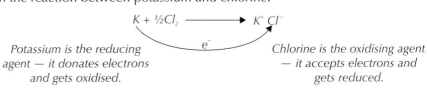

$$K + \tfrac{1}{2}Cl_2 \longrightarrow K^+ Cl^-$$

Potassium is the reducing agent — it donates electrons and gets oxidised.

e^-

Chlorine is the oxidising agent — it accepts electrons and gets reduced.

Tip: Don't forget:
<u>OIL RIG</u>
<u>O</u>xidation <u>I</u>s <u>L</u>oss
<u>R</u>eduction <u>I</u>s <u>G</u>ain
(...of electrons)

Oxidation numbers

The **oxidation number** of an element tells you the total number of electrons it has donated or accepted. There is a set of rules for assigning oxidation numbers:

- Uncombined elements have an oxidation number of 0.

- Elements just bonded to identical atoms also have an oxidation number of 0. E.g. oxygen in O_2 has an oxidation number of 0.

- The oxidation number of a simple monatomic ion is the same as its charge. E.g. Na^+ has an oxidation number of +1.

- In compound ions, the overall oxidation number is just the ion charge. E.g. SO_4^{2-} has an overall oxidation number of −2.

- The sum of the oxidation numbers for a neutral compound is 0. E.g. the sum of the oxidation numbers of the atoms in Fe_2O_3 is 0.

- Combined oxygen is almost always −2.

- Combined hydrogen is +1 (except in metal hydrides where it is −1 and H_2 where it's 0).

You can use all these rules to work out the oxidation number of an element in a compound.

Tip: Oxidation numbers are also known as oxidation states.

Tip: The only times oxygen doesn't have an oxidation number of −2 are in peroxides (where it's −1), fluorides (where it can be +1 or +2) and O_2 (where it's 0).

Example

What is the oxidation number of chromium in Cr_2O_3?

The sum of oxidation numbers for a neutral compound is 0 — so the overall oxidation number of Cr_2O_3 is 0.

Combined oxygen has an oxidation number of −2.

There are three oxygen atoms and two chromium atoms in the compound. So the oxidation number of the chromium atoms must be:

$(0 - (3 \times -2)) \div 2 = \mathbf{+3}$

Exam Tip
It's really important that you know how to assign oxidation numbers so make sure you learn all the rules on this page and understand this example.

Changes in oxidation number

Oxidation numbers go up or down as electrons are lost or gained. To work out which atoms are oxidised and which are reduced in a reaction, you need to look at the oxidation numbers. The oxidation number for an atom will increase by one for each electron lost. The oxidation number will decrease by one for each electron gained.

Tip: You covered oxidation numbers and how they change in redox reactions at AS-level, so if you need a more detailed reminder dig out the old AS notes and you should be fine.

Example

The reaction between vanadium(V) oxide and sulfur dioxide is shown below:

$$V_2O_5 + SO_2 \rightarrow V_2O_4 + SO_3$$

Oxidation number of V: $+5$ $\rightarrow$ $+4$ reduction
Oxidation number of S: $+4$ $\rightarrow$ $+6$ oxidation

In this reaction, vanadium is reduced from $+5$ to $+4$ (it gains 1 electron) and sulfur is oxidised from $+4$ to $+6$ (it loses two electrons).

Tip: If you see Roman numerals in a chemical name, it's an oxidation number. For example, in manganate(VII) ions, manganese has an oxidation number of $+7$.

Half-equations

A redox reaction is made up of an oxidation half-reaction and a reduction half-reaction. You can write an ionic **half-equation** for each of these half-reactions — see Figure 1.

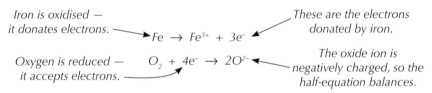

Iron is oxidised — it donates electrons. $Fe \rightarrow Fe^{3+} + 3e^-$ These are the electrons donated by iron.

Oxygen is reduced — it accepts electrons. $O_2 + 4e^- \rightarrow 2O^{2-}$ The oxide ion is negatively charged, so the half-equation balances.

Figure 1: Half-equations for the oxidation of iron and the reduction of oxygen.

Tip: Electrons are shown in half-equations so that the charges balance.

An oxidation half-equation can be combined with a reduction half-equation to make a full equation.

Example

Zinc metal displaces silver ions from silver nitrate solution to form a solution of zinc ions and a deposit of silver metal.

The zinc atoms each lose 2 electrons (oxidation): $Zn_{(s)} \rightarrow Zn^{2+}_{(aq)} + 2e^-$
The silver ions each gain 1 electron (reduction): $Ag^+_{(aq)} + e^- \rightarrow Ag_{(s)}$

Two silver ions are needed to accept the two electrons released by each zinc atom. So you need to double the silver half-equation before the two half-equations can be combined:

$$2Ag^+_{(aq)} + 2e^- \rightarrow 2Ag_{(s)}$$

Now the number of electrons lost and gained balance, so the half-equations can be combined:

$$Zn_{(s)} + 2Ag^+_{(aq)} \rightarrow Zn^{2+}_{(aq)} + 2Ag_{(s)}$$

Tip: Electrons aren't included in overall equations because they cancel out. If yours don't, go back and check your half-equations are right.

Adding H⁺ ions to half-equations

If your oxidising agent contains oxygen, you might need to add some H^+ ions and H_2O to the half-equation to make it balance. Oxidising agents like manganate(VII) ions are usually acidified (H^+ is added) before they're used.

Manganate(VII) ions, MnO_4^-, contain Mn with an oxidation number of $+7$. When these ions are reduced they gain five electrons to become Mn^{2+} ions, with an oxidation number of $+2$.

Tip: Electrons, H^+ ions, and water are the only things that you're allowed to add to balance half-equations.

Tip: The same principle applies to many other oxidising agents too — for example, dichromate(VI) ions ($Cr_2O_7^{2-}$) are also acidified.

Tip: In the exam, you'll often be asked to balance half-equations before writing out the full equation, so make sure you know how to do this — have a look back at your AS notes if you're unsure.

Exam Tip
You should always finish by checking that the charges balance — that way you know you haven't made a mistake.

In a +2 state, Mn can exist as simple $Mn^{2+}_{(aq)}$ ions. But in a +7 state, Mn combines with oxygen to form MnO_4^- ions ($Mn^{7+}_{(aq)}$ ions aren't stable on their own). MnO_4^- ions are good oxidising agents. But when the manganese gets reduced to Mn^{2+} the four O^{2-} ions have to go somewhere. That's why the H^+ ions are added — they react with the O^{2-} ions to form $4H_2O$.

Here's how to write an equation for this type of reaction:

Example

Acidified manganate(VII) ions (MnO_4^-) can be reduced to Mn^{2+} by Fe^{2+} ions. The Fe^{2+} ions are oxidised to Fe^{3+}. Write an equation for this reaction.

The half-equations for this reaction are:
$$Fe^{2+} \rightarrow Fe^{3+} + e^-$$
$$MnO_4^- + 8H^+ + 5e^- \rightarrow Mn^{2+} + 4H_2O$$

To balance the electrons you need to multiply the first half-equation by 5:
$$5Fe^{2+}_{(aq)} \rightarrow 5Fe^{3+}_{(aq)} + 5e^-$$

Now you can combine the half-equations:
$$MnO_4^-{}_{(aq)} + 8H^+_{(aq)} + 5Fe^{2+}_{(aq)} \rightarrow Mn^{2+}_{(aq)} + 4H_2O_{(l)} + 5Fe^{3+}_{(aq)}$$

Finish by checking that the charges balance:
$$MnO_4^-{}_{(aq)} + 8H^+_{(aq)} + 5Fe^{2+}_{(aq)} \rightarrow Mn^{2+}_{(aq)} + 4H_2O_{(l)} + 5Fe^{3+}_{(aq)}$$
Charges: (-1) $(+1 \times 8)$ $(+2 \times 5)$ $\rightarrow$ $(+2)$ 0 $(+3 \times 5)$
$$+17 \rightarrow +17$$

Practice Questions — Application

Q1 Give the oxidation numbers of:
a) Na in NaOH   b) Cr in CrO_4^{2-} c) O in H_2O_2

Q2 Copper metal can displace silver(I) ions in solution to form a solution of copper(II) ions and a deposit of silver metal. The half equations are:
$$Cu_{(s)} \rightarrow Cu^{2+}_{(aq)} + 2e^- \qquad Ag^+_{(aq)} + e^- \rightarrow Ag_{(s)}$$
Combine these half-equations to give the full redox equation for this reaction.

Q3 The following reaction occurs between iron and chlorine:
$$Cl_{2(g)} + 2Fe^{2+}_{(aq)} \rightarrow 2Cl^-_{(aq)} + 2Fe^{3+}_{(aq)}$$
One of the half equations is $Fe^{2+}_{(aq)} \rightarrow Fe^{3+}_{(aq)} + e^-$. Find the other.

Q4 Dichromate ions ($Cr_2O_7^{2-}$) are reduced by zinc. The half equations for this reaction are:
$$Zn \rightarrow Zn^{2+} + e^- \qquad Cr_2O_7^{2-} + H^+ + e^- \rightarrow Cr^{3+} + H_2O$$
a) Balance these two half equations
b) Give the full redox equation for this reaction.

Practice Questions — Fact Recall

Q1 a) What is oxidation?
b) What is an oxidising agent?

Q2 a) What is the oxidation number of an uncombined element?
b) Hydrogen has an oxidation number of –1 in metal hydrides, but what is the usual oxidation number of hydrogen?

Q3 What happens to the oxidation number of elements that gain an electron?

Figure 2: Iron(II) reacting with chlorine gas to produce iron(III) chloride. The iron is oxidised and the chlorine is reduced.

8. Electrode Potentials

In redox reactions, electrons move from one atom to another. When electrons move, you get electricity. So redox reactions can be used to make electricity.

Electrochemical Cells

Electrochemical cells can be made from two different metals dipped in salt solutions of their own ions and connected by a wire (the external circuit). There are always two reactions within an electrochemical cell — one's an oxidation and one's a reduction — so it's a **redox** process.

Learning Objectives:

- Be able to define the term standard electrode (redox) potential, $E^{\ominus}$.
- Be able to describe how to measure, using a hydrogen electrode, standard electrode potentials of:
  (i) metals or non-metals in contact with their ions in aqueous solution.
  (ii) ions of the same element in different oxidation states.

Specification Reference 5.2.3

Example

The diagram below shows an electrochemical cell made using copper and zinc.

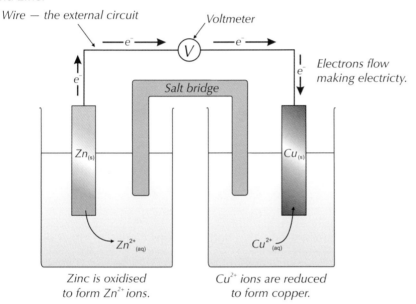

Zinc is oxidised to form Zn^{2+} ions.

Cu^{2+} ions are reduced to form copper.

A copper electrode is dipped in a solution of Cu^{2+} ions and a zinc electrode is dipped in a solution of Zn^{2+} ions. Zinc loses electrons more easily than copper. So in the half-cell on the left, zinc (from the zinc electrode) is oxidised to form $Zn^{2+}_{(aq)}$ ions. This releases electrons into the external circuit. In the other half-cell, the same number of electrons are taken from the external circuit, reducing the Cu^{2+} ions to copper atoms.

The solutions are connected by a **salt bridge**, e.g. a strip of filter paper soaked in $KNO_{3(aq)}$. This allows ions to flow through and balance out the charges — it completes the circuit.

Tip: See page 178 for more on redox reactions

Figure 1: *An electrochemical cell.*

Tip: The two different sides of the electrochemical cell are called half-cells — two half-cells make a whole.

Electrons flow through the wire from the most reactive metal to the least. A voltmeter in the external circuit shows the voltage between the two half-cells. This is the **cell potential** or e.m.f., E_{cell}.

You can also have half-cells involving solutions of two aqueous ions of the same element in different oxidation states.

Tip: e.m.f. stands for electromotive force.

Example

You can make an electrochemical half-cell using solutions of Fe^{2+} and Fe^{3+} ions. A platinum electrode is dipped into the solution (as shown on the next page).

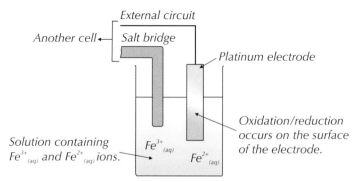

External circuit

Another cell ← Salt bridge

Platinum electrode

Solution containing $Fe^{3+}_{(aq)}$ and $Fe^{2+}_{(aq)}$ ions.

$Fe^{3+}_{(aq)}$

$Fe^{2+}_{(aq)}$

Oxidation/reduction occurs on the surface of the electrode.

Tip: An electrode has to be a <u>solid</u> that <u>conducts electricity</u>. If a half-cell doesn't contain anything like this, you can use something else (like platinum) as an electrode.

Tip: <u>Inert</u> means it won't react with anything. (The electrode has to be inert or it could react with the solution it's in.)

Platinum is used as the electrode because it is inert and conducts electricity. The conversion from Fe^{2+} to Fe^{3+}, or vice versa, happens on the surface of the electrode.

The direction of the conversion depends on the other half-cell in the circuit. If the other cell contains a metal that is less reactive than iron then Fe^{2+} will be oxidised to Fe^{3+} at the electrode. But if the other cell contains a more reactive metal, Fe^{3+} will be reduced to Fe^{2+} at the electrode.

Standard electrode potentials

The reactions that occur at each electrode in a cell are reversible.

Tip: These are half-equations for the reactions occurring in the electrochemical cell. See page 179 for more on half-equations.

┌─ Example ───

The reactions that occur at each electrode in the zinc/copper cell are:

$$Zn^{2+}_{(aq)} + 2e^- \rightleftharpoons Zn_{(s)}$$
$$Cu^{2+}_{(aq)} + 2e^- \rightleftharpoons Cu_{(s)}$$

The reversible arrows show that both reactions can go in either direction.

Which direction each reaction goes in depends on how easily each metal loses electrons (i.e. how easily it's oxidised). How easily a metal is oxidised is measured using **electrode potentials**. A metal that's easily oxidised has a very negative electrode potential, while one that's harder to oxidise has a less negative (or positive) electrode potential.

Figure 2: Analogue or digital voltmeters can be used to measure electrode potentials.

┌─ Example ───

The table below shows the electrode potentials for the copper and zinc half-cells:

Half-cell	Electrode potential (V)
$Zn^{2+}_{(aq)}/Zn_{(s)}$	−0.76
$Cu^{2+}_{(aq)}/Cu_{(s)}$	+0.34

The zinc half-cell has a more negative electrode potential, so in a zinc/copper cell, zinc is oxidised (the reaction goes backwards), while copper is reduced (the reaction goes forwards).

Tip: There's more on how electrode potentials are measured coming up.

Tip: See pages 128-129 for more on how changes in concentration temperature and pressure affect the position of equilibrium.

Because half-cell reactions are reversible, the equilibrium position is affected by changes in temperature, pressure and concentration. Changing the equilibrium position changes the cell potential. To get around this, **standard conditions** are used to measure electrode potentials — this gives you a **standard electrode potential** ($E^{\ominus}$). Standard electrode potentials are always the same so you can compare values for different cells.

Measuring standard electrode potentials

The standard electrode potential of a half-cell is the voltage measured under standard conditions when the half-cell is connected to a **standard hydrogen electrode**. In the standard hydrogen electrode, hydrogen gas is bubbled into a solution of aqueous H^+ ions. A platinum electrode is used as a platform for the oxidation/reduction reactions — see Figure 3.

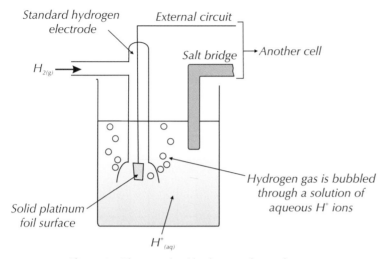

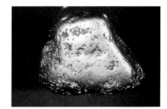

Figure 4: A nugget of platinum. Platinum is used as the electrode in the standard hydrogen electrode.

Figure 3: The standard hydrogen electrode

When measuring electrode potentials using the standard hydrogen electrode it is important that everything is done under standard conditions:

1. Any solutions of ions must have a concentration of 1.00 mol dm^{-3}.
2. The temperature must be 298 K (25 °C).
3. The pressure must be 100 kPa.

Tip: The standard hydrogen electrode has an electrode potential of 0.00 V by definition.

If standard conditions are maintained, the reading on the voltmeter when a half-cell is connected to the standard hydrogen electrode will be the standard electrode potential of that half-cell — see Figure 5.

Tip: The reading on the voltmeter could be positive or negative, depending on which way the electrons flow.

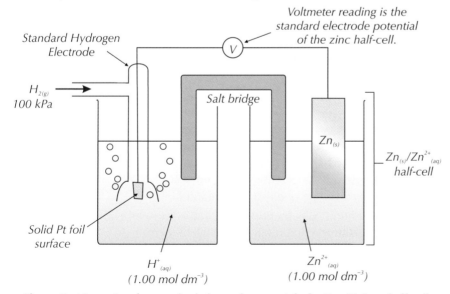

Tip: Notice how the H$_2$ gas is at a pressure of 100 kPa and the H$^+$ and Zn^{2+} solutions both have concentrations of 1.00 mol dm^{-3}. These are the standard conditions.

Figure 5: Measuring the standard electrode potential of a $Zn_{(s)}/Zn^{2+}_{(aq)}$ half-cell.

Exam Tip
You could also be asked to draw a diagram of an electrochemical cell that doesn't contain a standard hydrogen electrode. If so, just follow these rules, but swap the standard hydrogen electrode for a different half-cell. See page 181 for an example of what your diagram should look like.

Tip: State symbols can give you a clue as to whether you need a platinum electrode or not. If one of the species in the half cell is a solid (e.g. $Ag_{(s)}/Ag^{2+}_{(aq)}$), you don't need a platinum electrode. If both of the species in the half cell are aqueous (e.g. $Br_{2(aq)}/Br^-_{(aq)}$) you'll need to include a platinum electrode.

In the exam, you could be asked to draw a diagram showing how the standard electrode potential of a particular half-cell could be measured. If you are, there are a few things you need to do:

- Always put the standard hydrogen electrode on the left.
- Make sure you draw a complete circuit — don't forget to include the salt bridge, the wire between the electrodes and the voltmeter.
- Label any solutions as being 1.00 mol dm⁻³.
- If your half-cell contains aqueous ions of the same element in different oxidation states, don't forget to include a platinum electrode.

Example

Draw a labelled diagram to show how the standard electrode potential of an $Fe^{3+}_{(aq)}/Fe^{2+}_{(aq)}$ half cell could be measured.

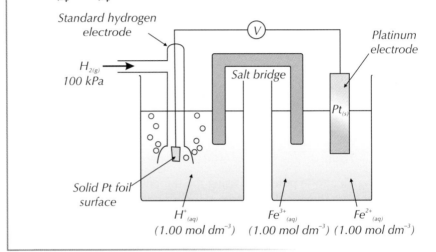

Practice Questions — Application

Q1 The following reactions occur in an electrochemical cell:

$$Ni^{2+}_{(aq)} + 2e^- \rightleftharpoons Ni_{(s)} \qquad E^\oplus = -0.25$$
$$Cl_{2(aq)} + 2e^- \rightleftharpoons 2Cl^-_{(aq)} \qquad E^\oplus = +1.36$$

a) Draw a diagram of this electrochemical cell.
b) Which of the above reactions goes in the direction of oxidation?

Q2 Draw diagrams to show how the standard electrode potentials of the following half-cells could be measured:

a) $Mg_{(s)}/Mg^{2+}_{(aq)}$ b) $Sn^{4+}_{(aq)}/Sn^{2+}_{(aq)}$ c) $Al_{(s)}/Al^{3+}_{(aq)}$

Practice Questions — Fact Recall

Q1 a) What type of electrode is used for half-cells involving solutions of two aqueous ions of the same element?
    b) Why is this type of electrode suitable?

Q2 Does oxidation or reduction occur in the half-cell with the more positive electrode potential?

Q3 Define the term "standard electrode potential".

Q4 Describe how a standard hydrogen electrode is set up and give the standard conditions used when measuring electrode potentials.

9. Electrochemical Series

The standard electrode potentials of different reactions are different (unsurprisingly). If you write a list of electrode potentials in order, you get an electrochemical series, which you can use to predict the outcome of a reaction.

What is an electrochemical series?

An **electrochemical series** is basically a big long list of electrode potentials for different electrochemical half-cells. They look something like this:

Half-reaction	$E^{\ominus}$ (V)
$Mg^{2+}_{(aq)} + 2e^- \rightleftharpoons Mg_{(s)}$	−2.37
$Al^{3+}_{(aq)} + 3e^- \rightleftharpoons Al_{(s)}$	−1.66
$Zn^{2+}_{(aq)} + 2e^- \rightleftharpoons Zn_{(s)}$	−0.76
$Ni^{2+}_{(aq)} + 2e^- \rightleftharpoons Ni_{(s)}$	−0.25
$2H^+_{(aq)} + 2e^- \rightleftharpoons H_{2(g)}$	0.00
$Sn^{4+}_{(aq)} + 2e^- \rightleftharpoons Sn^{2+}_{(aq)}$	+0.15
$Cu^{2+}_{(aq)} + 2e^- \rightleftharpoons Cu_{(s)}$	+0.34
$Fe^{3+}_{(aq)} + e^- \rightleftharpoons Fe^{2+}_{(aq)}$	+0.77
$Ag^+_{(aq)} + e^- \rightleftharpoons Ag_{(s)}$	+0.80
$Br_{2(aq)} + 2e^- \rightleftharpoons 2Br^-_{(aq)}$	+1.09
$Cr_2O_7^{2-}_{(aq)} + 14H^+_{(aq)} + 6e^- \rightleftharpoons 2Cr^{3+}_{(aq)} + 7H_2O_{(l)}$	+1.33
$Cl_{2(aq)} + 2e^- \rightleftharpoons 2Cl^-_{(aq)}$	+1.36
$MnO_4^-_{(aq)} + 8H^+_{(aq)} + 5e^- \rightleftharpoons Mn^{2+}_{(aq)} + 4H_2O_{(l)}$	+1.52

The electrode potentials are written in order, starting from the most negative and going down to the most positive. The half-equations are always written as reduction reactions — but the reactions are reversible and can go the opposite way. When two half-equations are put together in an electrochemical cell, the one with the more negative electrode potential goes in the direction of oxidation (backwards) and the one with the more positive electrode potential goes in the direction of reduction (forwards).

Electrochemical series and reactivity

An electrochemical series shows you what's reactive and what's not. The more reactive a metal is, the more it wants to lose electrons to form a positive ion. More reactive metals have more negative standard electrode potentials.

Example

Magnesium is more reactive than zinc — so it's more eager to form 2+ ions than zinc is. The list of standard electrode potentials shows that Mg^{2+}/Mg has a more negative value than Zn^{2+}/Zn — its −2.37 V for Mg^{2+}/Mg and −0.76 V for Zn^{2+}/Zn. In terms of oxidation and reduction, magnesium would reduce Zn^{2+} (or Zn^{2+} would oxidise magnesium).

The more reactive a non-metal the more it wants to gain electrons to form a negative ion. More reactive non-metals have more positive standard electrode potentials.

Figure 1: Chlorine will displace bromide ions — this confirms that chlorine is more reactive than bromine.

Tip: Don't forget — cell potential is the voltage between two half-cells. See page 181 for more.

Tip: If $E^{\ominus}_{cell}$ is positive, the reaction is feasible (it could happen).

Tip: If you can't remember which half-reaction in a cell goes backwards and which goes forwards, think <u>NO P.R.</u> — the more <u>N</u>egative electrode potential will go in the <u>O</u>xidation direction and the more <u>P</u>ositive electrode potential will go in the <u>R</u>eduction direction.

Tip: Once you know these steps, you can apply them to predict the outcome of any redox reaction.

Example

Chlorine is more reactive than bromine — so it's more eager to form a negative ion than bromine is. The list of standard electrode potentials shows that $Cl_2/2Cl^-$ is more positive than $Br_2/2Br^-$ — it's +1.36 V for $Cl_2/2Cl^-$ and +1.09 V for $Br_2/2Br^-$. In terms of oxidation and reduction, chlorine would oxidise Br^- (or Br^- would reduce chlorine).

Calculating cell potentials

You can use the information in an electrochemical series to calculate the **standard cell potential** or **e.m.f.**, when two half-cells are connected together. All you have to do is work out which half-reaction is going in the direction of oxidation and which half-reaction is going in the direction of reduction. Then just substitute the $E^{\ominus}$ values into this equation:

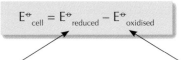

$$E^{\ominus}_{cell} = E^{\ominus}_{reduced} - E^{\ominus}_{oxidised}$$

This is the standard electrode potential of the half-cell which goes in the direction of reduction (the one with the more positive electrode potential).

This is the standard electrode potential of the half-cell which goes in the direction of oxidation (the one with the more negative electrode potential).

Examples

Calculate the e.m.f. of an Mg/Ag electrochemical cell using the two redox reaction equations shown below:

$$Mg^{2+}_{(aq)} + 2e^- \rightleftharpoons Mg_{(s)} \qquad E^{\ominus} = -2.37$$
$$Ag^+_{(aq)} + e^- \rightleftharpoons Ag_{(s)} \qquad E^{\ominus} = +0.80$$

The Mg/Mg^{2+} half-cell has the more negative electrode potential, so this half reaction will go in the direction of oxidation. The Ag/Ag^+ half-cell has the more positive electrode potential and so will go in the direction of reduction.

$$E^{\ominus}_{cell} = E^{\ominus}_{reduced} - E^{\ominus}_{oxidised} = 0.80 - (-2.37) = +3.17 \text{ V}$$

Predicting the outcome of reactions

You can use the anticlockwise rule to predict whether a redox reaction will happen and to show which direction it will go in. Just follow these steps:

1. Find the two half-equations for the redox reaction, and write them both out as reduction reactions.

2. Use an electrochemical series to work out which half-equation has the more negative electrode potential.

3. Put the half-equation with the more negative electrode potential on top of the other one.

4. Draw on two anticlockwise arrows — one going from the products of the top equation to the reactants of the top equation and one going from the reactants of the bottom equation to the products of the bottom equation.

5. If you mix the substances at the non-pointy ends of the arrows a redox reaction will occur — the arrows show the direction that the half-equations will go. But if you use any other combination of reactants there will be no reaction.

Will zinc react with aqueous copper ions?

1. Write down the two half-equations for the redox reaction as reduction reactions:

$$Zn^{2+}_{(aq)} + 2e^- \rightleftharpoons Zn_{(s)} \quad \text{and} \quad Cu^{2+}_{(aq)} + 2e^- \rightleftharpoons Cu_{(s)}$$

2. Find out the electrode potentials for the two half-equations:

$$Zn^{2+}/Zn = -0.76 \text{ V}$$
$$Cu^{2+}/Cu = +0.34 \text{ V}$$

Tip: These values for the electrode potentials came from the electrochemical series on page 185.

3. Put the half-equation with the more negative electrode potential on top:

$$Zn^{2+}_{(aq)} + 2e^- \rightleftharpoons Zn_{(s)}$$
$$Cu^{2+}_{(aq)} + 2e^- \rightleftharpoons Cu_{(s)}$$

4. Draw on the anticlockwise arrows:

$$Zn^{2+}_{(aq)} + 2e^- \rightleftharpoons Zn_{(s)}$$
$$Cu^{2+}_{(aq)} + 2e^- \rightleftharpoons Cu_{(s)}$$

Exam Tip
Remember — the arrows <u>must</u> go anticlockwise. If your arrows are clockwise you'll get the answer wrong. Look at the clock in the exam room if you can't picture which way is clockwise and which way is anticlockwise.

5. Look at the non-pointy ends of the arrows to work out if the reaction would happen:

   The substances at the ends of the arrows are $Zn_{(s)}$ and $Cu^{2+}_{(aq)}$. So zinc will react with aqueous copper(II) ions. (The arrows show that the zinc half-reaction goes backwards and the copper half-reaction goes forwards, so the overall equation is: $Zn_{(s)} + Cu^{2+}_{(aq)} \rightarrow Zn^{2+}_{(aq)} + Cu_{(s)}$)

Will silver react with aqueous magnesium ions?

Following the same steps as before, you get:

$$Mg^{2+}_{(aq)} + 2e^- \rightleftharpoons Mg_{(s)} \qquad E^{\ominus} = -2.37 \text{ V}$$
$$Ag^{+}_{(aq)} + e^- \rightleftharpoons Ag_{(s)} \qquad E^{\ominus} = +0.80 \text{ V}$$

Here, the substances at the non-pointy ends of the arrows are $Mg_{(s)}$ and $Ag^{+}_{(aq)}$. So, magnesium will react with aqueous silver ions, but silver and aqueous magnesium ions will not react.

Exam Tip
In the exam, don't assume you'll always be given a reaction that will happen — you're just as likely to get given one that won't.

You can use the rule to work out whether any two substances will react — just remember to put the half-cell with the more negative standard electrode potential on the top.

Making predictions without using the anticlockwise rule

For any two reduction half-equations, things on the right side of the one with the more negative electrode potential will react with things on the left side of the other one. That's why the anticlockwise rule works. But once you know that, you can make predictions just by looking at electrode potentials.

Tip: It's easier to explain how you know that two things will react using this method, because you can talk about their electrode potentials. But it's easier to make mistakes with too — so stick with the anticlockwise rule if you're finding it tricky.

Example

Will aluminium metal react with aqueous nickel ions? Explain your answer.

Here are the half-equations and their electrode potentials:

$$Al^{3+}_{(aq)} + 3e^- \rightleftharpoons Al_{(s)} \qquad E^\ominus = -1.66\text{ V}$$
$$Ni^{2+}_{(aq)} + 2e^- \rightleftharpoons Ni_{(s)} \qquad E^\ominus = -0.25\text{ V}$$

$E^\ominus$ is more negative for the Al^{3+}/Al half-equation than for the Ni^{2+}/Ni half-equation. So aluminium will react with Ni^{2+} ions.

Problems with predicting reactions

A prediction using $E^\ominus$ and the anticlockwise rule only states if a reaction is possible under standard conditions. The prediction might be wrong if...

...the conditions are not standard

Changing the concentration (or temperature) of the solution can cause the electrode potential to change. For example, the zinc/copper cell has these half equations in equilibrium...

$$Zn_{(s)} \rightleftharpoons Zn^{2+}_{(aq)} + 2e^-$$
$$Cu^{2+}_{(aq)} + 2e^- \rightleftharpoons Cu_{(s)}$$

Tip: Remember — just because a reaction is <u>feasible</u> doesn't mean that it will <u>actually happen</u>.

...if you increase the concentration of Zn^{2+}, the equilibrium will shift to the left, reducing the ease of electron loss. The whole cell potential will be lower. If you increase the concentration of Cu^{2+}, the equilibrium will shift to the right, increasing the ease of electron gain. The whole cell potential will be higher.

...the reaction kinetics are not favourable

The rate of a reaction may be so slow that the reaction might not appear to happen. If a reaction has a high activation energy, this may stop it happening.

Practice Questions — Application

Q1 Use the anticlockwise rule to say whether these reactions will happen:

a) $Mg_{(s)} + Ni^{2+}_{(aq)} \rightarrow Mg^{2+}_{(aq)} + Ni_{(s)}$

b) $2Br^-_{(aq)} + Fe^{3+}_{(aq)} \rightarrow Fe^{2+}_{(aq)} + Br_{2(aq)}$

c) $Sn^{2+}_{(aq)} + Cu^{2+}_{(aq)} \rightarrow Sn^{4+}_{(aq)} + Cu_{(s)}$

Q2 Calculate $E^\ominus_{cell}$ for the following reactions:

Tip: You'll find the electrode potentials that you need to answer these questions in the electrochemical series on page 185.

a) $Al_{(s)} + Ag^+_{(aq)} \rightarrow Al^{3+}_{(aq)} + Ag_{(s)}$

b) $Cu_{(s)} + Cl_{2(aq)} \rightarrow Cu^{2+}_{(aq)} + 2Cl^-_{(aq)}$

c) $Sn^{2+}_{(aq)} + Fe^{3+}_{(aq)} \rightarrow Sn^{4+}_{(aq)} + Fe^{2+}_{(aq)}$

Practice Questions — Fact Recall

Q1 What is an electrochemical series?

Q2 In what direction are half-equations written in electrochemical series?

Q3 A half-reaction has a very positive electrode potential. Is it more likely to go in the direction of oxidation or reduction?

Q4 Give two reasons why a prediction made using the anticlockwise rule might be wrong.

10. Energy Storage Cells

The last few topics told you all about electrochemical cells. This one's all about what electrochemical cells are actually used for — in particular, how electrochemical cells are used as energy storage cells (batteries).

Learning Objective:

▪ Be able to apply principles of electrode potentials to modern storage cells.

Specification Reference 5.2.3

What are energy storage cells?

Energy storage cells (fancy name for batteries) have been around for ages and modern ones work just like an electrochemical cell. For example the nickel-iron cell was developed way back at the start of the 1900s and is often used as a back-up power supply because it can be repeatedly charged and is very robust. You can work out the voltage produced by these cells by using the electrode potentials of the substances used in the cell.

There are lots of different cells and you won't be asked to remember the $E^{\ominus}$ for the reactions, but you might be asked to work out the cell potential (cell voltage) for a given cell... so here's an example I prepared earlier.

Figure 1: *An assortment of batteries — these are all electrochemical cells.*

--- Example ---

The nickel-iron cell has a nickel oxide hydroxide (NiOOH) cathode and an iron (Fe) anode with potassium hydroxide as the electrolyte. Using the half-equations given:

a) **write out the full equation for the reaction.**

b) **calculate the cell voltage produced by the nickel-iron cell.**

$$Fe(OH)_2 + 2e^- \rightleftharpoons Fe + 2OH^- \qquad E^{\ominus} = -0.44 \text{ V}$$
$$NiOOH + H_2O + e^- \rightleftharpoons Ni(OH)_2 + OH^- \qquad E^{\ominus} = +0.76 \text{ V}$$

a) First work out which half-equation will go in the forward (reduction) direction and which in the reverse (oxidation) direction. The iron half-equation has the more negative electrode potential, so it will go in the direction of oxidation: $Fe + 2OH^- \rightleftharpoons Fe(OH)_2 + 2e^-$
Now to find the overall equation for the reaction, just balance the number of electrons and then combine the two half-equations. So, the overall reaction in this cell is...

$$2NiOOH + 2H_2O + Fe \rightleftharpoons 2Ni(OH)_2 + Fe(OH)_2$$

The e^- and the OH^- are not shown because they cancel out.

b) To calculate the cell voltage you use the same formula that you use to work out cell potential (see page 186). So the cell voltage is...

$$E^{\ominus}_{cell} = E^{\ominus}_{reduced} - E^{\ominus}_{oxidised}$$
$$= +0.76 - (-0.44) = 1.2 \text{ V}$$

Tip: The cathode is the negative electrode and the anode is the positive electrode.

Tip: See page 179 for more on combining half-equations into full equations.

Recharging energy storage cells

Some energy storage cells, like the nickel-iron cell, are rechargeable. Rechargeable energy storage cells can be recharged because the reactions that occur within them are reversible. To recharge these batteries, a current is supplied to force electrons to flow in the opposite direction around the circuit and reverse the reactions. This is possible because none of the substances in a rechargeable battery escape or are used up. In the exam you could be asked to write equations for the reaction that occurs when an energy storage cell is recharged. These are just the equations for the storage cell in reverse.

Figure 2: *A lithium ion battery being recharged.*

Example

When the nickel-iron cell on the previous page is recharged, the half-equations for the reaction are:

$$Fe(OH)_2 + 2e^- \rightleftharpoons Fe + 2OH^-$$
$$Ni(OH)_2 + OH^- \rightleftharpoons NiOOH + H_2O + e^-$$

So, the overall equation when a nickel-iron cell is recharged is:

$$2Ni(OH)_2 + Fe(OH)_2 \rightleftharpoons 2NiOOH + 2H_2O + Fe$$

Practice Questions — Application

Q1 Nickel/cadmium batteries are a common type of rechargeable battery. The two half-equations for the reactions happening in this type of battery are shown below:

$$Cd(OH)_{2(s)} + 2e^- \rightleftharpoons Cd_{(s)} + 2OH^-_{(aq)} \qquad E^\ominus = -0.88$$
$$NiO(OH)_{(s)} + H_2O + e^- \rightleftharpoons Ni(OH)_{2(s)} + OH^- \qquad E^\ominus = +0.52$$

a) Calculate $E^\ominus_{cell}$ for this cell.

b) Write an equation for the overall reaction occurring in this cell.

c) Suggest an equation for the reaction that occurs when this type of battery is recharged.

Q2 Zinc-carbon dry cell batteries are commonly used in TV remote controls and torches. The half-equations for the reaction that occurs in this type of battery are shown below:

$$Zn^{2+}_{(aq)} + 2e^- \rightarrow Zn_{(s)} \qquad E^\ominus = -0.76 \text{ V}$$
$$2MnO_{2(s)} + 2NH_4^+{}_{(aq)} + 2e^- \rightarrow Mn_2O_{3(s)} + 2NH_{3(aq)} + H_2O_{(l)} \quad E^\ominus = +0.75 \text{ V}$$

a) Calculate $E^\ominus_{cell}$ for this cell.

b) Write an equation for the overall reaction occurring in this cell.

c) Explain why this type of battery is not rechargeable.

Q3 Lead acid cells are used in car batteries. The half-equations for the reaction happening in this type of battery are shown below:

$$PbSO_{4(s)} + 2e^- \rightleftharpoons Pb_{(s)} + SO_4^{2-}{}_{(aq)} \qquad E^\ominus = -0.36 \text{ V}$$
$$PbO_{2(s)} + SO_4^{2-}{}_{(aq)} + 4H^+_{(aq)} + 2e^- \rightleftharpoons PbSO_{4(s)} + 2H_2O_{(l)} \quad E^\ominus = +1.69 \text{ V}$$

a) Calculate $E^\ominus_{cell}$ for this cell.

b) Write an equation for the overall reaction occurring in this cell.

c) Suggest half-equations for the reaction that occurs when this type of battery is recharged.

Figure 3: Lead-acid car batteries being recharged.

Practice Questions — Fact Recall

Q1 What is the common name for an energy storage cell?

Q2 Give the equation you would use to calculate the cell potential of an energy storage cell.

Q3 Why can some energy storage cells be recharged?

11. Fuel Cells

Fuel cells are really handy — they can generate electricity without producing too much pollution and they're more efficient than petrol engines. But there are disadvantages to using fuel cells too. Read on to find out more...

Hydrogen-oxygen fuel cells

A **fuel cell** produces electricity by reacting a fuel, usually hydrogen, with an oxidant, which is most likely to be oxygen. The diagram below shows how a hydrogen-oxygen fuel cell works:

1. *At the anode the platinum catalyst splits the H_2 into protons and electrons.*

2. *The polymer electrolyte membrane (PEM) only allows the H+ across and this forces the e⁻ to travel around the circuit to get to the cathode.*

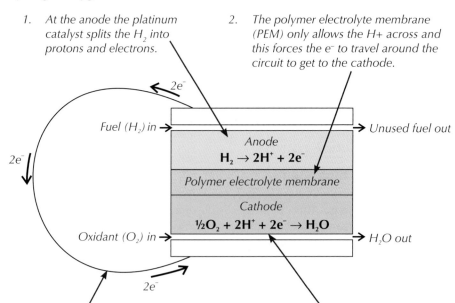

Fuel (H_2) in →

Unused fuel out →

$2e^-$

$2e^-$

Anode
$$H_2 \rightarrow 2H^+ + 2e^-$$

Polymer electrolyte membrane

Cathode
$$\tfrac{1}{2}O_2 + 2H^+ + 2e^- \rightarrow H_2O$$

Oxidant (O_2) in →

H_2O out →

$2e^-$

3. *An electric current is created in the circuit, which is used to power something like a car or a bike or a dancing Santa.*

4. *At the cathode, O_2 combines with the H⁺ from the anode and the e⁻ from the circuit to make H_2O. This is the only waste product.*

Fuel cell vehicles

Fuel cell vehicles (FCVs) are, unsurprisingly, electric vehicles powered by fuel cells as opposed to petrol or diesel. Using a hydrogen fuel cell does give FCVs some important advantages over regular cars:

- They produce a lot less pollution because the only waste product is water.

- The fuel cell is twice as efficient at converting fuel to power compared to a petrol engine.

Fuel cells don't just use hydrogen — they can also be powered by **hydrogen-rich fuels**. Hydrogen-rich fuels include methanol, natural gas, or petrol. These are converted into hydrogen gas by a reformer before being used in the fuel cell. Hydrogen-rich fuels only release small amounts of pollutants and CO_2 when used in a fuel cell compared to burning them in a conventional engine.

Problems with hydrogen fuel cells

Hydrogen might sound like the perfect fuel but there are some other things to think about...

Learning Objectives:

- Be able to explain that a fuel cell uses the energy from the reaction of a fuel with oxygen to create a voltage.

- Be able to explain the changes that take place at each electrode in a hydrogen-oxygen fuel cell.

- Be able to outline that scientists in the car industry are developing fuel cell vehicles (FCVs), fuelled by hydrogen gas and hydrogen-rich fuels.

- Know the advantages of FCVs over conventional petrol or diesel-powered vehicles.

- Understand how hydrogen might be stored in FCVs.

- Be able to consider the limitations of hydrogen fuel cells, for example: (i) storing and transporting hydrogen. (ii) limited lifetime and high production costs. (iii) the use of toxic chemicals in their production.

- Know that a 'hydrogen economy' may contribute largely to future energy needs but limitations include: (i) public and political acceptance of hydrogen as a fuel. (ii) handling and maintenance of hydrogen systems. (iii) initial manufacture of hydrogen requiring energy.

Specification Reference 5.2.3

Figure 1: A hydrogen-oxygen fuel cell.

Tip: <u>Adsorption</u> is when something forms a layer on a surface. <u>Absorption</u> is when something is taken up by another substance.

Figure 2: Electrolysis of water being used to make hydrogen and oxygen.

Tip: See page 4 for more on science and decision-making.

Figure 3: A bus powered by a hydrogen-oxygen fuel cell.

Production and life span

Hydrogen fuel cells are not easy to make. The platinum catalysts and membrane are expensive and the production of a fuel cell involves the use of toxic chemicals, which you need to dispose of afterwards.

Plus, fuel cells only have a limited life span so need to be replaced, which means new ones have to be made, and old ones disposed of. Disposing of a fuel cell is an expensive process because of the chemicals they contain and the need to recycle some of the materials.

Storage and transportation

Storing and transporting hydrogen can be a pain. For example:

- If you store it as a gas it is very explosive.
- If you try to store it as a liquid you need really expensive fridges because it has such a low boiling point.
- You can also store it adsorbed to the surface of a solid like charcoal or absorbed into a material like palladium but these can be very expensive and often have a limited life span.

The problems with storage could be overcome by using a hydrogen-rich fuel such as methanol as a source of hydrogen. Methanol is a liquid and can easily be stored and transported.

Manufacturing hydrogen

Hydrogen fuel cells are not as green as they seem because manufacturing hydrogen takes energy. Most hydrogen is currently produced from reacting natural gas with steam, which produces carbon dioxide as a waste product. Not only is one of the reactants a fossil fuel, but fossil fuels are also used to heat the process. Hydrogen can be produced by the electrolysis of water but the large amounts of electricity needed are produced by conventional power stations using fossil fuels. Hydrogen is described as an **energy carrier** and not an energy source because it requires energy to make it.

A hydrogen economy

Lots of people think that hydrogen will be really important in the future. They think there will be a hydrogen economy instead of an oil economy where all the energy needs of cars, buildings and electronics will be powered by hydrogen fuel cells. Sounds great but there are a few things to overcome first...

(HOW SCIENCE WORKS)

People accepting hydrogen as a fuel

Many people have concerns about the safety and reliability of hydrogen as a fuel. Most people are happy filling their cars with petrol but might think doing the same with hydrogen is more dangerous.

The cost of the new system

If hydrogen is going to be the future it needs to be as cheap or cheaper than existing energy systems to convince people to change. The infrastructure for hydrogen fuel supplies would also be very expensive to set up.

Producing the hydrogen

Hydrogen is an energy carrier, which means it needs an energy source to make it. So if you want to make clean hydrogen you need to make it using a clean energy source, e.g. solar or wind energy. Unfortunately these methods are expensive and currently don't supply large amounts of energy.

Q1 How does a fuel cell produce electricity?

Q2 Describe how a hydrogen-oxygen fuel cell works.

Q3 a) What are FCVs?

b) Give two advantages of using FCVs.

Q4 a) Describe three ways in which hydrogen could be stored in FCVs.

b) Give a disadvantage of each storage method.

Q5 Give three problems with using hydrogen-oxygen fuel cells.

Q6 a) What is meant by the term 'hydrogen economy'?

b) Give three limitations which may prevent the widespread acceptance of a hydrogen economy.

Section Summary

Make sure you know...

- How enthalpy changes can be determined using calorimeter experiments.
- The definition of enthalpy change of neutralisation, $\Delta H^{\ominus}_{neutralisation}$.
- How to calculate the enthalpy change of a neutralisation reaction from experimental results.
- The definition of the standard lattice enthalpy, $\Delta H^{\ominus}_{latt}$.
- How standard lattice enthalpy is affected by ionic charge and ionic radius.
- How to construct Born-Haber cycles and use them to calculate standard lattice enthalpies.
- The definitions of enthalpy change of hydration, $\Delta H^{\ominus}_{hyd}$, and enthalpy change of solution, $\Delta H^{\ominus}_{solution}$.
- How to use enthalpy cycles to calculate enthalpies of solution.
- How enthalpy of hydration is influenced by ionic charge and ionic radius.
- That entropy, S, is a measure of the amount of disorder in a system and that a system becomes energetically more stable when it becomes more disordered.
- How entropy is affected by physical state, dissolution and number of particles.
- That endothermic reactions can be spontaneous if there is a large enough increase in entropy.
- How to calculate the entropy change for a reaction.
- That the tendency of a reaction to happen depends on temperature, entropy and enthalpy.
- What free-energy is and how to calculate it using $\Delta G = \Delta H - T\Delta S$.
- How to use ΔG to determine whether or not a reaction is feasible at a particular temperature.
- The meaning of the terms redox, oxidation number, half-reaction, oxidising agent and reducing agent.
- What half-equations are and how to use them to write full equations for redox reactions.
- What electrochemical cells are and how to draw them.
- The definition for the standard electrode potential of a half-cell.
- What an electrochemical series is.
- How to calculate standard cell potentials by combining two standard electrode potentials.
- How to use standard electrode potentials to predict the outcome of a reaction.
- Why reaction predictions are sometimes wrong.
- How to write equations and calculate cell potentials for energy storage cells.
- What fuel cells are and how they work.
- The advantages and disadvantages of using fuel cells in FCVs and the limitations of a hydrogen economy.

Exam-style Questions

1   Rubidium chloride is an ionic compound that dissolves easily in water and can be used as a cell marker in laboratories. The table below shows thermodynamic data for rubidium chloride.

Enthalpy change	ΔH°/ kJ mol^{-1}
Enthalpy change of atomisation of rubidium	+81
First ionisation enthalpy of rubidium	+403
Enthalpy change of hydration of Rb$^+$ ions	−296
Enthalpy change of atomisation of chlorine	+122
Electron affinity of chlorine	−349
Enthalpy change of hydration of Cl$^-$ ions	−364
Enthalpy of change formation of rubidium chloride	−435

(a)   Define the term standard lattice enthalpy.

(3 marks)

(b)   Complete the Born-Haber cycle for the formation of rubidium chloride by filling in the blank lines. You should include chemical symbols and state symbols.

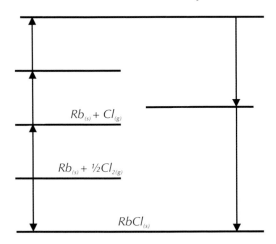

(3 marks)

(c)   Use the data in the table to calculate the standard lattice enthalpy of rubidium chloride.

(3 marks)

(d)   The standard lattice enthalpy of sodium chloride is more exothermic than that of rubidium chloride. Explain why.

(3 marks)

(e)   Calculate the enthalpy change of solution for rubidium chloride.
(If you have not been able to answer **(c)** use the value of −300 kJ mol^{-1} for the standard lattice enthalpy of rubidium chloride. This value is incorrect.)

(2 marks)

2 Manganese can be extracted from its ore manganese(IV) oxide, MnO_2, by reduction using carbon at 1473 K. The reaction is shown in the equation below.

$$MnO_{2\,(s)} + C_{(s)} \rightarrow Mn_{(s)} + CO_{2\,(g)} \qquad \Delta H^\circ = +127 \text{ kJ mol}^{-1}$$

	$MnO_{2\,(s)}$	$C_{(s)}$	$Mn_{(s)}$	$CO_{2\,(g)}$
S°/ J K^{-1}mol^{-1}	53	5.7	32	214

(a) (i) Use the balanced equation to explain whether you would expect entropy to decrease or increase during this reaction.

(2 marks)

(ii) Calculate the free energy change for the extraction of manganese from its ore.

(4 marks)

(iii) Explain how the free energy change of a reaction relates to the feasibility of that reaction.

(2 marks)

(b) (i) Give the equation which links the temperature at which a reaction becomes feasible, T, the enthalpy change for the reaction, ΔH, and the entropy change of the system, ΔS_{system}.

(1 mark)

(ii) Calculate the temperature at which the reduction of manganese oxide using carbon becomes feasible.

(2 marks)

3 The table below shows a short electrochemical series:

Half-reaction	E° (V)
$Mg^{2+}_{(aq)} + 2e^- \rightleftharpoons Mg_{(s)}$	−2.38
$V^{2+}_{(aq)} + 2e^- \rightleftharpoons V_{(s)}$	−1.18
$V^{3+}_{(aq)} + e^- \rightleftharpoons V^{2+}_{(aq)}$	−0.26
$Sn^{4+}_{(aq)} + 2e^- \rightleftharpoons Sn^{2+}_{(aq)}$	+0.15
$VO^{2+}_{(aq)} + 2H^+_{(aq)} + e^- \rightleftharpoons V^{3+}_{(aq)} + H_2O_{(l)}$	+0.34
$Fe^{3+}_{(aq)} + e^- \rightleftharpoons Fe^{2+}_{(aq)}$	+0.77
$VO_2^+{}_{(aq)} + 2H^+_{(aq)} + e^- \rightleftharpoons VO^{2+}_{(aq)} + H_2O_{(l)}$	+1.00

(a) (i) Using the information in the table, predict what reactions, if any, occur when aqueous Sn^{2+} ions are mixed with an acidified solution of VO_2^+ ions. Explain your answer.

(4 marks)

(ii) Suggest two reasons why your predictions may be incorrect.

(2 marks)

(b) An electrochemical cell can be made by connecting an Mg^{2+}/Mg half-cell to an Fe^{2+}/Fe^{3+} half-cell.

    (i) Draw a diagram to show how this cell could be set up in a laboratory.

        (3 marks)

    (ii) Calculate the cell potential (e.m.f.) of this cell.

        (1 mark)

    (iii) Write an equation for the overall reaction occurring in this cell.

        (2 marks)

(c) Standard electrode potentials are measured relative to the standard hydrogen electrode.

    (i) Explain what is meant by 'standard conditions'.

        (3 marks)

    (ii) The electrode itself is made of platinum. Suggest why platinum is a suitable metal to use for this purpose.

        (1 mark)

(d) When a standard hydrogen electrode was connected to an Ag^+/Ag half-cell, the reading on the voltmeter was +0.80 V.

    (i) What is the standard electrode potential for the reaction $Ag^+_{(aq)} + e^- \rightleftharpoons Ag_{(s)}$?

        (1 mark)

    (ii) What does this electrode potential tell you about the reactivity of silver compared to vanadium? Explain your answer.

        (2 marks)

4 Nickel-zinc cells are a type of rechargeable battery used in digital cameras. The half-equations for the reactions that occur in a nickel-zinc cell are shown below:

$$NiOOH_{(s)} + H_2O_{(l)} + e^- \rightleftharpoons Ni(OH)_{2(s)} + OH^-_{(aq)} \qquad E^\ominus = \ ? \ V$$

$$Zn(OH)_{2(s)} + 2e^- \rightleftharpoons Zn_{(s)} + 2OH^-_{(aq)} \qquad E^\ominus = -1.25 \ V$$

(a) When the cell discharges the $Zn/Zn(OH)_2$ half-reaction goes in the oxidation direction.

    (i) Give the equation for the overall reaction occurring in this cell as it discharges.

        (2 marks)

    (ii) The standard cell potential is +1.73 V. Calculate the standard electrode potential of the $NiOOH/Ni(OH)_2$ half-reaction.

        (3 marks)

(b) Hydrogen-oxygen fuel cells can be used as an alternative source of commercially available electrical energy.

    • Write equations for the oxidation and reduction reactions occurring in a hydrogen-oxygen fuel cell.

    • Give two advantages and two disadvantages of using hydrogen-oxygen fuel cells over standard petrol engines.

 In your answer you should explain your reasoning clearly and concisely.

        (6 marks)

1. Transition Elements

Learning Objectives:
- Be able to describe the elements Ti–Cu as transition elements, i.e. d-block elements that have an ion with an incomplete d sub-shell.
- Be able to deduce the electron configurations of atoms and ions of the d-block elements of Period 4 (Sc–Zn), given the atomic number and charge.

Specification Reference 5.3.1

You've already learnt about the halogens and the alkaline earth metals at AS. This section is about another important set of elements — the transition metals.

The d-block

The **d-block** is the block of elements in the middle of the periodic table. Most of the elements in the d-block are **transition elements** (or transition metals). You mainly need to know about the ones in the first row of the d-block. These are the elements from titanium to copper — see Figure 1.

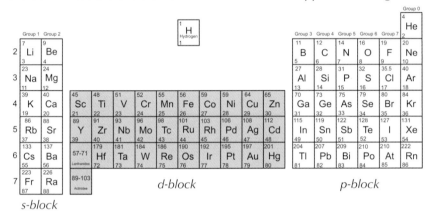

Figure 1: The three main blocks of the periodic table. The transition elements are in the d-block.

What is a transition metal?

Here's the definition of a transition metal:

> A transition metal is a metal that can form one or more stable ions with an incomplete d-subshell.

A **d-subshell** can take ten electrons. So transition metals form at least one ion with between one and nine electrons in the d-subshell. All the Period 4 d-block elements are transition metals apart from scandium and zinc (see page 199).

Figure 2: A variety of transition metals.

Electron configurations

At AS level you saw that the electron configurations of elements can be figured out by following a few simple rules:

- Electrons fill up the lowest energy **subshells** first.
- Electrons fill **orbitals** singly before they start sharing.

The transition metals generally follow the same rules — see Figure 3. The 4s subshell usually fills up first because it has lower energy than the 3d subshell. Once the 4s subshell is full, the 3d subshell starts to fill up. The 3d orbitals are occupied singly at first. They only double up when they have to. But, there are a couple of exceptions...

Tip: Electron orbitals and electron configurations were covered at AS level, so if you've forgotten what they are have a quick skim over your AS notes.

- Chromium prefers to have one electron in each orbital of the 3d subshell and just one in the 4s subshell — this gives it more stability.
- Copper prefers to have a full 3d subshell and just one electron in the 4s subshell — it's more stable that way.

Tip: Subshells are made up of orbitals — for example, s-subshells contain one orbital, p-subshells contain three orbitals and d-subshells contain five orbitals. Each orbital can hold two electrons.

		3d					*4s*	
Ti	[Ar]	↑	↑				↑↓	[Ar] $3d^2 4s^2$
V	[Ar]	↑	↑	↑			↑↓	[Ar] $3d^3 4s^2$
Cr	[Ar]	↑	↑	↑	↑	↑	↑	[Ar] $3d^5 4s^1$
Mn	[Ar]	↑	↑	↑	↑	↑	↑↓	[Ar] $3d^5 4s^2$
Fe	[Ar]	↑↓	↑	↑	↑	↑	↑↓	[Ar] $3d^6 4s^2$
Co	[Ar]	↑↓	↑↓	↑	↑	↑	↑↓	[Ar] $3d^7 4s^2$
Ni	[Ar]	↑↓	↑↓	↑↓	↑	↑	↑↓	[Ar] $3d^8 4s^2$
Cu	[Ar]	↑↓	↑↓	↑↓	↑↓	↑↓	↑	[Ar] $3d^{10} 4s^1$

Figure 3: *The electron configurations of the Period 4 d-block transition metals.*

Tip: The electron configurations of all the Period 4 transition metals start in the same way — $1s^2 2s^2 2p^6 3s^2 3p^6$. This is the same as the electron configuration of the element argon, so [Ar] is used as a short way of writing it.

Transition metal ions

Transition metal atoms form positive ions. When this happens, the s electrons are removed first, then the d electrons.

Example

Iron forms Fe^{2+} ions and Fe^{3+} ions.

When it forms 2^+ ions, it loses both its 4s electrons:

$$Fe = [Ar]3d^6\,4s^2 \rightarrow Fe^{2+} = [Ar]3d^6$$

Only once the 4s electrons are removed can a 3d electron be removed.

$$\text{E.g. } Fe^{2+} = [Ar]3d^6 \rightarrow Fe^{3+} = [Ar]3d^5$$

Exam Tip
The atomic number in the periodic table tells you how many electrons each atom has — you should be able to work the electron configuration out from there.

You might be asked to write the electron configuration of a transition metal ion in the exam. To do this, just follow these steps:

- Write down the electron configuration of the element.
- Work out how many electrons have been removed to make the ion.
- Remove that number of electrons from the electron configuration taking them out of the s-orbital first and then the d-orbitals.

Tip: You can work out how many electrons have been lost using oxidation states — see page 178.

Example

Write out the electron configuration of Mn^{2+} ions.

- The electron configuration of Mn atoms is $[Ar]3d^5 4s^2$.
- Two electrons are removed to convert Mn atoms into Mn^{2+} ions.
- Removing the electrons starting from the s-orbitals gives $[Ar]3d^5 4s^0$.
- So the electron configuration of Mn^{2+} ions is $[Ar]3d^5$.

Scandium and zinc

Sc and Zn aren't transition metals as their stable ions don't have partially filled d-subshells.

Scandium only forms one ion, Sc^{3+}, which has an empty d-subshell. Scandium has the electron configuration $1s^2 2s^2 2p^6 3s^2 3p^6 3d^1 4s^2$, so when it loses three electrons to form Sc^{3+}, it ends up with the electron configuration $1s^2 2s^2 2p^6 3s^2 3p^6$.

Zinc only forms one ion, Zn^{2+}, which has a full d-subshell. Zinc has the electron configuration $1s^2 2s^2 2p^6 3s^2 3p^6 3d^{10} 4s^2$. When it forms Zn^{2+} it loses two electrons, both from the 4s subshell. This means it keeps its full 3d subshell and becomes $1s^2 2s^2 2p^6 3s^2 3p^6 3d^{10}$.

Figure 4: *A lump of zinc.*

Practice Questions — Application

Q1 Write out the electron configurations for the following transition metal elements:

   a) V   b) Co   c) Cu   d) Ni

Q2 Write out the electron configurations for the following transition metal ions:

   a) V^{3+} b) Co^{2+} c) Cu^{2+} d) Ni^{2+}

   e) Cr^{2+} f) Ti^{3+} g) Ti^{4+}

Q3 Using electron configurations, explain why zinc is not a transition metal, despite being in the d-block of the periodic table.

Exam Tip
If you're asked for an electron configuration it's fine to use shorthand and start them with [Ar], but if you're asked for a <u>full</u> electron configuration you need to write it all out starting from $1s^2$.

Practice Questions — Fact Recall

Q1 Where in the periodic table are transition elements found?

Q2 What is the definition of a transition metal?

Q3 How many electrons can a d-subshell hold?

Q4 Give two rules that are usually followed when working out electron configurations.

Q5 a) Explain why chromium has the electron configuration $[Ar]3d^5 4s^1$ and not $[Ar]3d^4 4s^2$ as you would expect.

   b) Explain why copper has the electron configuration $[Ar]3d^{10} 4s^1$ and not $[Ar]3d^9 4s^2$ as you would expect.

Exam Tip
Chromium and copper have slightly odd electron configurations (see previous page). I'm afraid there's no easy way to work them out in the exam — you'll just have to learn 'em...

- Be able to illustrate the formation of coloured transition metal ions.
- Be able to illustrate the catalytic behaviour of the transition elements and/or their compounds.
- Be able to illustrate the existence of more than one oxidation state for each transition element in its compounds.
- Be able to describe, including ionic equations, the simple precipitation reactions and the accompanying colour changes of $Cu^{2+}_{(aq)}$, $Co^{2+}_{(aq)}$, $Fe^{2+}_{(aq)}$ and $Fe^{3+}_{(aq)}$ with aqueous sodium hydroxide.

Specification Reference 5.3.1

2. Transition Element Properties

The chemical properties of transition metals makes them great for things like indicators, colouring agents, catalysts and even drugs. But before you can learn about these fascinating applications you have to learn the basics...

Chemical properties

The transition metals have a few special chemical properties that you need to know about:

- They can form **complex ions** — see pages 203-205.
  E.g. iron forms a complex ion with water — $[Fe(H_2O)_6]^{2+}$.
- They form coloured ions — see below.
  E.g. $Fe^{2+}_{(aq)}$ ions are pale green and $Fe^{3+}_{(aq)}$ ions are yellow.
- They're good **catalysts** because they can change oxidation states by gaining or losing electrons within their d orbitals. This means they can transfer electrons to speed up reactions.
  E.g. iron is the catalyst used in the Haber process to produce ammonia. Vanadium(V) oxide, V_2O_5, is the catalyst used in the contact process to make sulfuric acid. Nickel is the catalyst used to harden margarine.
- They can exist in variable **oxidation states** — see below.
  E.g. iron can exist in the +2 oxidation state as Fe^{2+} ions and in the +3 oxidation state as Fe^{3+} ions.

Oxidation states and coloured ions

Some common coloured ions and oxidation states are shown below. The colours refer to the aqueous ions.

Figure 1: The different colours of the aqueous transition metal ions.

Tip: The colour of the Cr^{3+} ion tends to change depending on what else is in solution with it. It's mostly green though, so stick with that and you can't go wrong.

Element	Ion	Oxidation state	Colour
Ti	Ti^{2+}	+2	violet
	Ti^{3+}	+3	purple
V	V^{2+}	+2	violet
	V^{3+}	+3	green
	VO^{2+}	+4	blue
	VO_2^+	+5	yellow
Cr	Cr^{3+}	+3	green/violet
	$Cr_2O_7^{2-}$	+6	orange
Mn	Mn^{2+}	+2	very pale pink/ colourless
	MnO_4^-	+7	purple
Fe	Fe^{2+}	+2	pale green
	Fe^{3+}	+3	yellow
Co	Co^{2+}	+2	pink
Ni	Ni^{2+}	+2	green
Cu	Cu^{2+}	+2	pale blue

These elements show variable oxidation states because the energy levels of the 4s and the 3d sub-shells are very close to one another. So different numbers of electrons can be gained or lost using fairly similar amounts of energy.

Tip: See page 178 for more on oxidation states and how to find them.

Transition metal hydroxides

When you mix a solution of transition metal ions with sodium hydroxide solution you get a coloured **precipitate**. You need to know the equations for the following reactions, and the colours of the hydroxide precipitates:

Tip: Remember that a precipitate is a solid formed in a solution.

Copper(II)

$$Cu^{2+}_{(aq)} + 2OH^-_{(aq)} \rightarrow Cu(OH)_{2\,(s)}$$

pale blue   *blue precipitate*

Cobalt(II)

$$Co^{2+}_{(aq)} + 2OH^-_{(aq)} \rightarrow Co(OH)_{2\,(s)}$$

pink   *blue precipitate*
                     (turns pink on standing)

Iron(II)

$$Fe^{2+}_{(aq)} + 2OH^-_{(aq)} \rightarrow Fe(OH)_{2\,(s)}$$

pale green   *green precipitate*
                   (darkens on standing)

Iron(III)

$$Fe^{3+}_{(aq)} + 3OH^-_{(aq)} \rightarrow Fe(OH)_{3\,(s)}$$

yellow   *orange precipitate*
                 (darkens on standing)

If you know which transition metal ion produces which colour precipitate, you can use these reactions to identify a transition metal ion solution.

Figure 2: Clockwise from top left — copper(II) hydroxide, cobalt(II) hydroxide, iron(II) hydroxide and iron(III) hydroxide.

The incomplete d-subshell

It's the incomplete d-subshell that causes the special chemical properties of transition metals. d-block elements without an incomplete d-subshell don't have these properties.

┌─ **Example** ──────────────────
Scandium and zinc don't form ions with incomplete d-subshells. As a result they don't have the same chemical properties as transition metals.

For example, they can't form complex ions, they don't form coloured ions, they can't exist in variable oxidation states and they don't catalyse any reactions.

Tip: There's more on scandium and zinc on page 199.

Practice Questions — Fact Recall

Q1 Transition elements have variable oxidation states.
State two other chemical properties of transition elements.

Q2 Name the catalyst used in the contact process.

Q3 Name one thing that nickel catalysts can be used for?

Q4 Match the transition metal ions (**A–D**) with the colour they'd be in solution (**1–4**).

A	Fe^{3+}	**1**	pale blue
B	Mn^{2+}	**2**	purple
C	MnO_4^-	**3**	yellow
D	Cu^{2+}	**4**	very pale pink

Q5 Write an equation for the reaction of cobalt(II) ions with sodium hydroxide solution.

Q6 What would you observe as sodium hydroxide solution is added to a solution of iron(III) ions?

Q7 A scientist has a solution of Fe ions. Describe a test the scientist could use to determine whether the ions are Fe^{2+} ions or Fe^{3+} ions.

Q8 What feature of transition metals causes their chemical properties?

Exam Tip
You could be asked to give the equation or describe the colour change for any of the metal ion and sodium hydroxide reactions on page 201 — so make sure you know them all.

3. Complex Ions

The ability to form complex ions is an important property of transition metals.
You probably haven't come across complex ions before, but the next few
pages should tell you everything you need to know.

What are complex ions?

A **complex ion** is a metal ion surrounded by coordinately bonded **ligands**.
A **coordinate bond** (or dative covalent bond) is a covalent bond in which both
electrons in the shared pair come from the same atom, ion or molecule.
In a complex ion, they come from the ligands. So, a ligand is an atom, ion
or molecule that donates a pair of electrons to a central metal ion.

Example

$[Cu(H_2O)_6]^{2+}$

The central metal ion is a Cu^{2+} ion and water molecules are acting as ligands.
There are six water molecules, each forming a coordinate bond with the
Cu^{2+} ion:

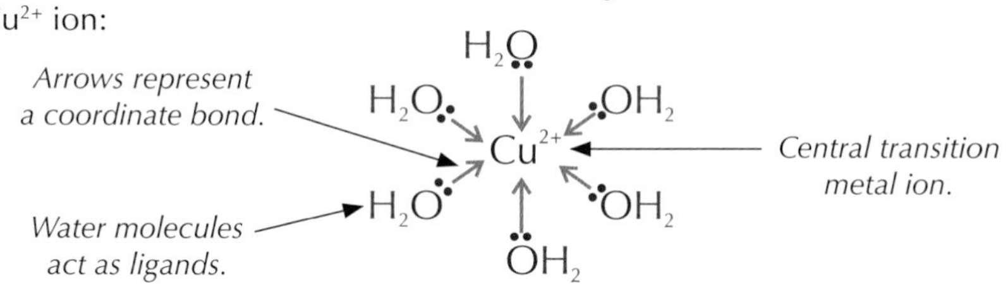

Arrows represent a coordinate bond.

Central transition metal ion.

Water molecules act as ligands.

The different types of ligand

A ligand must have at least one lone pair of electrons, or it won't have anything
to use to form a coordinate bond. But, different ligands can have different
numbers of lone pairs and can form different numbers of coordinate bonds.
Ligands that can only form one coordinate bond are called **monodentate**.

Examples

Here are some examples of monodentate ligands:

ammonia   *chloride ions*   *cyanide ions*   *water*

Ammonia only has one lone pair of electrons to donate to form a coordinate
bond. Water has two lone pairs of electrons but because they are so close
together, it can only form one coordinate bond at a time. Chloride ions and
cyanide ions can also only form one coordinate bond with a metal ion.

Ligands that can form more than one coordinate bond are called **multidentate**.

Example

$EDTA^{4-}$ is a
multidentate ligand:

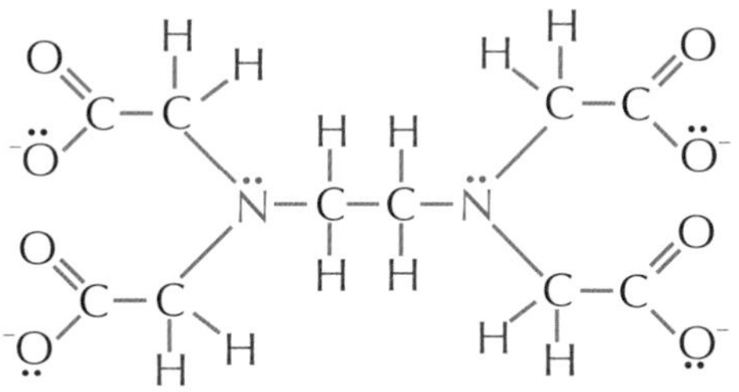

Learning Objectives:

- Be able to explain the term ligand in terms of coordinate bonding.
- Be able to state and use the terms complex ion and coordination number.
- Be able to explain and use the term bidentate ligand (e.g. $NH_2CH_2CH_2NH_2$, 'en').
- Be able to state and give examples of complexes with sixfold coordination with an octahedral shape.

Specification Reference 5.3.1

Tip: Complex ions
are always written in
square brackets, e.g.
$[NiCl_2(NH_3)_2]$.
If the complex ion
has a charge, it's put
to the top right of the
square brackets,
e.g. $[Cu(H_2O)_6]^{2+}$.

Tip: Monodentate
ligands are also called
unidentate ligands.

Tip: Chloride ions and
cyanide ions both have
more than one lone
pair of electrons, but
they are only able to
donate <u>one</u> lone pair
to a central metal ion
to form a coordinate
bond — so they are both
monodentate ligands.

Tip: EDTA stands for
ethylenediaminetetra-
acetic acid.

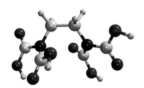

***Figure 1:** Molecular model of EDTA.*

EDTA⁴⁻ has six lone pairs (two on nitrogen atoms and four on oxygen atoms) so it can form six coordinate bonds with a metal ion.

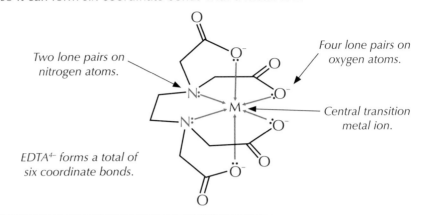

Two lone pairs on nitrogen atoms.

Four lone pairs on oxygen atoms.

Central transition metal ion.

EDTA⁴⁻ forms a total of six coordinate bonds.

Multidentate ligands that can form two coordinate bonds are called **bidentate**.

--- Example ---

Ethane-1,2-diamine ($\overset{\bullet\bullet}{N}H_2CH_2CH_2\overset{\bullet\bullet}{N}H_2$) is a bidentate ligand. It has two amine groups, each of which has a lone pair of electrons that it can donate to form a coordinate bond. In complex ions, each ethane-1,2-diamine molecule forms two coordinate bonds with the metal ion. In the complex ion below, there are three ethane-1,2-diamine molecules forming six coordinate bonds:

Each ethane-1,2-diamine molecule forms two coordinate bonds with the central metal ion.

Shapes of complex ions

The shape of a complex ion depends on its **coordination number**. This is the number of coordinate bonds that are formed with the central metal ion. The usual coordination numbers are 6 and 4. If the ligands are small, like H_2O, CN^- or NH_3, 6 can fit around the central metal ion. But if the ligands are larger, like Cl^-, only 4 can fit around the central metal ion.

Six coordinate bonds

Complex ions that contain six coordinate bonds have an octahedral shape. In an octahedral structure all of the bond angles are 90°.

--- Examples ---

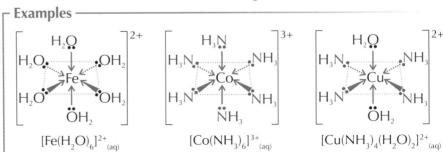

$[Fe(H_2O)_6]^{2+}_{(aq)}$ $[Co(NH_3)_6]^{3+}_{(aq)}$ $[Cu(NH_3)_4(H_2O)_2]^{2+}_{(aq)}$

The different types of bond arrow show that the complex is 3D. The wedge-shaped arrows represent bonds coming towards you and the dashed arrows represent bonds sticking out behind the molecule.

Four coordinate bonds

Complex ions with four coordinate bonds usually have a tetrahedral shape and 109.5° bond angles.

Examples

$[CuCl_4]^{2-}$

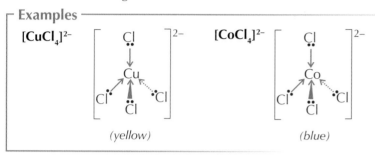

(yellow)

$[CoCl_4]^{2-}$

(blue)

But in a few complexes four coordinate bonds form a square planar shape. All of the bond angles in a square-planar structure are 90°.

Example

Cisplatin $[Pt(NH_3)_2Cl_2]$ (see page 207) has a square planar shape:

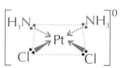

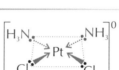

Figure 2: *The flask on the left shows the pink colour of hexaaquacobalt(II) ions. The flask on the right shows the blue colour of cobalt(II) ions complexed as $[CoCl_4]^{2-}$.*

Tip: Cisplatin is used as an anti-cancer drug. See page 207 for more information on this.

Practice Questions — Application

Q1 Give the shapes of the following complex ions and draw them:
   a) $[AlF_6]^{3-}$ b) $[Fe(H_2O)_4(OH)_2]$ c) $[Fe(en)_3]^{3+}$

Q2 What is the coordination number of the transition metal in each of the complex ions in Q1?

Q3 $C_2O_4^{2-}$ is a bidentate ligand. Its structure is shown on the right.

   a) Copy the diagram and circle the atoms that could form a coordinate bond with a metal ion.

   b) $C_2O_4^{2-}$ forms an octahedral complex with Cr^{3+}. Give the formula of the complex ion formed.

Q4 $[Ni(CN)_4]^{2-}$ is a complex ion. In $[Ni(CN)_4]^{2-}$, the carbon from the CN^- ion donates one lone pair to the central Ni atom.

   a) It does not have a tetrahedral shape. What shape could it have instead?

   b) Draw the structure of $[Ni(CN)_4]^{2-}$.

Tip: Remember, 'en' stands for one ethane-1,2-diamine ligand.

Tip: To work out the overall change on a complex ion you just add up all the charges of the ions in the complex.

Practice Questions — Fact Recall

Q1 Define the following terms:
   a) Ligand   b) Coordinate bond   c) Complex ion

Q2 What is a bidentate ligand?

Q3 Give an example of an octahedral complex ion.

- Be able to describe the types of stereoisomerism shown by complexes, including those associated with bidentate and multidentate ligands.
- Know that complexes can show optical isomerism, e.g. $[Ni(en)_3]^{2+}$.
- Know that complexes can show cis-trans isomerism, e.g. $Ni(NH_3)_2Cl_2$.
- Be able to describe the use of cis-platin as an anti-cancer drug and its action by binding to DNA in cancer cells, preventing division.

Specification Reference 5.3.1

4. Isomerism in Complex Ions

Complex ions can show optical and cis-trans isomerism because the ligands can be arranged in various different ways around the central metal ion.

Optical isomerism in complex ions

Optical isomerism is a type of stereoisomerism (see pages 65-67). For compounds containing tetrahedral carbon atoms, optical isomers only form when the carbon atom is attached to four different groups. For complex ions, optical isomers form when an ion can exist as two non-superimposable mirror images. Optical isomers are also known as enantiomers.

--- Example ---

When three ethane-1,2-diamine molecules ($H_2NCH_2CH_2NH_2$), use the lone pairs on both nitrogen atoms to coordinately bond with nickel, two optical isomers are formed.

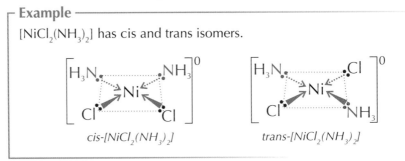

mirror line

Cis-trans isomerism in complex ions

Cis-trans isomerism is a special case of E/Z isomerism (see page 65).

Cis-trans isomerism in square planar complex ions

Square planar complex ions that have two pairs of ligands show cis-trans isomerism. When two paired ligands are directly opposite each other it's the trans isomer and when they're next to each other it's the cis isomer.

--- Example ---

$[NiCl_2(NH_3)_2]$ has cis and trans isomers.

cis-[NiCl$_2$(NH$_3$)$_2$]   *trans-[NiCl$_2$(NH$_3$)$_2$]*

Cis-platin

Cis-platin is a complex of platinum(II) with two chloride ions and two ammonia molecules in a square planar shape (see Figure 1). It is used as an anti-cancer drug.

Tip: If you're finding it difficult to see that the complexes in the example are mirror images of each other try building their 3D structures using a molecular model kit (or matchsticks and modelling clay).

Exam Tip
If you're asked to draw a complex ion in the exam make sure you use dashed bonds and wedged bonds to show that the structure is 3D — you'll lose marks if you don't.

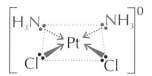

Figure 1: *The structure of cisplatin.*

Cisplatin can be used to treat some types of cancer. Cancer is caused by cells in the body dividing uncontrollably and forming tumours. Cisplatin is active against a variety of cancers, including lung and bladder cancer, because it prevents cancer cells from reproducing.

Before a cell can divide it has to replicate its DNA, which involves unwinding the two strands of the DNA double helix so that they can be copied. Cisplatin easily loses its chlorine ligands through a displacement reaction and forms coordinate bonds with nitrogen atoms in the DNA molecule. This prevents the two strands from unwinding. So, the cell can no longer replicate its DNA and it can't divide.

Cis-trans isomerism in octahedral complex ions

Octahedral complexes with four ligands of one type and two ligands of another type can also exhibit cis-trans isomerism. If the two odd ligands are opposite each other you've got the trans isomer, if they're next to each other then you've got the cis isomer.

> **Tip:** If the two chlorine atoms were on opposite sides of the complex to each other the molecule would be trans-platin. Trans-platin has different biological effects to cis-platin.

> **Tip:** The downside is that cisplatin also prevents normal cells from reproducing — including blood and hair cells. This can cause hair loss and suppress the immune system, increasing the risk of infection. Cisplatin may also cause damage to the kidneys. Scientists always need to weigh up the benefits and risks of new inventions before releasing them for public use. See page 4 for more on decision-making in science.

HOW SCIENCE WORKS

Example

$[Ni(H_2O)_4Cl_2]$ has a trans and a cis isomer.

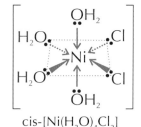

trans-$[Ni(H_2O)_4Cl_2]$ cis-$[Ni(H_2O)_4Cl_2]$

Practice Questions — Application

Q1 State what type of stereoisomerism the following complex ions will exhibit:

a) $[PtCl_2(H_2O)_2]$

b) $[Co(en)_3]^{3+}$

c) $[Cu(H_2O)_4(OH)_2]$

Q2 Draw the cis and trans isomers of $[Ni(H_2O)_2Cl_2]$.

> **Tip:** If you're asked about the isomerism shown in a complex ion sometimes it helps to draw out the structure of the ion first — then you'll get a better idea of the possible isomers.

Practice Questions — Fact Recall

Q1 Name two types of stereoisomerism that complex ions can exhibit.

Q2 a) Draw the structure of cis-platin.

b) Cis-platin can be used to treat some types of cancer. Explain how cis-platin can work as an anti-cancer drug.

Learning Objectives:

- Be able to describe the process of ligand substitution and the accompanying colour changes in the formation of $[Cu(NH_3)_4(H_2O)_2]^{2+}$ and $[CuCl_4]^{2-}$ from $[Cu(H_2O)_6]^{2+}$.

- Be able to describe the process of ligand substitution and the accompanying colour changes in the formation of $[CoCl_4]^{2-}$ from $[Co(H_2O)_6]^{2+}$.

- Be able to explain the biochemical importance of iron in haemoglobin, including ligand substitution involving O_2 and CO.

Specification Reference 5.3.1

Tip: The word 'aqua' is just a fancy name for water. So, a chromium-aqua complex is a complex that contains only chromium and water ($[Cr(H_2O)_6]^{3+}$).

Exam Tip
You don't need to memorise all the ligand substitution reactions on these pages — check out the Learning Objective box at the top of this page for which reactions you have to learn.

Tip: Have a look back at pages 204-205 for a reminder about the shapes of complex ions.

5. Ligand Substitution

Ligands around a central metal ion can switch places with other ligands in ligand substitution reactions.

Ligand substitution reactions

One ligand can be swapped for another ligand — this is **ligand substitution** (or ligand exchange). It pretty much always causes a colour change.

Substitution of similarly sized ligands

If the ligands are of similar size then the coordination number of the complex ion doesn't change, and neither does the shape.

> **Examples**
>
> H_2O and NH_3 ligands are similarly sized and are both uncharged. This means that H_2O ligands can be exchanged with NH_3 ligands without any change in coordination number or shape. There will still be a colour change due to the change of ligand.
>
> $$[Co(H_2O)_6]^{2+}{}_{(aq)} + 6NH_{3(aq)} \rightarrow [Co(NH_3)_6]^{2+}{}_{(aq)} + 6H_2O_{(l)}$$
>
>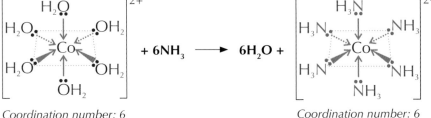
>
> Coordination number: 6   Coordination number: 6
> octahedral   octahedral
> pink   straw coloured
>
> In a chromium-aqua complex, the H_2O ligands can be exchanged with OH^- ligands without any change in coordination number or shape because the ligands are similar sizes.
>
> $$[Cr(H_2O)_6]^{3+}{}_{(aq)} + 6OH^-{}_{(aq)} \rightarrow [Cr(OH)_6]^{3-}{}_{(aq)} + 6H_2O_{(l)}$$
>
>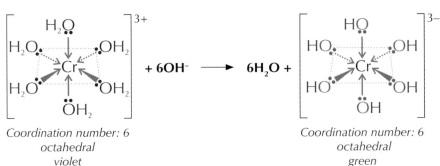
>
> Coordination number: 6   Coordination number: 6
> octahedral   octahedral
> violet   green

Substitution of different sized ligands

If the ligands are different sizes there's a change of coordination number and a change of shape.

- Complex ions with a coordination number of four are usually tetrahedral.
- Complex ions with a coordination number of six are usually octahedral.

Examples

In a copper-aqua complex, the H_2O ligands can be exchanged with Cl^- ligands. The shape of the complex changes from octahedral to tetrahedral because fewer of the larger Cl^- ligands can fit around the central metal ion. There is also a colour change during this reaction.

$$[Cu(H_2O)_6]^{2+}_{(aq)} + 4Cl^-_{(aq)} \rightleftharpoons [CuCl_4]^{2-}_{(aq)} + 6H_2O_{(l)}$$

Tip: You can add Cl^- ions to a solution by adding hydrochloric acid (HCl).

Coordination number: 6
octahedral
pale blue

+ 4Cl⁻ ⟶ 6H₂O +

Coordination number: 4
tetrahedral
yellow-green

In a cobalt-aqua complex, the H_2O ligands can be exchanged with the larger Cl^- ligands. The shape of the complex changes from octahedral to tetrahedral and there is also a colour change (see Figure 1).

$$[Co(H_2O)_6]^{2+}_{(aq)} + 4Cl^-_{(aq)} \rightleftharpoons [CoCl_4]^{2-}_{(aq)} + 6H_2O_{(l)}$$

Figure 1: The flask on the left contains pale blue $[Cu(H_2O)_6]^{2+}$ ions, the flask on the right contains $[CuCl_4]^{2-}$ ions.

Coordination number: 6
octahedral
pink

+ 4Cl⁻ ⟶ 6H₂O +

Coordination number: 4
tetrahedral
blue

For this process, the forward reaction is endothermic, so the equilibrium can be shifted to the right-hand side by heating. The equilibrium will also shift to the right if you add more concentrated hydrochloric acid. Adding water to this equilibrium shifts it back to the left.

Tip: You'll only be asked about a few types of ligand in the exam so try to remember that H_2O, NH_3 and OH^- ligands are about the same size but Cl^- ions are a lot larger.

Partial substitution of ligands

Sometimes the substitution is only partial — not all of the six H_2O ligands are substituted.

Tip: In partial ligand substitution reactions of octahedral complexes either 1, 2, 3, 4 or 5 ligands are substituted during the reaction.

Examples

In a copper-aqua complex, some of the H_2O ligands can be exchanged with NH_3 ligands whilst some H_2O ligands remain where they are.

In this example, four of the H_2O ligands are substituted with NH_3 ligands. The shape of the complex changes from octahedral to elongated octahedral and there is also a colour change.

$$[Cu(H_2O)_6]^{2+}_{(aq)} + 4NH_{3(aq)} \rightarrow [Cu(NH_3)_4(H_2O)_2]^{2+}_{(aq)} + 4H_2O_{(l)}$$

octahedral　　　　*elongated octahedral*
pale blue　　　　　*deep blue*

Tip: In the example on the left you only get trans-[Cu(NH₃)₄(H₂O)₂]²⁺ when an <u>excess</u> of NH_3 is added. Otherwise you get [Cu(H₂O)₄(OH)₂] (a blue precipitate) instead.

In an iron(III)-aqua complex, some of the H_2O ligands can be exchanged with SCN^- ligands whilst some of them remain where they are.

In this example, one of the H_2O ligands is exchanged with an SCN^- ligand. The shape of the complex changes from octahedral to distorted octahedral and there is also a colour change.

$$[Fe(H_2O)_6]^{3+}_{(aq)} + SCN^-_{(aq)} \rightarrow [Fe(H_2O)_5SCN]^{2+}_{(aq)} + H_2O_{(l)}$$

octahedral
pale violet when pure
(but it usually looks yellow)

distorted octahedral
blood red

Haem and haemoglobin

Haemoglobin is a protein found in blood that helps to transport oxygen around the body. It contains Fe^{2+} ions, which are hexa-coordinated — six lone pairs are donated to them to form six coordinate bonds. Four of the lone pairs come from nitrogen atoms, which form a circle around the Fe^{2+}. This part of the molecule is called haem. The molecule that the four nitrogen atoms are part of is a multidentate ligand called a **porphyrin**. A protein called a globin and either an oxygen or a water molecule also bind to the Fe^{2+} ion to form an octahedral structure — see Figure 2.

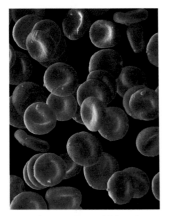

Figure 3: Red blood cells are packed full of haemoglobin.

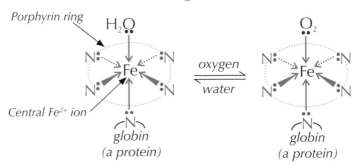

Figure 2: The structure of haemoglobin when it is bound to oxygen or water.

Tip: When the Fe^{2+} ion is bound to water the complex is called deoxyhaemoglobin and when it's bound to oxygen it's called oxyhaemoglobin.

In the body, both water and oxygen will bind to the Fe^{2+} ions as ligands, so the complex can transport oxygen to where it's needed, and then swap it for a water molecule — here's how it works:

▪ In the lungs, where the oxygen concentration is high, water ligands are substituted for oxygen molecules to form oxyhaemoglobin, which is carried around the body in the blood.

▪ When the oxyhaemoglobin gets to a place where oxygen is needed, the oxygen molecules are exchanged for water molecules. The haemoglobin then returns to the lungs and the whole process starts again.

The process of oxygen transport is summarised in Figure 5 (on the next page).

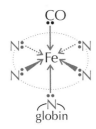

Figure 4: Carboxyhaemoglobin.

Carbon monoxide poisoning

When carbon monoxide is inhaled, the haemoglobin can substitute its water ligands for carbon monoxide ligands, forming carboxyhaemoglobin (Figure 4). This is bad news because carbon monoxide forms a very strong bond with the Fe^{2+} ion and doesn't readily exchange with oxygen or water ligands, meaning the haemoglobin can't transport oxygen any more. Carbon monoxide poisoning starves the organs of oxygen — it can cause headaches, dizziness, unconsciousness and even death if it's not treated.

Summary of the oxygen transport process

Here's an overview of how haemoglobin transports oxygen round the body:

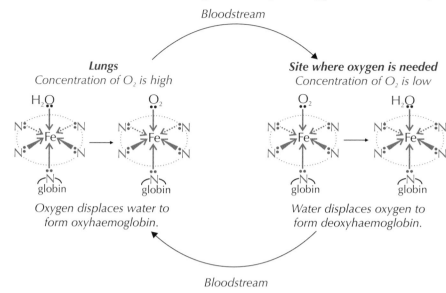

Figure 5: The role of haemoglobin in the transport of oxygen around the body.

Practice Questions — Fact Recall

Q1 State whether the colour, coordination number and/or the shape of the complex ion changes in the following situations.

a) Ligand exchange of similarly sized ligands.

b) Ligand exchange of differently sized ligands.

Q2 The H_2O ligands in $[Co(H_2O)_6]^{2+}$ can be exchanged for other ligands. Predict the shape of the complex ions formed after the following substitutions:

a) All the H_2O ligands exchanged for NH_3 ligands.

b) The six H_2O ligands exchanged for four Cl^- ligands.

Q3 a) Write an equation for the formation of $[CuCl_4]^{2-}$ from a hexa-aqua copper(II) ion and chloride ions.

b) State the colour change that occurs during this reaction.

Q4 The metal-aqua ion $[Cu(H_2O)_6]^{2+}$ will undergo a ligand substitution reaction with excess ammonia to form $[Cu(NH_3)_4(H_2O)_2]^{2+}$.

a) Write an equation for this reaction.

b) State the shape of $[Cu(NH_3)_4(H_2O)_2]^{2+}$.

Q5 a) What is the role of haemoglobin in the body?

b) Where do the six coordinate bonds come from in haemoglobin?

Q6 Haemoglobin is found in red blood cells.

a) Explain what happens to haemoglobin in the lungs.

b) Explain what happens to haemoglobin at sites where oxygen is needed.

Q7 Explain why carbon monoxide is toxic.

Figure 6: The reaction between $Cu^{2+}_{(aq)}$ ions and excess ammonia. A $[Cu(NH_3)_4(H_2O)_2]^{2+}$ complex ion is formed which has a deep blue colour.

- Know that the stability constant, K_{stab}, of a complex ion is the equilibrium constant for the formation of the complex ion in a solvent from its constituent ions.

- Be able to deduce expressions for the stability constant, K_{stab}, of a ligand substitution, e.g. $M^{2+}_{(aq)} + 6X^-_{(aq)} \rightleftharpoons MX_6^{4-}_{(aq)}$ where $K_{stab} = [MX_6^{4-}_{(aq)}]/[M^{2+}_{(aq)}][X^-_{(aq)}]^6$.

- Be able to relate ligand substitution reactions of complexes to stability constants and understand that a large K_{stab} results in formation of a stable complex ion.

Specification Reference 5.3.1

Tip: If you want a reminder of just how equilibrium constants work, have a look back at pages 124-126.

Tip: The square brackets in the K_{stab} expression mean 'the concentrations of the ions'. Don't mix them up with the square brackets you'd use in the formula of a complex ion — they just keep everything together.

6. Stability Constants

All complex ions have a stability constant. This stability constant tells you how likely the formation of the ion is. The higher the stability constant, the more stable the complex ion and the more likely that the ion will form. Easy...

What is a stability constant?

The stability constant of a complex ion is just what it sounds like — it tells you how stable a complex ion is in solution. Here's the official definition:

> The stability constant, K_{stab}, of a complex ion is the equilibrium constant for the formation of the complex ion from its constituent ions in solution.

Like the equilibrium constant, K_c, K_{stab} is worked out from the concentrations of the reactants and the products after equilibrium is reached.

Finding the stability constant

To write an expression for the stability constant of a complex ion, you first need to write down the equation for the formation of the complex ion in solution. Remember to make sure the equation is balanced. K_{stab} is the concentration of the products divided by the concentration of the reactants. If there's more than one mole of a particular ion in the equation put the number of moles of ions as a power to the right of the square brackets.

--- Examples ---

Write an expression for the stability constant for the formation of the complex ion $[Fe(CN)_6]^{4-}$.

Here is the equation for the formation of this ion in solution:

$$Fe^{2+}_{(aq)} + 6CN^-_{(aq)} \rightleftharpoons [Fe(CN)_6]^{4-}_{(aq)}$$

And here is the expression for the stability constant:

product ion

$$K_{stab} = \frac{[[Fe(CN)_6]^{4-}]}{[Fe^{2+}][CN^-]^6}$$

reactant ions

There are six moles of CN^- ions in the balanced formation equation so you need to put a 6 to the top right of the square brackets.

Write an expression for the stability constant for the formation of the complex ion $[CoCl_4]^{2-}$.

Here is the equation for the formation of this ion in solution:

$$Co^{2+}_{(aq)} + 4Cl^-_{(aq)} \rightleftharpoons [CoCl_4]^{2-}_{(aq)}$$

And here is the expression for the stability constant:

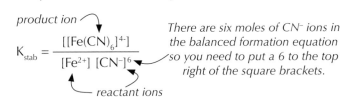

product ion

$$K_{stab} = \frac{[[CoCl_4]^{2-}]}{[Co^{2+}][Cl^-]^4}$$

reactant ions

There are four moles of Cl^- ions so you need to put a 4 here.

The stability constant of ligand substitution reactions

All ligand substitution reactions are reversible — so you can write a ligand substitution reaction as an equilibrium. The equilibrium constant will also be the stability constant, or K_{stab}, for this ligand substitution reaction.

If the complex that you start with only has water ligands, don't include $[H_2O]$ in the stability constant expression. Since all the ions are in solution, there's so much water around that the few extra molecules produced don't alter its concentration much — it's practically constant.

┌─ **Example** ─────────────────

Write an expression for the stability constant, K_{stab}, of the following ligand substitution reaction:

$$[Cu(H_2O)_6]^{2+}_{(aq)} + 4Cl^-_{(aq)} \rightleftharpoons [CuCl_4]^{2-}_{(aq)} + 6H_2O_{(l)}$$

So the stability constant for this reaction is:

$$K_{stab} = \frac{[[CuCl_4]^{2-}]}{[[Cu(H_2O)_6]^{2+}]\ [Cl^-]^4}$$

Remember that you don't need to include $[H_2O]$ in the expression.

─────────────────────────────

Predicting ligand substitution reactions

The size of the stability constant tells you how stable the new complex ion is, and how likely it is to form.

┌─ **Example** ─────────────────

The stability constant for the substitution reaction in the example above is 4.2×10^5 dm^{12} mol^{-4} at 291 K.

This is a large stability constant — which tells you that the $[CuCl_4]^{2-}$ complex ion is very stable. So if you add chloride ions to a solution containing $[Cu(H_2O)_6]^{2+}$ ions, it's very likely that a ligand substitution reaction will happen, and you'll end up with $[CuCl_4]^{2-}$ ions.

─────────────────────────────

Practice Questions — Application

Q1 Write an expression for the stability constant for the formation of the complex ion $[Cr(OH)_6]^{3-}$.

Q2 Write an expression for the stability constant for the formation of the complex ion $[Al(H_2O)_3(OH)_3]$.

Q3 a) Write an expression for the stability constant for this reaction:

$$[Co(H_2O)_6]^{2+} + 6NH_{3(aq)} \rightarrow [Co(NH_3)_6]^{2+} + 6H_2O_{(l)}$$

    b) The stability constant for this reaction is 2.45×10^4 dm^{18} mol^{-6} at 303 K. The stability constant for the formation of $[Ni(NH_3)_6]^{2+}$ from $[Ni(H_2O)_6]^{2+}$ is 1.02×10^8 dm^{18} mol^{-6}. Which complex ion, $[Co(NH_3)_6]^{2+}$ or $[Ni(NH_3)_6]^{2+}$ is more stable? Explain your answer.

Practice Questions — Fact Recall

Q1 What is the stability constant, K_{stab}, of a complex ion?

Q2 Explain why you don't have to include water ligands in the stability constant expression.

Q3 What does the size of the stability constant tell you?

Tip: This applies to ligand formation reactions too — if there's loads of water around you don't have to include water in the expression for the stability constant.

Tip: If you included water in the equation it would look like this:

$$\frac{[[CuCl_4]^{2-}]\ [H_2O]^{loads\ +\ 6}}{[[Cu(H_2O)_6]^{2+}]\ [Cl^-]^4\ [H_2O]^{loads}}$$

The concentration of water ions on the top and the bottom cancel each other out.

Tip: It's difficult to say what a 'large' or a 'small' stability constant is, but don't worry — you're usually given another stability constant so you can compare the values.

- Be able to describe, using suitable examples, redox behaviour in transition elements.

- Know how to carry out redox titrations, and be able to carry out structured calculations, involving MnO_4^-.

- Be able to perform non-structured titration calculations, based on experimental results.

Specification Reference 5.3.1

7. Redox Reactions

You learnt all about redox reactions on pages 178-180 (and if you haven't, you should). But here's a nice topic all about how you can use redox reactions in experimental chemistry.

Oxidising and reducing agents

Transition elements can exist in many different **oxidation states** (see page 178). They can change oxidation state by gaining or losing electrons in redox reactions (see page 179). The ability to gain or lose electrons easily makes transition metal ions good oxidising or reducing agents.

Here are a couple of examples:

┌─ **Examples** ─────────────────────────────

The oxidation of Fe^{2+} to Fe^{3+} by manganate(VII) ions in solution

Acidified potassium manganate(VII) solution, $KMnO_{4(aq)}$, is used as an oxidising agent. It contains manganate(VII) ions (MnO_4^-), in which manganese has an oxidation state of +7. They can be reduced to Mn^{2+} ions during a redox reaction with Fe^{2+} ions.

Half equations:
$$MnO_4^- + 8H^+ + 5e^- \rightarrow Mn^{2+} + 4H_2O$$
$$5Fe^{2+} \rightarrow 5Fe^{3+} + 5e^-$$
$$\overline{MnO_4^- + 8H^+ + 5Fe^{2+} \rightarrow Mn^{2+} + 4H_2O + 5Fe^{3+}}$$

In this reaction the manganese is reduced and the iron is oxidised.

$MnO_{4\,(aq)}^-$ is purple and $[Mn(H_2O)_6]^{2+}_{(aq)}$ is colourless so, during this reaction, you'll see a colour change from purple to colourless.

Figure 1: The colour change seen during the reaction of potassium manganate(VII) solution with iron(II) ions. The solution goes from purple to colourless as the manganate(VII) ions are reduced to Mn^{2+} ions.

The oxidation of Zn to Zn^{2+} by dichromate(VI) ions in solution.

Acidified potassium dichromate(VI) solution, $K_2Cr_2O_{7(aq)}$, is another oxidising agent. It contains dichromate(VI) ions ($Cr_2O_7^{2-}$), in which chromium has an oxidation state of +6. They can be reduced to Cr^{3+} ions during a redox reaction with Zn metal.

Half equations:
$$Cr_2O_7^{2-} + 14H^+ + 6e^- \rightarrow 2Cr^{3+} + 7H_2O$$
$$3Zn \rightarrow 3Zn^{2+} + 6e^-$$
$$\overline{Cr_2O_7^{2-} + 14H^+ + 3Zn \rightarrow 2Cr^{3+} + 7H_2O + 3Zn^{2+}}$$

In this reaction the chromium is reduced and the zinc is oxidised.

$Cr_2O_7^{2-}{}_{(aq)}$ is orange and $[Cr(H_2O)_6]^{3+}_{(aq)}$ is violet but usually looks green so, during this reaction, you'll see a colour change from orange to green.

Figure 2: The colour change seen during the reaction of potassium dichromate(VI) solution with zinc. The solution goes from orange to green as the dichromate(VI) ions are reduced to Cr^{3+} ions.

The pretty colours of transition metal ion solutions make them really useful as indicators. The sharp colour changes let you know when a reaction has taken place. This characteristic of transition metal ions is especially useful in titrations, as you'll see on the next few pages...

Performing titrations

Titrations using transition element ions let you find out how much oxidising agent is needed to exactly react with a quantity of reducing agent — they're **redox titrations**. If you know the concentration of either the oxidising agent or the reducing agent, you can use the titration results to work out the concentration of the other.

Tip: You've already seen how to do an acid-base titration — that was covered on page 149.

- First you measure out a quantity of reducing agent, e.g. aqueous Fe^{2+} ions, using a pipette, and put it in a conical flask.

- Using a measuring cylinder, you add about 20 cm^3 of dilute sulfuric acid to the flask — this is an excess, so you don't have to be too exact. The acid is added to make sure there are plenty of H^+ ions to allow the oxidising agent to be reduced.

- Now you add the oxidising agent, e.g. aqueous potassium manganate(VII), to the reducing agent using a burette, swirling the conical flask as you go.

- The oxidising agent that you add reacts with the reducing agent. This reaction will continue until all of the reducing agent is used up.

Tip: You can also do titrations the other way round — adding the reducing agent to the oxidising agent.

- The very next drop you add to the flask will give the mixture the colour of the oxidising agent. (You could use a coloured reducing agent and a colourless oxidising agent instead — then you'd be watching for the moment that the colour in the flask disappears.)

- Stop when the mixture in the flask just becomes tainted with the colour of the oxidising agent (the end point) and record the volume of the oxidising agent added. This is the rough titration.

- Now you do some accurate titrations. You need to do a few until you get two or more readings that are within 0.10 cm^3 of each other.

The equipment you'll need to do a titration is shown in Figure 3.

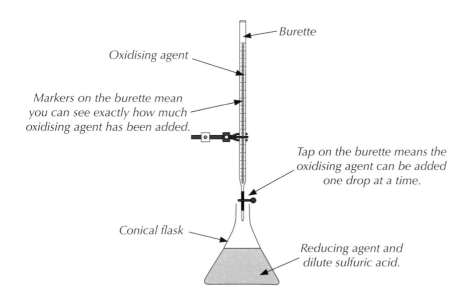

Burette

Oxidising agent

Markers on the burette mean you can see exactly how much oxidising agent has been added.

Tap on the burette means the oxidising agent can be added one drop at a time.

Conical flask

Reducing agent and dilute sulfuric acid.

Figure 3: The equipment needed to perform a redox titration.

Figure 4: A student reading a burette during a titration experiment.

Figure 5: *KMnO₄ being added to Fe²⁺ ions. The solution turns purple at the end point.*

Titrations using KMnO₄

Manganate(VII) ions (MnO_4^-) in aqueous potassium manganate(VII) ($KMnO_4$) are purple. When they're added to the reducing agent, they start reacting. This reaction will continue until all of the reducing agent is used up and the solution turns purple. The exact point at which the solution turns from colourless to purple is the end point of the reaction.

Calculating the concentration of a reagent

Once you've done a titration you can use your results to calculate the concentration of either the oxidising agent or the reducing agent. To do this:

Step 1: Write out a balanced equation for the redox reaction that's happening in the conical flask.

Step 2: Decide what you know already and what you need to know — usually you'll know the two volumes and the concentration of one of the reagents and want to find the concentration of the other reagent.

Step 3: For the reagent you know both the concentration and the volume for, calculate the number of moles of this reagent using the equation:

$$\text{moles} = \frac{\text{concentration (mol dm}^{-3}) \times \text{volume (cm}^3)}{1000}$$

Tip: These calculations are the same as the ones for acid-base titrations, which are covered on pages 153-154.

Step 4: Use the molar ratios in the balanced equation to find out how many moles of the other reagent were present in the solution.

Step 5: Calculate the unknown concentration using the equation:

$$\text{concentration (mol dm}^{-3}) = \frac{\text{moles} \times 1000}{\text{volume (cm}^3)}$$

Example

27.5 cm³ of 0.0200 mol dm⁻³ aqueous potassium manganate(VII) reacted with 25.0 cm³ of acidified iron(II) sulfate solution.
Calculate the concentration of Fe²⁺ ions in the solution.

1. The balanced equation for this titration reaction is:

$$MnO_{4\ (aq)}^- + 8H^+_{(aq)} + 5Fe^{2+}_{(aq)} \rightarrow Mn^{2+}_{(aq)} + 4H_2O_{(l)} + 5Fe^{3+}_{(aq)}$$

2. You know the concentration and the volume of the MnO_4^- ion solution (0.0200 mol dm⁻³ and 27.5 cm³) and the volume of the Fe²⁺ solution (25.0 cm³). You need to know the concentration of the Fe²⁺ solution.

3. Work out the number of moles of MnO_4^- ions added to the flask.

$$\text{moles } MnO_4^- = \frac{\text{conc.} \times \text{volume}}{1000} = \frac{0.0200 \times 27.5}{1000} = 5.50 \times 10^{-4} \text{ moles}$$

4. From the molar ratios in the equation, you know 1 mole of MnO_4^- reacts with 5 moles of Fe²⁺. So 5.50 × 10⁻⁴ moles of MnO_4^- must react with (5.50 × 10⁻⁴) × 5 = 2.75 × 10⁻³ moles of Fe²⁺.

Tip: In these calculations the units of concentration should always be mol dm⁻³.

5. Calculate the concentration of Fe²⁺:

$$\text{conc. } Fe^{2+} = \frac{\text{moles} \times 1000}{\text{volume}} = \frac{(2.75 \times 10^{-3}) \times 1000}{25.0} = \textbf{0.110 mol dm}^{-3}$$

Practice Questions — Application

Q1 28.3 cm³ of a 0.0500 mol dm⁻³ acidified iron(II) sulfate solution reacted exactly with 30.0 cm³ of aqueous potassium manganate(VII).

  a) Write down the ionic equation for the reaction between Fe^{2+} ions and MnO_4^- ions.

  b) Calculate the number of moles of acidified iron(II) sulfate solution that reacted with the aqueous potassium manganate(VII).

  c) Calculate the concentration of the potassium manganate(VII) solution.

Exam Tip
These questions are quite wordy. You might find it helpful to highlight the key bits of information in the question.

Q2 Aqueous potassium manganate(VII) with a concentration of 0.0750 mol dm⁻³ was used to completely react with 28.0 cm³ of a 0.600 mol dm⁻³ solution of acidified iron(II) sulfate. Calculate the volume of potassium manganate(VII) solution that reacted.

Q3 22.5 cm³ of 0.150 mol dm⁻³ aqueous potassium dichromate(VI) was needed to completely react with 20.0 cm³ of an acidified iron(II) sulfate solution.

  a) Write down the balanced ionic equation for the reaction between Fe^{2+} ions and $Cr_2O_7^{2-}$ ions.

  b) Calculate the number of moles of aqueous potassium dichromate(VI) that reacted with the acidified iron(II) sulfate solution.

  c) Calculate the concentration of Fe^{2+} ions in the solution.

Q4 A 0.450 mol dm⁻³ solution of acidified iron(II) sulfate completely reacted with 24.0 cm³ of a 0.0550 mol dm⁻³ solution of aqueous potassium dichromate(VI). Calculate the volume of iron(II) sulfate solution used.

Q5 A lump of zinc metal was dropped into 30.0 cm³ of a 0.230 mol dm⁻³ solution of acidified dichromate(VI) ions.

  a) Write an equation for this reaction.

  b) Calculate the number of moles of dichromate(VI) ions present in the solution.

  c) The lump of zinc fully dissolved in the solution. Calculate the mass of zinc that was added to the solution. Assume that all of the acidified dichromate(VI) solution reacted. (You will need to use the equation mass = moles × M_r).

Tip: Question 5 is a bit different because there's a solid and a solution involved. But you still start your calculations by following the same steps.

Practice Questions — Fact Recall

Q1 Give an example of an oxidising agent.

Q2 Why is acid added to the reducing agent in redox titrations?

Q3 How do you know when you've reached the end point of a titration?

Learning Objectives:

- Know how to carry out redox titrations, and be able to carry out structured calculations, involving $I_2/S_2O_3^{2-}$.
- Be able to perform non-structured titration calculations, based on experimental results.

Specification Reference 5.3.1

Exam Tip
If you have to write out these equations in the exam make sure they're <u>balanced</u>. You'll lose easy marks if they're not.

Exam Tip
Make sure you learn this equation for the exam.

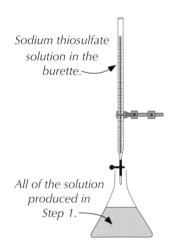

Sodium thiosulfate solution in the burette.

All of the solution produced in Step 1.

Figure 1: *The apparatus used to perform an iodine-sodium thiosulfate titration.*

Tip: The molar ratio is the ratio of one ion (or compound to another ion (or compound) in the balanced equation.

8. More Titrations

More titrations... hurrah. As well as knowing all about acid-base titrations (pages 149-154) and MnO_4^- titrations (pages 215-216) you also need to know about iodine-sodium thiosulfate titrations. Keeeeep learning...

Iodine-sodium thiosulfate titrations

Iodine-sodium thiosulfate titrations are a way of finding the amount of iodine in a solution. If the iodine has been formed in a redox reaction, knowing the amount of iodine allows you to work out the amount of other substances involved in the reaction too — for example, the amount of oxidising agent present. So here's how you can find out the concentration of a solution of the oxidising agent potassium iodate(V):

Step 1: Oxidise the iodide ions to iodine

Measure out a certain volume of potassium iodate(V) solution (KIO_3) (the oxidising agent) — say 25 cm³. Add this to an excess of acidified potassium iodide solution (KI). The iodate(V) ions in the potassium iodate(V) solution oxidise some of the iodide ions to iodine — the solution will be bright yellow.

$$IO_3^-{}_{(aq)} + 5I^-{}_{(aq)} + 6H^+{}_{(aq)} \rightarrow 3I_2{}_{(aq)} + 3H_2O_{(l)}$$

Step 2: Titrate the iodine solution with sodium thiosulfate

You need to titrate the solution formed in step 1 with sodium thiosulfate ($Na_2S_2O_3$) of a known concentration. The iodine in the solution reacts with thiosulfate ions like this:

$$I_2{}_{(aq)} + 2S_2O_3^{2-}{}_{(aq)} \rightarrow 2I^-{}_{(aq)} + S_4O_6^{2-}{}_{(aq)}$$

Here's how you do the titration:

- Take the flask containing the solution that was produced in Stage 1.
- From a burette, add sodium thiosulfate solution to the flask drop by drop.
- It's hard to see the end point, so when the iodine colour fades to a pale yellow, add 2 cm³ of starch solution (to detect the presence of iodine). The solution in the conical flask will go dark blue, showing there's still some iodine there.
- Add sodium thiosulfate one drop at a time until the blue colour disappears.
- When this happens, it means all the iodine has just been reacted.
- Jot down the volume of sodium thiosulfate added to the solution.

Step 3: Calculate the number of moles of iodine present

To do this you need to:

- Calculate the number of moles of thiosulfate ions used in the titration.
- Then use the 1 : 2 molar ratio of $I_2 : S_2O_3^{2-}$ in the balanced equation for the reaction to work out how many moles of iodine were present in the solution.

Step 4: Calculate the concentration of the oxidising agent

This bit's the same as the last few steps for an acid-base titration (see page 153).

- Use the 3 : 1 molar ratio of $I_2 : IO_3^-$ from the balanced equation in step 1 to work out how many moles of potassium iodate(V) were present in the solution.
- You can then use this to work out the concentration of potassium iodate(V).

25.0 cm³ of potassium iodate(V) solution was added to an excess of acidified potassium iodide. This solution was then titrated against a 0.120 mol dm⁻³ solution of sodium thiosulfate. 11.1 cm³ of thiosulfate solution was required to react fully with the solution. Find the concentration of the potassium iodate(V) solution.

Because you're given the titration data in the question you can start at step 3 for this one:

First calculate the number of moles of thiosulfate ions used in the titration...

$$\text{Number of moles of thiosulfate} = \frac{\text{concentration} \times \text{volume (cm}^3)}{1000}$$

$$= \frac{0.120 \times 11.1}{1000}$$

$$= 1.33 \times 10^{-3} \text{ moles}$$

Figure 2: *Titrating iodine with sodium thiosulfate.*

Then use the balanced equation and the molar ratio to calculate the number of moles of iodine in the solution.

Balanced equation: $I_2 + 2S_2O_3^{2-} \rightarrow 2I^- + S_4O_6^{2-}$

1 mole of iodine reacts with 2 moles of thiosulfate. So,
Number of moles of iodine in the solution = $1.33 \times 10^{-3} \div 2$

$$= 6.65 \times 10^{-4} \text{ moles}$$

Step 4... Use the balanced equation from step 1 and the molar ratio to calculate the number of moles of potassium iodate(V) present in the solution.

Balanced equation: $IO_3^-{}_{(aq)} + 5I^-{}_{(aq)} + 6H^+{}_{(aq)} \rightarrow 3I_{2\,(aq)} + 3H_2O$

25.0 cm³ of potassium iodate(V) solution produced 6.65×10^{-4} moles of iodine. The equation shows that one mole of iodate(V) ions will produce three moles of iodine.

That means there must have been $(6.65 \times 10^{-4}) \div 3 = 2.22 \times 10^{-4}$ moles of iodate(V) ions in the original solution. So now it's straightforward to find the concentration of the potassium iodate(V) solution, which is what you're after:

$$\text{Number of moles of iodate(V) ions} = \frac{\text{concentration} \times \text{volume (cm}^3)}{1000}$$

$$2.22 \times 10^{-4} = \frac{\text{concentration} \times 25.0}{1000}$$

$$\text{concentration of } KIO_3 = \mathbf{0.00888 \text{ mol dm}^{-3}}$$

Tip: Don't forget that in step 3 and step 4 you are using different balanced equations and different molar ratios. First you need to calculate the number of moles of iodine then you can use this information to calculate the moles of iodate(V) ions.

Tip: Remember:
moles = conc. × vol (dm³)

Tip: Always remember to give units with your answer. It'd be crazy to get through all those steps just to lose marks 'cause you didn't put down your units.

You don't have to use potassium iodate(V) solution (KIO₃) as the oxidising agent for this reaction — the method works the same way with any oxidising agent.

Practice Questions — Application

Q1 13.2 cm³ of potassium iodate(V) solution was added to an excess of acidified potassium iodide. This solution was then titrated against a 0.200 mol dm⁻³ solution of sodium thiosulfate. 41.1 cm³ of thiosulfate solution was required to react fully with the solution. Here's the equation for the titration: $I_{2(aq)} + 2Na_2S_2O_{3(aq)} \rightarrow 2NaI_{(aq)} + Na_2S_4O_{6(aq)}$

a) Calculate the number of moles of sodium thiosulfate used in the reaction.

b) Calculate the number of moles of iodine formed by adding the potassium iodate(V) solution to the acidified potassium iodide.

c) Work out the number of moles of potassium iodate present.

d) Work out the concentration of the potassium iodate(V) solution used in this experiment.

Tip: These questions are pretty calculation heavy, so if you find yourself struggling have a look back at pages 153 and 218 for a quick recap.

Q2 39.0 cm³ of potassium manganate(VII) solution was added to 61.0 cm³ (an excess) of acidified potassium iodide. 25.0 cm³ of this solution was then titrated against a 0.750 mol dm⁻³ solution of sodium thiosulfate. 4.00 cm³ of thiosulfate solution was required to react fully with the solution. Here are the reactions that occur in this experiment:

$$2MnO_4^-{}_{(aq)} + 10I^-{}_{(aq)} + 16H^+{}_{(aq)} \rightarrow 5I_{2\,(aq)} + 8H_2O_{\,(l)} + 2Mn^{2+}{}_{(aq)}$$

$$I_{2(aq)} + 2Na_2S_2O_{3(aq)} \rightarrow 2NaI_{(aq)} + Na_2S_4O_{6(aq)}$$

a) Calculate the number of moles of sodium thiosulfate used in the reaction.

b) Calculate the total number of moles of iodine formed by adding the potassium manganate(VII) solution to the acidified potassium iodide.

c) Work out the concentration of the potassium manganate(VII) solution used in this experiment.

Exam Tip
In the exam you could be asked to complete a calculation like this one step at a time, or you could be dumped in at the deep end and asked to do the whole calculation in one go (like in Q3). So you need to be really clear on how to work them through.

Q3 15.0 cm³ of potassium dichromate(VI) solution was added to an excess of acidified potassium iodide. This solution was then titrated against a 0.0600 mol dm⁻³ solution of sodium thiosulfate. If 22.3 cm³ of sodium thiosulfate solution was required to react fully with the solution, what was the concentration of the potassium dichromate(VI) solution?

Here are the equations for the two steps of the experiment:

$$Cr_2O_7^{2-}{}_{(aq)} + 6I^-{}_{(aq)} + 14H^+{}_{(aq)} \rightarrow 2Cr^{3+}{}_{(aq)} + 3I_{2\,(aq)} + 7H_2O$$

$$I_2 + 2S_2O_3^{2-} \rightarrow 2I^- + S_4O_6^{2-}$$

Practice Questions — Fact Recall

Q1 Write out the ionic equation for a reaction between iodate(V) ions, and acidified potassium iodide solution.

Q2 Write down the ionic equation for the reaction between iodine and thiosulfate ions.

Q3 Describe how you would carry out a titration between an iodine solution and sodium thiosulfate.

Section Summary

Make sure you know...

- That transition elements are d-block elements that have an ion with an incomplete d sub-shell.
- That the elements Ti–Cu are transition elements
- How to work out the electron configurations of atoms and ions of the d-block elements of Period 4 (Sc–Zn).
- Why scandium and zinc aren't transition elements.
- That transition elements can form complex ions.
- That transition elements can form coloured ions.
- That transition elements have variable oxidation states.
- That transition elements make great catalysts because of their variable oxidation states.
- The common colours of different transition metal ions and their oxidation states.
- The ionic equations for the precipitation reactions of $Cu^{2+}_{(aq)}$, $Co^{2+}_{(aq)}$, $Fe^{2+}_{(aq)}$ and $Fe^{3+}_{(aq)}$ with aqueous sodium hydroxide.
- The colour change that happens when $Cu^{2+}_{(aq)}$, $Co^{2+}_{(aq)}$, $Fe^{2+}_{(aq)}$ and $Fe^{3+}_{(aq)}$ react with aqueous sodium hydroxide.
- What complex ions are.
- That a ligand is an atom, ion or molecule that can form coordinate bonds with a central metal ion.
- What coordination numbers are.
- What bidentate ligands are and that $NH_2CH_2CH_2NH_2$ (en) is a bidentate ligand.
- Examples of complexes with a coordination number of six and an octahedral shape.
- Examples of complexes with a coordination number of four and a tetrahedral or square-planar shape.
- That complexes such as $[Ni(en)_3]^{2+}$ can show optical isomerism.
- That complexes such as $Ni(NH_3)_2Cl_2$ can show cis-trans isomerism.
- That cis-platin is used as an anti-cancer drug and how it works.
- That ligands can be substituted for one another in ligand substitution reactions.
- The ligand substitution reactions and the colour changes for the formation of $[Cu(NH_3)_4(H_2O)_2]^{2+}$ and $[CuCl_4]^{2-}$ from $[Cu(H_2O)_6]^{2+}$.
- The ligand substitution reaction and the colour change for the formation of $[CoCl_4]^{2-}$ from $[Co(H_2O)_6]^{2+}$.
- How the iron in haemoglobin allows oxygen to be transported around the body.
- Why the ligand substitution of carbon monoxide for oxygen or water in haemoglobin is so dangerous.
- That the stability constant, K_{stab}, of a complex ion is the equilibrium constant for the formation of the complex ion from its constituent ions in solution.
- How to write expressions for the stability constant, K_{stab}, of ligand formation reactions.
- How to write expressions for the stability constant, K_{stab}, of ligand substitution reactions.
- That a large K_{stab} results in the formation of a stable complex ion and if a ligand substitution reaction has a large K_{stab} then the reaction is very likely to occur.
- That transition elements can undergo redox reactions.
- How to carry out redox titrations involving the manganate(VII) ion (MnO_4^-).
- How to carry out iodine-sodium thiosulfate ($I_2/S_2O_3^{2-}$) redox titrations.
- How to perform calculations based on experimental titration results.

Exam-style Questions

1   Brass is an alloy of mainly copper and zinc. The percentage composition of copper in brass can be determined using an iodine-sodium thiosulfate titration because the copper ion (Cu^{2+}) is an oxidising agent.

(a)   The first step of the experiment is to dissolve the brass in acid. The resulting solution contains aqueous copper ions.

    (i)   What colour is the aqueous Cu^{2+} ion?

(1 mark)

    (ii)   Write down the electronic configuration of the copper atom and the Cu^{2+} ion.

(2 marks)

    (iii)   Explain why the Cu^{2+} ion has the chemical properties associated with transition metal elements.

(1 mark)

(b)   In the solution the $[Cu(H_2O)_6]^{2+}$ complex ion forms.

    (i)   In this complex ion, water acts as a ligand. Explain the meaning of the term ligand.

(1 mark)

    (ii)   Draw the 3D structure of $[Cu(H_2O)_6]^{2+}$ and state its shape.

(2 marks)

    (iii)   What is the coordination number of this ion?

(1 mark)

(c)   1.00 g of brass was dissolved and added to an excess of acidified potassium iodide solution. The equation for the reaction that took place is shown below.

$$2Cu^{2+}_{(aq)} + 4I^-_{(aq)} \rightarrow 2CuI_{(aq)} + I_{2\,(aq)}$$

    This solution was then titrated against sodium thiosulfate. The equation for this reaction is shown below.

$$I_{2\,(aq)} + 2S_2O_3^{2-}{}_{(aq)} \rightarrow 2I^-_{(aq)} + S_4O_6^{2-}{}_{(aq)}$$

    It took 23.6 cm^3 of 0.500 mol dm^{-3} sodium thiosulfate solution to reach the end point of the reaction.

    (i)   Describe how you would perform the titration part of the experiment.

    In your answer you should make it clear what type of specialist laboratory equipment you are using in each step.

(5 marks)

    (ii)   Use the information given above to calculate the number of moles of Cu^{2+} ions present in the brass solution.

(3 marks)

    (iii)   Work out the percentage composition by mass of copper in the 1 g sample of brass.

(2 marks)

2   Many complex ions exist as stereoisomers.

(a) $[Co(NH_3)_2Cl_2]$ exists as two stereoisomers.

    (i)   Give the shape of the $[Co(NH_3)_2Cl_2]$ ion.

(1 mark)

    (ii) What type of stereoisomerism does $[Co(NH_3)_2Cl_2]$ exhibit?

(1 mark)

    (iii) Draw the two possible stereoisomers of $[Co(NH_3)_2Cl_2]$.

(2 marks)

(b)   The ethanedioate ion is a bidentate ligand. When it binds to chromium(III) ions it forms a complex ion with stereoisomers. The structure of the ethanedioate ion is shown below.

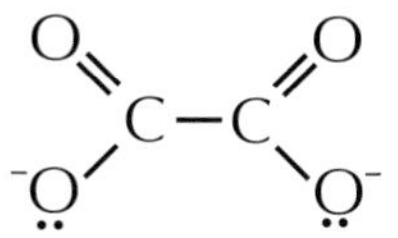

Ethanedioate ion

    (i)   What type of stereoisomerism does $[Cr(C_2O_4)_3]^{3-}$ exhibit?

(1 mark)

    (ii) Describe how the ethanedioate ion bonds to the chromium ion.

(2 marks)

    (iii) Draw two stereoisomers of $[Cr(C_2O_4)_3]^{3-}$.
          You can simplify the structure of the ethanedioate ion if you wish.

(2 marks)

(c)   Cisplatin ($[Pt(NH_3)_2Cl_2]$) is another complex that exhibits stereoisomerism.

    (i)   Explain how cisplatin works as an anticancer drug.

(2 marks)

    (ii) Use your knowledge of how cisplatin works to give one disadvantage of using cisplatin.

(1 mark)

3   A solution of VO^{2+} ions was titrated against acidified potassium manganate(VII) to determine the concentration of VO^{2+} ions in the solution. The equation for the reaction is shown below:

$$MnO_4^- + H_2O + 5VO^{2+} \rightarrow Mn^{2+} + 5VO_2^+ + 2H^+$$

(a)   Write down the oxidation states of vanadium in the VO^{2+} and VO_2^+ ions.

(2 marks)

(b) (i) What has been reduced in this titration?

(1 mark)

    (ii) What has been oxidised in this titration?

(1 mark)

(c)   14.2 cm^3 of a 0.0500 mol dm^{-3} solution of potassium manganate(VII) reacted with 20.0 cm^3 of the VO^{2+} solution during the titration.
    Calculate the concentration of VO^{2+} ions found in the original solution.

(3 marks)

4 Fe^{2+} is a transition element ion that can undergo a wide variety of reactions.

(a)   What is a transition element?

(1 mark)

(b) $Fe^{2+}_{(aq)}$ can react with sodium hydroxide to form a precipitate.
   (i)   Write down the ionic equation for this reaction.

(1 mark)

   (ii)   What colour is the precipitate?

(1 mark)

(c) Fe^{2+} can combine with ligands to form complex ions.
   (i)   What is a complex ion?

(1 mark)

   (ii)   Write an equation for the reaction between $Fe^{2+}_{(aq)}$ and $Cl^-_{(aq)}$ to form a tetrahedral complex.

(2 marks)

   (iii)   Draw the structure of the complex ion formed in part **(c) (ii)**.

(1 mark)

(d)   The hexaaqua iron(II) ion ($[Fe(H_2O)_6]^{2+}$) will react with six CN^- ions in a ligand substitution reaction.
   (i)   Write down the equation for this reaction.

(1 mark)

   (ii)   State whether you expect the coordination number, shape and/or colour of the complex ion to change during this reaction. Explain your answer

(3 marks)

(e)   The Fe^{2+} ion has an important role in haemoglobin as an oxygen carrier.
   (i)   Describe how ligand substitution reactions are used in the body to transport oxygen.

(2 marks)

   (ii)   Explain what happens to haemoglobin when carbon monoxide is inhaled. Why is this dangerous?

(2 marks)

(f)   The stability constants for two reactions of Fe^{2+} ions are shown below.

A: $[Fe(H_2O)_6]^{2+} + OH^- \rightarrow [Fe(OH)(H_2O)_5]^+ + H_2O$ $K_{stab} = 5.01 \times 10^5 \ dm^3 \ mol^{-3}$

B: $[Fe(H_2O)_6]^{2+} + EDTA^{4-} \rightarrow [Fe(EDTA)]^{2-} + 6H_2O$ $K_{stab} = 2.00 \times 10^{14} \ dm^{18} \ mol^{-6}$

   (i)   Write out an expression for the stability constant of reaction **A**.

(2 marks)

   (ii)   Which reaction is more likely to occur? Explain your answer.

(2 marks)

Practical Skills in Chemistry

1. Variables and Data

When you're planning an experiment you need to think carefully about what things you're going to change, what things you're going to measure and how you're going to record your results.

Variables

You probably know this all off by heart but it's easy to get mixed up sometimes. So here's a quick recap. A **variable** is a quantity that has the potential to change, e.g. mass. There are two types of variable commonly referred to in experiments:

Independent variable — the thing that you change in an experiment.

Dependent variable — the thing that you measure in an experiment.

Tip: When drawing graphs, the dependent variable should go on the y-axis, the independent variable on the x-axis.

Example

You could investigate the effect of temperature on rate of reaction using the apparatus in Figure 1 below:

Thermometer — to check the temperature of the reaction mixture.

Gas syringe — to measure the volume of gas given off over time.

Figure 1: *Apparatus for measuring the rate of reaction.*

- The independent variable will be temperature.
- The dependent variable will be the volume of gas produced.
- All the other variables must be kept the same. These include the concentration and volume of solutions, mass of solids, pressure, the presence of a catalyst and the surface area of any solid reactants.

Types of data

Experiments always involve some sort of measurement to provide data. There are different types of data — and you need to know what they are.

1. Discrete data

You get discrete data by counting. E.g. the number of bubbles produced in a reaction would be discrete (see Figure 2). You can't have 1.25 bubbles. That'd be daft. Shoe size is another good example of a discrete variable.

Figure 2: *Zinc reacting with an acid. The number of bubbles produced is discrete data, but the volume of gas produced is continuous data.*

2. Continuous data

A continuous variable can have any value on a scale. For example, the volume of gas produced or the mass of products from a reaction. You can never measure the exact value of a continuous variable.

3. Categoric data

A categoric variable has values that can be sorted into categories. For example, the colours of solutions might be blue, red and green (see Figure 3). Or types of material might be wood, steel, glass.

4. Ordered (ordinal) data

Ordered data is similar to categoric, but the categories can be put in order. For example, if you classify reactions as 'slow', 'fairly fast' and 'very fast' you'd have ordered data.

Figure 3: *Different coloured solutions. Colour is a type of categoric data.*

Tables of data

Before you start your experiment, make a table to write your results in. You'll need to repeat each test at least three times to check your results are reliable (see page 229 for more on reliable results). Figure 4 (below) is the sort of table you might end up with when you investigate the effect of temperature on reaction rate. (You'd then have to do the same thing at other temperatures.)

Tip: To find the average of each set of repeated measurements you need to add them all up and divide by how many there are.

For example, for the average volume of gas evolved after 10 s, it's:

$8 + 7 + 8 ÷ 3 = 7.7$ cm³

Temperature	Time (s)	Volume of gas evolved (cm³) Run 1	Volume of gas evolved (cm³) Run 2	Volume of gas evolved (cm³) Run 3	Average volume of gas evolved (cm³)
20 °C	10	8	7	8	**7.7**
	20	17	19	20	**18.7**
	30	28	20	30	**29**

Figure 4: *Table of results showing the effect of temperature on the rate of reaction.* See example below.

Watch out for **anomalous results**. These are ones that don't fit in with the other values and are likely to be wrong. They're usually due to random errors, such as making a mistake when measuring. You should ignore anomalous results when you calculate averages.

Tip: Just because you ignore anomalous results in your calculations you shouldn't ignore them in your write-up. Try to find an explanation for what went wrong so that it can be avoided in future experiments.

Example

Look at the table in Figure 4 again — the volume of gas evolved after 30 s in Run 2 looks like it might be an anomalous result. It's much lower than the values in the other two runs. It could have been caused by the syringe plunger getting stuck.

The anomalous result has been ignored when the average was calculated — that's why the average volume of gas evolved after 30 s is 29 cm³ ((28 + 30) ÷ 2 = 29), rather than 26 cm³ ((28 + 20 + 30) ÷ 3 = 26).

2. Graphs and Charts

You'll usually be expected to make a graph of your results. Graphs make your data easier to understand — so long as you choose the right type.

Types of graphs and charts

Bar charts

You should use a bar chart when one of your data sets is categoric or ordered data, as in Figure 1.

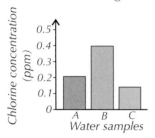

Figure 1: Bar chart to show chlorine concentration in water samples.

Pie charts

Pie charts are normally used to display categoric data, as in Figure 2.

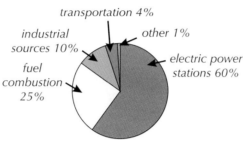

Figure 2: Pie chart to show sources of a country's sulfur dioxide emissions.

Line Graphs

Line graphs are best when you have two sets of continuous data, as in Figure 3. Volume of gas and time are both continuous variables — you could get any value on the x or y-axis.

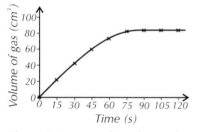

Figure 3: Line graph to show volume of gas evolved against time.

Scatter graphs

Scatter graphs, like Figure 4, are great for showing how two sets of data are related (or correlated — see below for more on correlation). Don't try to join all the points — draw a line of best fit to show the trend.

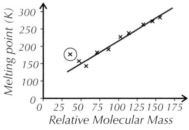

Figure 4: Scatter graph showing the relationship between M_r and melting point of some alcohols.

> **Tip:** Use simple scales when you draw graphs — this'll make it easier to plot points.

> **Tip:** Whatever type of graph you make, you'll only get full marks if you:
>
> 1. Choose a sensible scale — don't do a tiny graph in the corner of the paper.
>
> 2. Label both axes — including units.
>
> 3. Plot your points accurately — using a sharp pencil.

> **Tip:** A line of best fit should have about half of the points above it and half of the points below. You can ignore any anomalous points like the one circled in Figure 4.

Scatter graphs and correlation

Correlation describes the relationship between two variables — usually the independent one and the dependent one. Data can show positive correlation, negative correlation or no correlation (see Figure 5).

Positive correlation
As one variable increases the other also increases.

Negative correlation
As one variable increases the other decreases.

No correlation
There is no relationship between the variables.

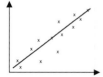

Figure 5: Scatter graphs showing positive, negative and no correlation.

> **Tip:** Computers can make it a lot quicker to collect, record and analyse big sets of data from experiments — but you've still got to understand what all the numbers and graphs they churn out mean.

3. Conclusions and Evaluations

Once you've got your results nicely presented in graphical form you can start to draw a conclusion. But be careful — you may have a graph showing a lovely correlation, but that doesn't always tell you as much as you might think.

Correlation and cause

Ideally, only two quantities would ever change in any experiment — everything else would remain constant. But in experiments or studies outside the lab, you can't usually control all the variables. So even if two variables are correlated, the change in one may not be causing the change in the other. Both changes might be caused be a third variable.

Tip: If an experiment really does confirm that changing one variable causes another to change, we say there's a <u>causal link</u> between them.

— Example —————————

Some studies have suggested that there may be a correlation between drinking chlorinated tap water and the risk of developing certain cancers. So some people argue that this means water shouldn't have chlorine added. But it's hard to control all the variables between people who drink tap water and people who don't. It could be many lifestyle factors. Or the risk could be affected by something else in tap water — or by what the non-tap water drinkers drink instead.

Tip: Watch out for bias too — for instance, a bottled water company might point these studies out to people without mentioning any of the doubts.

Drawing conclusions

The data should always support the conclusion. This may sound obvious but it's easy to jump to conclusions. Conclusions have to be specific — not make sweeping generalisations.

— Example —————————

The rate of an enzyme-controlled reaction was measured at 10 °C, 20 °C, 30 °C, 40 °C, 50 °C and 60 °C. All other variables were kept constant, and the results are shown in Figure 1.

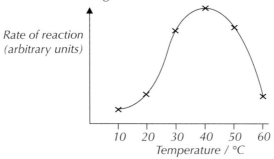

Figure 1: *Graph to show the effect of temperature on the rate of an enzyme-controlled reaction.*

A science magazine concluded from this data that enzyme X works best at 40 °C. The data doesn't support this. The enzyme could work best at 42 °C or 47 °C but you can't tell from the data because increases of 10 °C at a time were used. The rate of reaction at in-between temperatures wasn't measured. All you know is that it's faster at 40 °C than at any of the other temperatures tested.

Also, the experiment only gives information about this particular enzyme-controlled reaction. You can't conclude that all enzyme-controlled reactions happen faster at a particular temperature — only this one.

Tip: Whoever funded the research (e.g. a chemical manufacturer) may want to have some influence on what conclusions are drawn from the results — but scientists have a responsibility to make sure that the conclusions they draw are supported by the data.

Evaluations

There are a few terms that you need to understand. They'll be useful when you're evaluating how convincing your results are.

1. Valid results

Valid results answer the original question, using reliable data. For example, if you haven't controlled all the variables your results won't be valid, because you won't be testing just the thing you wanted to.

2. Accurate results

Accurate results are those that are really close to the true answer.

3. Precise results

These are results taken using sensitive instruments that measure in small increments.

> **Example**
>
> A pH measured with a meter (pH 7.692) will be more precise than pH measured with paper (pH 7).

4. Reliable results

Reliable means the results can be consistently reproduced in independent experiments. And if the results are reproducible they're more likely to be true. If the data isn't reliable for whatever reason you can't draw a valid conclusion. For experiments, the more repeats you do, the more reliable the data. If you get the same result twice, it could be the correct answer. But if you get the same result 20 times, it'd be much more reliable. And it'd be even more reliable if everyone in the class got about the same results.

5. Percentage error

You may have to calculate the percentage error of a measurement. If you know the precision that the measuring equipment is calibrated to, just divide this by the measurement taken and multiply by 100, as shown below.

> **Example**
>
> A balance is calibrated to within 0.1 g, and you measure a mass as 4.0 g.
> The percentage error is: $(0.1 \div 4.0) \times 100 = 2.5\%$.
>
> Using a larger quantity reduces the percentage error —
> a mass of 40.0 g has a percentage error of: $(0.1 \div 40.0) \times 100 = 0.25\%$.

Most measuring equipment has the precision it's calibrated to written on it. Where it doesn't, you can usually use the scale as a guide (e.g. if a measuring cylinder has a 1 ml scale, it is probably calibrated to within 0.5 ml).

Risks, hazards and ethical considerations

In any experiment you'll be expected to show that you've thought about the risks and hazards. It's generally a good thing to wear a lab coat and goggles, but you may need to take additional safety measures, depending on the experiment. For example, anything involving nasty gases will need to be done in a fume cupboard.

You need to make sure you're working ethically too. This is most important if there are other people or animals involved. You have to put their welfare first.

Tip: It's possible for results to be precise but not accurate, e.g. a balance that weighs to 1/1000th of a gram will give precise results, but if it's not calibrated properly the results won't be accurate.

Tip: Part of the scientific process involves other scientists repeating your experiment too (see pages 2-3) — if they get the same results, you can be more certain they're reliable.

Tip: You should always choose appropriate measuring equipment for the precision you need to work with.

Tip: After evaluating your results, you can suggest improvements to the experiment — e.g. use more precise equipment or repeat the experiment more times.

Figure 2: *A scientist wearing protective clothing.*

1. Exam Structure and Technique

Revision is really, really important when it comes to exams, but it's not the only thing that'll help. Good exam technique and knowing the exam structure can help you pick up marks and make sure you do as well as you possibly can.

Exam structure

For OCR A2-level Chemistry you're going to have to sit through two exams (Unit F324 and Unit F325) and complete an internal assessment (Unit F326). This book covers Unit F324 in Unit 4 and Unit F325 in Unit 5.

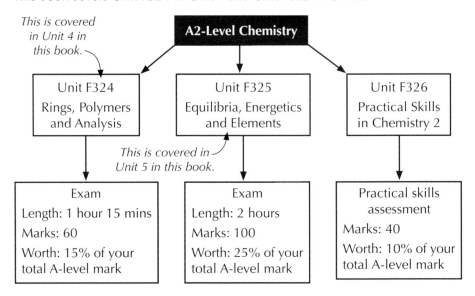

This is covered in Unit 4 in this book.

A2-Level Chemistry

| Unit F324
Rings, Polymers and Analysis | Unit F325
Equilibria, Energetics and Elements | Unit F326
Practical Skills in Chemistry 2 |

This is covered in Unit 5 in this book.

| Exam
Length: 1 hour 15 mins
Marks: 60
Worth: 15% of your total A-level mark | Exam
Length: 2 hours
Marks: 100
Worth: 25% of your total A-level mark | Practical skills assessment
Marks: 40
Worth: 10% of your total A-level mark |

Tip: The percentages on this page only add up to 50%. The other 50% comes from your AS-level exams.

Unit F326 — Practical Skills in Chemistry 2

You'll do this unit in school with your teacher. It'll test your understanding of chemistry and your ability to plan, carry out and evaluate experiments in the lab. It's worth 10% of your total A-level.

The assessments in Unit F326 test that you can demonstrate safe and skilful practical techniques, make and record suitable observations, take measurements with precision and accuracy, correctly record data and analyse, interpret and evaluate your experiment. This may sound a bit scary, but there's some stuff on pages 225-229 to help you out.

Figure 1: *Fun times in a chemistry lesson.*

Synoptic assessment

At A2-level, some of the questions will have a synoptic element. This basically means that the examiner could ask you about things that you learnt at AS-level. So, you can't just forget all of the stuff you learnt at AS-level once you've finished your AS exams — you might need it for your A2 exams too. You could also be given a question where you have to use knowledge from lots of different areas of chemistry. But don't worry — as long as you know your stuff you'll be just fine.

Tip: This book covers everything on the A2 course and recaps some bits from AS, but you'll need to have a look back over your AS notes as well.

Quality of written communication (QWC)

All of the units you take for A2-level Chemistry will have a quality of written communication element — this means that the examiner will assess your ability to write properly. This may seem like a bit of a drag but you will lose marks if you don't do it. You need to make sure that:

- your writing is legible,
- your spelling, punctuation and grammar are accurate,
- your writing style is appropriate,
- you organise your answer clearly and coherently,
- you use specialist scientific vocabulary where it's appropriate.

In your F324 and F325 exams certain questions will be designated as QWC questions — they'll be the ones with a nice picture of a pencil (see Figure 2) next to them. On these questions make sure you write in full sentences and check your spelling — you don't want to lose marks for something as simple as spelling 'quartet' incorrectly.

Figure 2: *A picture of a pencil next to a question means that you'll be assessed on the quality of your written communication in your answer.*

Time management

This is one of the most important exam skills to have. How long you spend on each question is really important in an exam — it could make all the difference to your grade. Some questions will require lots of work for only a few marks but other questions will be much quicker. Don't spend ages struggling with questions that are only worth a couple of marks — move on. You can come back to them later when you've bagged loads of other marks elsewhere.

> **Exam Tip**
> Everyone has their own method of coping with time pressure in exams. The most important thing is to find out the way that suits you best <u>before</u> the exam — that means doing all the practice exams you can.

┌ **Example** ─────────────

The questions below are both worth the same number of marks but require different amounts of work.

1 (a) Define the term 'standard enthalpy change of neutralisation'.

(2 marks)

2 (a) Compounds A and B are hydrocarbons with relative molecular masses of 78 and 58 respectively. In their ^1H NMR spectra, A has only one peak and B has two peaks. Draw a possible structure for each compound.

(2 marks)

Question 1 (a) only requires you to write down a definition — if you can remember it this shouldn't take you too long.

Question 2 (a) requires you to apply your knowledge of NMR spectra and draw the structure of two compounds — this may take you a lot longer, especially if you have to draw out a few structures before getting it right.

So, if you're running out of time it makes sense to do questions like 1(a) first and come back to 2 (a) if you've got time at the end.

> **Exam Tip**
> Don't forget to go back and do any questions that you left the first time round — you don't want to miss out on marks because you forgot to do the question. Fold over the corner of the page or put a big star next to the questions to remind yourself to go back.

Calculations

There's no getting away from those pesky calculation questions — they come up a lot in A2-level Chemistry. The most important thing to remember is to show your working. You've probably heard it a million times before but it makes perfect sense. It only takes a few seconds more to write down what's in your head and it'll stop you from making silly errors and losing out on easy marks. You won't get a mark for a wrong answer but you could get marks for the method you used to work out the answer.

> **Exam Tip**
> It's so easy to mis-type numbers into a calculator when you're under pressure in an exam. Always double check your calculations and make sure the answer looks sensible.

Units

Make sure that you always give the correct units for your answers (there's more about finding the right units coming up on pages 237-238).

Exam Tip
When you calculate a value in chemistry you'll nearly always need to give its units — see pages 235-236 for the units used in different formulas and pages 237-238 for how to convert between different units.

--- Example ---

Here's an example of a question where you need to change the units so they match the answer the examiner wants.

1   Calculate the free energy change for the following reaction at 298 K, giving your answer in kJ mol^{-1}:

$$MgCO_3 \rightarrow MgO + CO_2 \qquad \begin{aligned} \Delta H^{\ominus} &= 1.17 \times 10^5 \text{ J mol}^{-1} \\ \Delta S^{\ominus} &= 175 \text{ J K}^{-1}\text{mol}^{-1} \end{aligned}$$

(2 marks)

Here you use the equation: $\Delta G = \Delta H - T\Delta S$. Plugging the numbers in gives you an answer of +64850 J mol^{-1}. But the question asks for the answer in kJ mol^{-1}, so you have to divide by 1000, giving an answer of 64.85 kJ mol^{-1}. If you left your answer as +64850 J mol^{-1} you'd lose a mark.

Significant figures

Tip: The first significant figure of a number is the first digit that isn't a zero. The second, third and fourth significant figures follow on immediately after the first (even if they are zeros).

Use the number of significant figures given in the question as a guide for how many to give in the answer. You should always give your answer to the lowest number of significant figures (s.f.) given in the question — if you're really unsure, write down the full answer and then round it to 3 s.f. It always helps to write down the number of significant figures you've rounded to after your answer — it shows the examiner you really know what you're talking about.

--- Examples ---

In this question the data given to you is a good indication of how many significant figures you should give your answer to.

1 **(b)** Calculate the pH of 0.410 mol dm^{-3} ethanoic acid at 298 K.

(2 marks)

The concentration in the question is given to 3 s.f. so it makes sense to give your answer to 3 s.f. too. But sometimes it isn't as clear as that.

3 **(b)** 18.5 cm^3 of a 0.65 mol dm^{-3} solution of potassium hydroxide reacts with 1.5 mol dm^{-3} sulfuric acid. Calculate the volume of sulfuric acid needed to neutralise the potassium hydroxide.

(2 marks)

Exam Tip
Sometimes the question might say how many significant figures or decimal places you should give your answer to. If you are told, make sure that you follow the instructions or you'll lose valuable marks.

There are two types of data in this question, volume data and concentration data. The volume data is given to 3 s.f. and the concentration data is given to 2 s.f. You should always give your answer to the lowest number of significant figures given — in this case that's to 2 s.f. The answer in full is 4.00833... cm^3 so the answer rounded correctly would be 4.0 cm^3 (2 s.f.).

Standard form

You might be asked to use numbers in standard form in your chemistry exams. Standard form is used for writing very big or very small numbers in a more convenient way. Standard form must always look like this:

This number must always be between 1 and 10. → $A \times 10^n$ ← *This number is the number of places the decimal point moves.*

Here's how to write 480 000 in standard form.

- First write the non-zero digits with a decimal point after the first number and a '× 10' after it:

$$4.8 \times 10$$

- Then count how many places the decimal point has moved to the left. This number sits to the top right of the 10.

$$4\,80000 = 4.8 \times 10^5$$

- Et voilà... that's 480 000 written in standard form.

Here are some more examples.

- You can write 3 200 000 as 3.2×10^6.
- The number 0.00073 is 7.3×10^{-4} in standard form — the n is negative because the decimal point has moved to the right instead of the left.
- You can write 0.008294 as 8.294×10^{-3}.

Tip: If your calculator already gives you your answer in standard form, you don't need to do anything — result.

Diagrams

When you're asked to draw diagrams or mechanisms in an exam it's important that you draw everything correctly.

― Examples ―

Drawing organic reaction mechanisms

When you're drawing organic reaction mechanisms the curly arrows must come from either a lone pair of electrons or from a bond, like this:

The mechanisms below are incorrect — you wouldn't get marks for them:

You won't get marks if the curly arrows come from atoms, like this...

or this...

You show the movement of an electron pair with a full curly arrow — don't use half curly arrows, it's just plain wrong...

 ✓

Tip: It's important that the curly arrows come from a lone pair or a bond because that's where the electrons are found. Remember, curly arrows are supposed to show the movement of electrons.

Drawing displayed formulas

If a question asks you for a displayed formula you have to show all of the bonds and all of the atoms in the molecule. That means you have to draw displayed formulas like this:

Exam Tip
Don't forget to draw in any charges too — carbocations need a full positive charge (+) and dipoles need to be labelled clearly with δ+ or δ–. You'll miss out on valuable marks if it isn't clear what you mean.

And not like this:

H CH₃ — *Some of the bonds between the carbon atoms and the hydrogen atoms haven't been shown, so it's not a displayed formula and you wouldn't get the marks.*

Cl–C–C–CH₃

H H

Tip: A displayed formula shows how all the atoms are arranged and all the bonds between them.

If you're not asked specifically for a displayed formula then either kind of diagram will do. Just make sure that the bonds are always drawn between the right atoms. For example, ethanol should be drawn like this:

H H
H–C–C–OH
H H

And not like this:

H H
H–C–C–HO
H H

It's the oxygen atom that's bonded to the carbon, not the hydrogen, so drawing it like this is just plain wrong.

Exam Tip
If you're having trouble drawing a skeletal formula, try sketching out the displayed formula first. It'll help you to see which atoms should go where in the skeletal formula.

Drawing skeletal formulas

There's a pretty good chance that you'll have to draw skeletal formulas in your exam so you need to be able to draw them properly. Bonds between carbon atoms are shown by a line and carbon atoms are found at each end. Atoms that aren't carbon or hydrogen have to be drawn on:

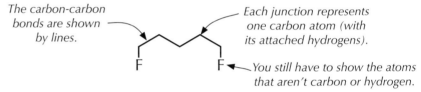

The carbon-carbon bonds are shown by lines.
Each junction represents one carbon atom (with its attached hydrogens).
You still have to show the atoms that aren't carbon or hydrogen.

Exam Tip
If you make a mistake when drawing a diagram, don't just scribble part of it out and try to fix it — it'll look messy and be difficult for the examiner to figure out what you're trying to show. Cross the whole thing out and start again from scratch.

You aren't allowed to draw any carbon or hydrogen atoms when you're drawing out skeletal formulas, so the diagrams below are both wrong...

You don't show the carbon atoms or the hydrogen atoms.

Drawing hydrogen bonding

Drawing hydrogen bonds is a common exam question. You need to know how to draw them properly to pick up all the marks you can.

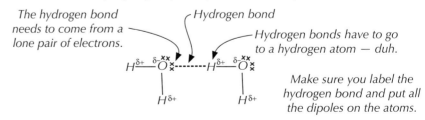

The hydrogen bond needs to come from a lone pair of electrons.
Hydrogen bond
Hydrogen bonds have to go to a hydrogen atom — duh.
Make sure you label the hydrogen bond and put all the dipoles on the atoms.

Exam Tip
Remember <u>intramolecular</u> bonding is the bonds within a molecule. <u>Intermolecular</u> bonding (like hydrogen bonding) is the bonds or forces between two molecules.

When you're drawing any diagram make sure it's really clear what you're drawing. A small scribble in the bottom corner of a page isn't going to show enough detail to get you the marks. Draw the diagrams nice and big, but make sure that you stay within the space given for that answer.

2. Formulas and Equations

You need to do a lot of calculations at A2-level, so there are loads of formulas you need to know. Here's a quick summary of the main formulas you'll need.

Formulas from A2

First up its the equation for calculating R_f values in thin-layer chromatography:

$$R_f \text{ value} = \frac{\text{distance travelled by spot}}{\text{distance travelled by solvent}}$$

Tip: If something in an equation is in [square brackets] it means it's a concentration.

Next, it's the rate equation. You'll need this when looking at rates of reaction...

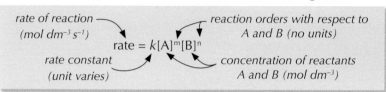

rate of reaction (mol dm⁻³ s⁻¹) — *reaction orders with respect to A and B (no units)*
$$\text{rate} = k[A]^m[B]^n$$
rate constant (unit varies) — *concentration of reactants A and B (mol dm⁻³)*

Tip: In this equation there are only two reactants (A and B), but you can have more. Here's the equation if you have three reactants: rate = $k[A]^m[B]^n[C]^x$

This is the equation for calculating the equilibrium constant (K_c)...

For the reaction $aA + bB \rightleftharpoons dD + eE$: $K_c = \dfrac{[D]^d[E]^e}{[A]^a[B]^b}$

lower case letters are the number of moles

Tip: You have to calculate the unit of K_c. It's not always the same.

These are the equations for the ionic product of water (K_w) and the acid dissociation constant (K_a)...

$$K_w = [H^+][OH^-]$$
in mol² dm⁻⁶

$$K_a = \frac{[H^+][A^-]}{[HA]}$$
in mol dm⁻³

Tip: In pure water, $[H^+] = [OH^-]$ so in pure water $K_w = [H^+]^2$.

And here are the equations for calculating pH and pK_a...

$$pH = -\log_{10}[H^+]$$
$$pK_a = -\log_{10}[K_a]$$

...which rearrange to...

$$[H^+] = 10^{-pH}$$
$$K_a = 10^{-pKa}$$

Tip: Make sure you know how to use the log button on your calculator.

You'll need a few formulas for enthalpy, entropy and free energy changes. To calculate the energy released during a reaction you would use:

(g) — *(K or °C)*
$$q = mc\Delta T$$
(J) — *(J g⁻¹ K⁻¹)*

For this formula it doesn't matter if the temperature is in K or °C — it's the <u>change</u> in temperature that goes into the formula (and that's the same whether it's K or °C).

To calculate the entropy change of a system you use:

$$\Delta S_{system} = S_{products} - S_{reactants}$$ where ΔS is the entropy change in J K⁻¹ mol⁻¹

Exam Tip
Make sure you learn all of these formulas. You could need any one of them in the exam and you'll be gutted if you can't remember them.

To calculate the entropy change of the surroundings you need:

$$\Delta S_{surrondings} = -\frac{\Delta H}{T}$$ where ΔH is the enthalpy change (J mol⁻¹) of the reaction and T is the temperature (K)

Once you know the entropy change of the system and the entropy change of the surroundings you can calculate the total entropy change using:

$$\Delta S_{total} = \Delta S_{system} + \Delta S_{surroundings}$$

Exam Tip
Make sure you can rearrange all these formulas and give the units of each quantity as well.

If you know the enthalpy change, the entropy change and temperature of a reaction, you can calculate the free energy change (ΔG) using:

Free energy change ($J\ mol^{-1}$)
Temperature (K)
$$\Delta G = \Delta H - T\Delta S$$
Enthalpy change ($J\ mol^{-1}$)
Entropy change ($J\ K^{-1}\ mol^{-1}$)

And here's an equation for calculating standard cell potentials:

Tip: Electrode potentials are always measured in volts (V).

$$E^{\ominus}_{cell} = \left(E^{\ominus}_{reduced} - E^{\ominus}_{oxidised} \right)$$

Formulas you might need from AS

Tip: See page 230 for more on synoptic assessment.

There are some synoptic elements in the A2 exam so you might need some of these formulas that you learnt at AS-level. First up...

$$\text{Number of moles} = \frac{\text{Number of particles you have}}{\text{Number of particles in a mole}}$$

Here is perhaps the most useful equation of all...

$$\text{Number of moles} = \frac{\text{Mass of substance}}{\text{Molar mass}} \quad \text{also written as...} \quad n = \frac{m}{M_r}$$

Tip: To convert cm^3 into dm^3 you divide by 1000. See page 237 for more.

You'll need this one when you're dealing with solutions...

$$\text{Number of moles} = \text{Concentration} \times \text{Volume (in } dm^3)$$

...and these when you've got gases at room temperature and pressure.

Tip: If you forget an equation in an exam, thinking about the units could help you out. For example, if you know concentration is in mol dm^{-3}, it tells you that to calculate a concentration you have to divide a number of moles by a volume in dm^3. So the equation is concentration = moles ÷ volume.

$$\frac{\text{Number}}{\text{of moles}} = \frac{\text{Volume (in } dm^3)}{24} \qquad \frac{\text{Number}}{\text{of moles}} = \frac{\text{Volume (in } cm^3)}{24\ 000}$$

Here are the equations for percentage yield and percentage atom economy...

$$\% \text{ yield} = \frac{\text{Actual yield}}{\text{Theoretical yield}} \times 100\%$$

$$\text{atom economy} = \frac{\text{Molecular mass of desired product}}{\text{Sum of molecular masses of all products}} \times 100\%$$

And finally...

$$\text{Enthalpy change of reaction} = \text{total energy absorbed} - \text{total energy released}$$

3. Units

Units aren't the most exciting bit of chemistry, but you need to be able to use them. Here's how to convert between units and work them out from scratch.

Converting between units

Volume

Volume can be measured in m³, dm³ and cm³.

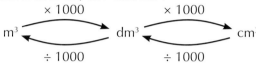

Figure 1: *Measuring cylinders like this one measure volumes in cm³.*

Example

Write 0.3 cm³ in dm³ and m³.

First, to convert 0.3 cm³ into dm³ you need to divide by 1000.

$$0.3 \text{ cm}^3 \div 1000 = 0.0003 \text{ dm}^3 = 3 \times 10^{-4} \text{ dm}^3$$

Then, to convert 0.0003 dm³ into m³ you need to divide by 1000.

$$0.0003 \text{ dm}^3 \div 1000 = 0.0000003 \text{ m}^3 = 3 \times 10^{-7} \text{ m}^3$$

Tip: Standard form (that's showing numbers as, for example, 3×10^{-7}) is covered on pages 232-233.

Temperature

Temperature can be measured in K and °C.

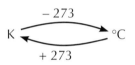

Examples

Write 25 °C in kelvins.

To convert 25 °C into K you need to add 273: $\quad 25 \text{ °C} + 273 = 298 \text{ K}$

Write 298 K in °C.

To convert 298 K into °C you need to subtract 273: $\quad 298 \text{ K} - 273 = 25 \text{ °C}$

Exam Tip
Make sure you practise these conversions. It could save you valuable time in the exam if you can change between units confidently.

Mass

Mass can be measured in kg and g.

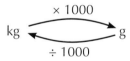

Example

Write 5.2 kg in g.

To convert 5.2 kg into g you need to multiply by 1000.

$$5.2 \text{ kg} \times 1000 = 5200 \text{ g}$$

Tip: A kg is bigger than a g, so you'd expect the number to get smaller when you convert from g to kg — each unit is worth more so you'll have fewer of them.

Energy

Energy can be measured in kJ and J.

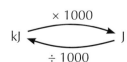

Example

Write 78 kJ in J.

To convert 78 kJ into J you need to multiply by 1000.

$$78 \text{ kJ} \times 1000 = 78\ 000 \text{ J} = 7.8 \times 10^4 \text{ J}$$

Figure 2: *This balance measures mass in g.*

Concentration

Concentration can be measured in mol dm^{-3} (M) and mol cm^{-3}.

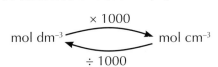

--- Example ---------------------------------

Write 0.5 mol dm^{-3} in mol cm^{-3}.

To convert 0.5 mol dm^{-3} into mol cm^{-3} you need to multiply by 1000.

$$0.5 \text{ mol dm}^{-3} \times 1000 = 500 \text{ mol cm}^{-3}$$

Life gets a bit confusing if you have to do lots of calculations one after the other — sometimes it can be difficult to keep track of your units.

To avoid this, always write down the units you're using with each line of the calculation. Then when you get to the end you know what units to give with your answer.

Calculating units

Some things, like the equilibrium constant (K_c) and the rate constant (k), have variable units. This means you'll need to work the units out — you can't just learn them. To work out the units, you just follow these steps:

- Substitute the units that you know into the equation you're using.

- Cancel out units wherever possible — if the same unit is present on the top and the bottom of a fraction, you can cancel them out.

- Get rid of any fractions by inversing the powers of the units on the bottom of the fraction — any positive powers become negative and any negative powers become positive.

Figure 3: *When you're under pressure in an exam it's really easy to make mistakes. So don't be afraid to use your calculator, even for really simple calculations.*

--- Examples ---------------------------------

The rate equation for the reaction $CH_3COCH_3 + I_2 \rightarrow CH_3COCH_2I + H^+ + I^-$ is Rate $= k[CH_3COCH_3][H^+]$. The rate of reaction is in mol dm^{-3} s^{-1} and the concentrations are in mol dm^{-3}. Find the units of k.

$$\text{Rate} = k[CH_3COCH_3][H^+] \qquad \text{so} \qquad k = \frac{\text{Rate}}{[CH_3COCH_3][H^+]}$$

First substitute in the units you know:

$$k = \frac{\text{mol dm}^{-3}\,\text{s}^{-1}}{(\text{mol dm}^{-3})(\text{mol dm}^{-3})}$$

Cancel out units where you can. In this case you can cancel a mol dm^{-3} from the top and the bottom of the fraction:

$$k = \frac{\cancel{\text{mol dm}^{-3}}\,\text{s}^{-1}}{(\cancel{\text{mol dm}^{-3}})(\text{mol dm}^{-3})} = \frac{\text{s}^{-1}}{\text{mol dm}^{-3}}$$

Then get rid of the fraction by inversing the powers from the bottom:

$$k = \text{s}^{-1}\,\text{mol}^{-1}\,\text{dm}^{3}$$

4. The Periodic Table — Facts and Trends

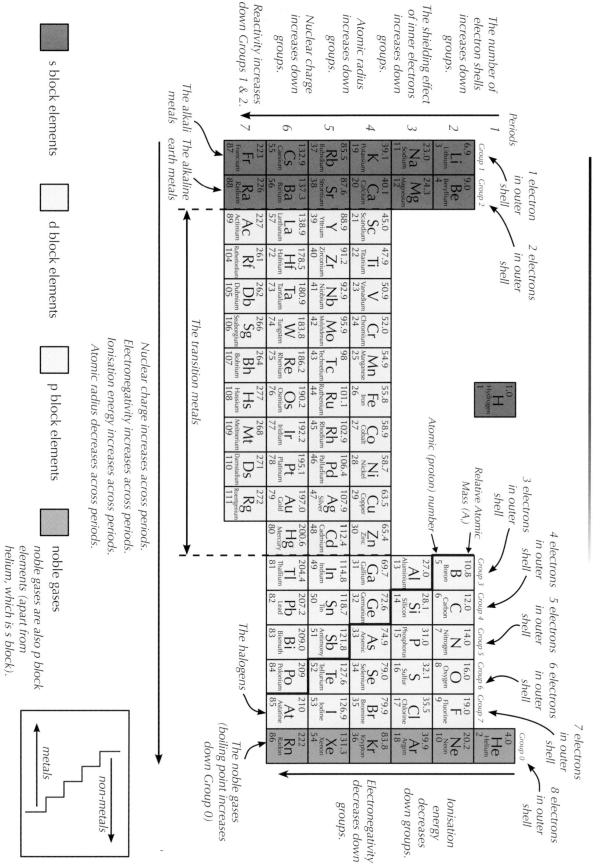

Answers

Unit 4

Module 1 — Rings, Acids and Amines

1. Benzene

Page 8 — Application Questions

Q1 a) 1,2-dinitrobenzene
   b) 4-methylphenol
   c) 2,4,6-trichlorophenylamine

Q2 a) Kekulé proposed that the structure of benzene was a ring of six carbons joined by alternating double and single bonds. He later adapted his model to say that the benzene molecule was constantly flipping between two isomers.
   b) The $\Delta H^{\ominus}_{\text{hydrogenation}}$ for cyclohexene is -120 kJ mol^{-1}. So if benzene had three double bonds you would expect it to have a $\Delta H^{\ominus}_{\text{hydrogenation}}$ of -360 kJ mol^{-1}. But, $\Delta H^{\ominus}_{\text{hydrogenation}}$ for benzene is only -208 kJ mol^{-1}. This is far less exothermic than expected, so benzene must be more stable than the proposed Kekulé structure and the Kekulé model cannot be correct.

Page 8 — Fact Recall Questions

Q1 According to the delocalised model, the p-orbitals of all six carbon atoms overlap to create π-bonds. This creates two ring-shaped clouds of electrons — one above and one below the plane of the six carbon atoms. All the bonds in the ring are the same and so are the same length.

Q2 If the Kekulé model were correct, half of the bonds in benzene would be the length of C=C double bonds (135 pm) and the other half would be the length of C–C single bonds (147 pm). But X-ray diffraction studies have shown that all the bonds in benzene are the same length (140 pm — between that of single and double bonds). So this is evidence for the delocalised model.

Q3 Compounds that contain a benzene ring.

2. Reactions of Benzene

Page 12 — Application Questions

Q1 a)

   b) E.g. AlCl$_3$ / FeCl$_3$ / Fe.
   c) E.g. AlCl$_3$Cl$^{\delta-}$–Cl$^{\delta+}$

You could another halogen carrier here (like Fe or FeCl$_3$) instead of AlCl$_3$.

Q2 a)

   b) An H$_2$SO$_4$ catalyst and a temperature below 55 °C.

Q3 a)

   b) The scientist needs to carry out the reaction at a temperature above 55 °C. Below this temperature he will only achieve monosubstitution.

Page 12 — Fact Recall Questions

Q1 In alkenes, the C=C bond is a localised area of high electron density. It attracts an electrophile, which adds to the C=C double bond, forming a stable alkane. The delocalised electrons in benzene make the benzene ring very stable, and spreads out the negative charge. So benzene is very unwilling to undergo addition reactions which would destroy the stable ring.

Q2 Aromatic compounds contain a benzene ring, which is a region of high electron density. Electrophiles are electron deficient so are attracted to the regions of high electron density found in aromatic compounds.

Q3 a) Any two from, e.g. AlCl$_3$ / Fe / FeCl$_3$.
   b) Br$_2$ isn't a strong enough electrophile to react with the benzene ring on its own.
   A halogen carrier will accept a lone pair of electrons from one of the bromine atoms, forming a polarised molecule, which is a much stronger electrophile than the original. This species is strong enough to react with the benzene ring.

Q4 HNO$_3$ + H$_2$SO$_4$ → HSO$_4^-$ + NO$_2^+$ + H$_2$O

3. Phenols

Page 15 — Application Questions

Q1 a) 4-bromophenol
   b) 3-methyl-5-nitrophenol
   This isn't called 3-nitro-5-methylphenol because methyl comes before nitro alphabetically.
   c) 3,5-dimethylphenol
   d) 4-chloro-3,5-dimethylphenol
   This isn't called 3,5-dimethyl-4-chlorophenol because chloro comes before methyl alphabetically.

Q2 a)

b)

$$\text{(3-methyl-5-nitrophenol)} + NaOH \longrightarrow \text{(sodium salt)} + H_2O$$

c)

$$\text{(3,5-dimethylphenol)} + NaOH \longrightarrow \text{(sodium salt)} + H_2O$$

d)

$$\text{(4-chloro-3,5-dimethylphenol)} + NaOH \longrightarrow \text{(sodium salt)} + H_2O$$

Q3 a)

$$2\,\text{(4-bromophenol)} + 2Na \longrightarrow \text{(sodium salt)} + H_2$$

b)

$$2\,\text{(3-methyl-5-nitrophenol)} + 2Na \longrightarrow \text{(sodium salt)} + H_2$$

c)

$$2\,\text{(3,5-dimethylphenol)} + 2Na \longrightarrow \text{(sodium salt)} + H_2$$

d)

$$2\,\text{(4-chloro-3,5-dimethylphenol)} + 2Na \longrightarrow \text{(sodium salt)} + H_2$$

Q4 Nothing would happen.
Sodium carbonate isn't a strong enough base to react with 2-methylphenol.

Page 15 — Fact Recall Questions
Q1 hydrogen gas / H_2
Q2 2,4,6-tribromophenol structure (OH with Br at 2, 4 and 6 positions)

Q3 In benzene the p-orbital electrons are delocalised. This makes the benzene ring very stable so it is unwilling to undergo addition reactions with halogens. In phenol, one of the lone pairs of electrons in a p-orbital of the oxygen atom overlaps with the delocalised ring of electrons and is partially delocalised into the ring. This increases the electron density of the ring. This higher electron density means that phenol can polarise Br_2 and cause a reaction. (Benzene can't polarise Br_2 so no reaction occurs).

Q4 Any two of: e.g. in the production of antiseptics and disinfectants. / In the production of polymers. / In the production of polycarbonates which are used to make bottles, spectacle lenses and CDs. / In the manufacture of resins (epoxies) which are used to make adhesives, paints and electrical insulators. / In the production of Bakelite™.

4. Aldehydes and Ketones
Pages 18-19 — Application Questions
Q1 a) butan-2-one / butanone
You don't really need to say which carbon the functional group is on here, because it has to be carbon-2 — but in exams it's best to use the full systematic name (butan-2-one) to make sure you get the marks.
  b) 2-ethyl-3-methylbutanal

Q2 a) butan-2-ol
     heat under reflux and acidic conditions
   b) 2-ethyl-3-methylbutan-1-ol
     heat in distillation apparatus under acidic conditions

Q3 heptanal

Q4 structure: $H_3C-CH(CH_2H)-C(CH_2CH_3)(H)-CH(OH)-CH_3$

Q5 **C** and **D**

Q6 $CH_3CH_2CH(CH_3)CH_2OH + 2[O] \rightarrow CH_3CH_2CH(CH_3)COOH + H_2O$

Q7 $CH_3CHO + [O] \rightarrow CH_3COOH$

Page 19 — Fact Recall Questions
Q1 Aldehydes have the carbonyl group at the end of the carbon chain, ketones have the carbonyl group in the middle of the carbon chain.
Q2 $Cr_2O_7^{2-}$
Q3 orange to green
Q4 A carboxylic acid.
Q5 refluxing apparatus (a round bottomed flask and a Liebig condenser, plus a heat source).

5. Reducing Carbonyls
Page 21 — Application Questions
Q1 a)

Reaction mechanism showing hydride ion addition to a carbonyl then protonation by water to give an alcohol, producing ^-OH.

b)

c)

d)

Q2 $CH_3COCH_2CH_2CH_3 + 2[H] \rightarrow CH_3CHOHCH_2CH_2CH_3$

Q3 $CHOCH(CH_3)CH_2CH_2CH_2CH_3 + 2[H] \rightarrow$
$CH_2OHCH(CH_3)CH_2CH_2CH_2CH_3$

Q4 $CH_3COCH_2COCH_3 + 4[H] \rightarrow CH_3CHOHCH_2CHOHCH_3$
This molecule started off with two ketone groups — so when it's reduced it will end up with two alcohol groups.

Q5 $CH_3COCH(CH_3)CHO$
This is tricky — it's all about working out that molecule X must have both a ketone group and an aldehyde group if it's going to produce the molecule given in the question.

Page 21 — Fact Recall Questions
Q1 E.g. $NaBH_4$
Q2 a ketone
Q3 nucleophilic addition

6. Tests for Carbonyls
Page 23 — Application Question
Q1 a) i)   orange precipitate formed
        ii)   nothing happens
        iii) orange precipitate formed
        iv)   orange precipitate formed
    b) i)   silver mirror formed
        ii)   nothing happens
        iii) nothing happens
        iv)   silver mirror formed

Page 23 — Fact Recall Questions
Q1 carbonyl groups / aldehydes and ketones
Q2 When reacted with Brady's reagent, carbonyl compounds form derivatives of 2,4-DNPH. Each different carbonyl compound produces a crystalline derivative with a different melting point. So if you measure the melting point of the crystals and compare it against the known melting points of the derivatives, you can identify the carbonyl compound.
Q3 A solution of silver nitrate ($AgNO_3$) dissolved in aqueous ammonia.
Q4 Ag^+

7. Carboxylic Acids
Page 25 — Application Questions
Q1 a) (i) methanoic acid
       (ii) 2-ethyl-4-hydroxypentanoic acid
    b) $2HCOOH_{(aq)} + Mg_{(s)} \rightarrow (HCOO)_2Mg_{(aq)} + H_{2(g)}$
    c) $2CH_3CHOHCH_2CH(C_2H_5)COOH_{(aq)} + Na_2CO_{3(s)} \rightarrow$
        $2CH_3CHOHCH_2CH(C_2H_5)COONa_{(aq)} + H_2O_{(l)} + CO_{2(g)}$
Q2 $CH_3CH_2CH(CH_3)COOH_{(aq)} + NaOH_{(aq)} \rightarrow$
    $CH_3CH_2CH(CH_3)COONa_{(aq)} + H_2O_{(l)}$
Q3 $CH_3CH_2COOH_{(aq)} \rightleftharpoons CH_3CH_2COO^-_{(aq)} + H^+_{(aq)}$

Page 25 — Fact Recall Questions
Q1 $-COOH$
Q2 Ethanoic acid is a polar molecule so it can form hydrogen bonds with water molecules. This means that it will easily dissolve in water.

Q3 A gas (hydrogen) would bubble out of the solution.

8. Esters
Page 27 — Application Question
Q1 a) i)   methyl methanoate
        ii) ethyl benzoate
    b) i)   methanol and methanoic acid
        ii) ethanol and benzoic acid

Page 28 — Application Questions
Q1 $HCOOCH_3 + CH_3CH_2CH_2CH_2OH \rightarrow$
    $CH_3CH_2CH_2CH_2OOCH_3 + HCOOH$
Q2 $CH_3CH_2CH_2OH + CH_3CH_2CH_2CH_2COOH \overset{H^+}{\rightleftharpoons}$
    $CH_3CH_2CH_2CH_2COOCH_2CH_2CH_3 + H_2O$

Page 29 — Application Question
Q1 a) $CH_3CH_2COOCH_3 + H_2O \overset{H^+}{\rightarrow} CH_3CH_2COOH + CH_3OH$
    b) $CH_3CH_2COOCH_3 + OH^- \rightarrow CH_3CH_2COO^- + CH_3OH$
    If you'd written an equation including the sodium from the sodium hydroxide that would have been fine here too
    ($CH_3CH_2COOCH_3 + NaOH \rightarrow CH_3CH_2COONa + CH_3OH$).

Page 29 — Fact Recall Questions

Q1 a) A carboxylic acid and an alcohol.
    b) A carboxylate ion and an alcohol.

Q2 Any two from, e.g. making perfumes / adding scents to products / as a flavouring in food/drinks/sweets.

9. Fatty Acids and Triglycerides

Page 33 — Application Questions

Q1 a) none
    b) three
    c) four

Q2 a) i)   decanoic acid
       ii) 10, 0
    b) i)   hept-3-enoic acid
       ii) 7, 1(3)
    c) i)   non-4-enoic acid
       ii) 9, 1(4)
    d) i)   pentadeca-6,10-dienoic acid
       ii) 15, 2(6, 10)

Q3

We've had to write the equation vertically here so it'll fit on the page. In the exam, write the equation horizontally like normal.

Q4 a) The molecule will be bent.
    The cis double bond makes a kink in the hydrocarbon chain.
    b) Yes, because almost all naturally occurring fatty acids are cis fatty acids.

Page 33 — Fact Recall Questions

Q1 An unsaturated fatty acid is a carboxylic acid with a long hydrocarbon chain that contains one or more carbon-carbon double bonds.

Q2

Q3 Glycerol (propane-1,2,3-triol) and fatty acids.

Q4 Trans fatty acids are almost always the product of human processing.

10. Fats

Page 35 — Application Question

Q1 a)

    b) e.g. KOH/potassium hydroxide

Page 35 — Fact Recall Questions

Q1 a) Cholesterol is a soft, waxy material found in cell membranes and transported in your blood stream.
    b) E.g. good cholesterol removes bad cholesterol, taking it to the liver to be destroyed.

Q2 Recent research has shown that trans fats increase the amount of bad cholesterol in your body and decrease the amount of good cholesterol. Bad cholesterol can clog up blood vessels, leading to heart attacks and strokes. Because of these health concerns there have been moves to reduce the use of trans fats and more clearly label foods that contain them.

Q3 Polyunsaturated oils have been shown to reduce bad cholesterol and help to prevent heart disease when eaten in moderation.

Q4 Biodiesel is made by reacting triglycerides (oils or fats) with methanol or ethanol.

Q5 Advantage: e.g. biodiesel is a renewable fuel so it won't run out.
    Disadvantage: e.g. large-scale use of biodiesel would mean that we'd need to devote huge areas of land to growing biodiesel crops rather than food crops.

11. Amines

Page 38 — Application Questions

Q1 a) ethylamine
    b) dipropylamine
    c) ethyldimethylamine

Q2 $N(CH_3)_3 + HCl \rightarrow HN(CH_3)_3^+Cl^-$

Q3 $CH_3Cl + 2NH_3 \rightarrow CH_3NH_2 + NH_4^+Cl^-$

Q4

Page 38 — Fact Recall Questions

Q1 A quaternary ammonium ion is a positively charged ion that consists of a nitrogen atom with four organic groups attached.

Q2 E.g. amines can act as proton acceptors by forming a dative bond with an H^+ ion. / Amines can donate their lone pair of electrons to an H^+ ion forming a dative covalent bond.

Q3 a) Heat the haloalkane with an excess of ethanolic ammonia.

b) More than one hydrogen on the ammonia can be substituted, so a mixture of primary, secondary and tertiary amines and quaternary ammonium ions is produced.

c) By distillation.

Q4 Take an aromatic nitro compound (e.g. nitrobenzene). Heat the nitro compound with tin metal and concentrated HCl under reflux to form a salt. Mix the salt with an alkali (e.g. NaOH) to produce an aromatic amine.

12. Azo Dyes

Page 41 — Application Question

Q1 a)

and

b)

$+ HNO_2 + HCl$

$+ 2H_2O$

c)

$+ NaOH$

$+ NaCl + H_2O$

Page 41 — Fact Recall Questions

Q1 Azo dyes are man-made dyes that contain the azo group, $-N=N-$.

Q2 The azo group becomes part of the delocalised electron system which stabilises the molecule.

Q3 E.g. $NaNO_2 + HCl \rightarrow HNO_2 + NaCl$

Q4 Because otherwise a phenol will be formed instead.

Q5 Any two from: e.g. food colourings / lightfast, permanent colours for clothing / paint pigments / indicators.

Q6 Enzymes in the body can break some azo dyes down to produce toxic or carcinogenic compounds. Some other azo dyes have been linked to hyperactivity in children.

Exam-style Questions — pages 43-46

Q1 a) (i) E.g. $AlCl_3$ / $FeCl_3$ / Fe *(1 mark)*.
You could write down any correct halogen carrier here and get the mark.

(ii) The Cl_2 isn't a strong enough electrophile to react with the benzene ring by itself *(1 mark)*. The halogen carrier (Catalyst X) pulls electrons away from the chlorine and forms a permanent dipole *(1 mark)*. This makes the chlorine a much stronger electrophile and gives it a strong enough charge to react with the benzene ring *(1 mark)*.

b) (i) $HNO_3 + H_2SO_4 \rightarrow HSO_4^- + NO_2^+ + H_2O$ *(1 mark)*

(ii)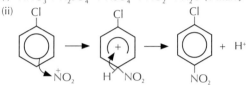

$+ H^+$

(1 mark for each correct curly arrow, 1 mark for correct intermediate, 1 mark for correct products)

(iii) 1-chloro-4-nitrobenzene *(1 mark)*

c) (i)

(1 mark)

(ii)

$+ 18[H] \longrightarrow$

$+ 6H_2O$

(1 mark for correct products and reactants, 1 mark for correctly balanced equation)

Q2 a) molecule X — propanal *(1 mark)*
molecule Y — propanoic acid *(1 mark)*
molecule Z — propanone *(1 mark)*

b) (i) E.g. $NaBH_4$ / sodium tetrahydridoborate(III) / sodium borohydride *(1 mark)*.

(ii)

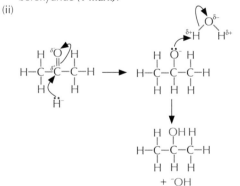

(1 mark for each correct curly arrow)

(iii) $CH_3COCH_3 + 2[H] \rightarrow CH_3CHOHCH_3$
(1 mark for correct products, 1 mark for correctly balanced equation)

c) (i) Molecule Y is polar because electrons are drawn from the carbon to the more electronegative oxygen atom *(1 mark)*. This means that molecule Y can form hydrogen bonds with the water molecule and so will be soluble *(1 mark)*.

(ii) $2CH_3CH_2COOH_{(aq)} + NaCO_{3(s)} \rightarrow$
$2CH_3CH_2COONa_{(aq)} + H_2O_{(l)} + CO_{2(g)}$
(1 mark for correct products, 1 mark for correctly balanced equation)

d) (i) E.g. acidified potassium dichromate(VI) / $K_2Cr_2O_7$/ H_2SO_4 *(1 mark)*. Distillation apparatus *(1 mark)*.
(ii) Before the reaction (orange ion) — $Cr_2O_7^{2-}$ *(1 mark)* After the reaction (green ion) — Cr^{3+} *(1 mark)*

e) Molecule X (an aldehyde) will form a silver mirror with Tollens' reagent and an orange precipitate with Brady's reagent *(1 mark)*. Molecule Y (a carboxylic acid) will not react with either reagent *(1 mark)*. Molecule Z (a ketone) will form an orange precipitate with Brady's reagent but will not react with Tollens' reagent *(1 mark)*.

Q3 All the carbon-carbon bonds in benzene are the same length / the length of the carbon-carbon bonds in benzene is between that of a C–C single and C=C double bond *(1 mark)*. In the delocalised model all the carbon-carbon bonds are the same (whereas in the Kekulé model three are single bonds and three are double bonds)*(1 mark)*.
The enthalpy of hydrogenation of benzene is lower than you would expect it to be if benzene had three double bonds / compared to cyclohexene *(1 mark)*. More energy is needed to break the bonds in benzene than would be needed to break the bonds in the Kekulé structure *(1 mark)*.
Benzene won't react easily with bromine whereas alkenes do *(1 mark)*. This suggests that the structure of benzene is more stable than a normal alkene as predicted by the delocalised model *(1 mark)*.
One of hydrogenation or enthalpy must be spelt correctly to gain full marks.

Q4 a) 2,4-dinitrophenyl hydrazine will form an orange precipitate with the compound *(1 mark)*. The scientist can measure the melting point of this precipitate/derivative *(1 mark)* and compare it to known melting points of the derivatives of 2,4-DNPH *(1 mark)*.

b) (i) amine *(1 mark)* and ketone groups *(1 mark)*
(ii) Bases are proton acceptors *(1 mark)*. The compound has an amine group with a nitrogen lone pair that can act as a proton acceptor *(1 mark)*.
or bases are electron donors *(1 mark)*. The compound has an amine group with a nitrogen lone pair that can act as an electron donor *(1 mark)*.

Q5 a) (i)

HO$_3$S—⬡—$\overset{+}{N}\equiv N$ Cl$^-$ *(1 mark)*

(ii) HCl and $NaNO_2$/hydrochloric acid and sodium nitrite present *(1 mark)*. Temperature must be below 10 °C *(1 mark)*.

b)

OH—⬡ + NaOH ⟶ O$^-$Na$^+$—⬡ + H$_2$O *(1 mark)*

c)

HO$_3$S—⬡—$\overset{+}{N}\equiv N$ Cl$^-$ + OH—⬡ + NaOH ⟶ HO$_3$S—⬡—N=N—⬡—OH + NaCl + H$_2$O

(1 mark for correct products, 1 mark for correct reactants)

d) E.g. as a food colouring / as a lightfast, permanent colour for clothes / to produce paint pigments *(1 mark)*.

Q6 a) (i)

H—C—OH   HO—C—R   H—C—O—C—R
| ‖ | ‖
H—C—OH + HO—C—R ⟶ H—C—O—C—R + 3 H$_2$O
| ‖ | ‖
H—C—OH   HO—C—R   H—C—O—C—R
| |
H   H

(1 mark for correct products, 1 mark for correct reactants)
(ii) tetradeca-3-enoic acid *(1 mark)*

b) (i) The fatty acid chain will be straight *(1 mark)*.
(ii) Bad cholesterol can clog blood vessels *(1 mark)*, which increases the risk of heart attacks and strokes *(1 mark)*. Recent research has shown that trans fats increase the amount of bad cholesterol *(1 mark)*.

c) (i)

H—C—O—C—R
| ‖
H—C—O—C—R   + 3CH$_3$OH
| ‖
H—C—O—C—R
|
H

⟶

H—C—OH
|
H—C—OH + 3 R—C(=O)O—CH$_3$
|
H—C—OH
|
H

(1 mark for correct products, 1 mark for correct reactants)
(ii) E.g. KOH *(1 mark)*.
(iii) Biodiesel is renewable so it won't run out *(1 mark)*.

d) The triglyceride must be heated under reflux *(1 mark)* with dilute sulfuric/hydrochloric acid *(1 mark for any named acid)*.

Module 2 — Polymers and Synthesis

1. Addition Polymers

Page 48 — Application Questions

Q1 a)

Br   H
 \   /
  C=C
 /   \
H   Br

b)

H$_3$C   H
  \   /
   C=C
  /   \
 H   OH

c)

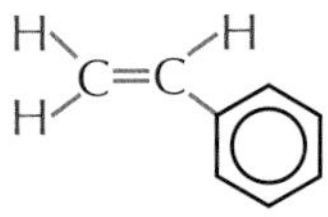

Q2 a) 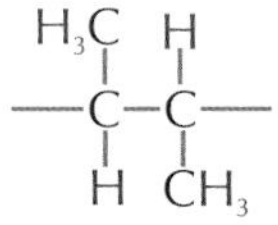   b) 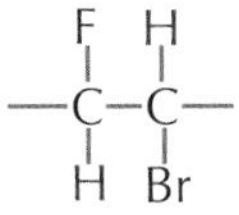   c)

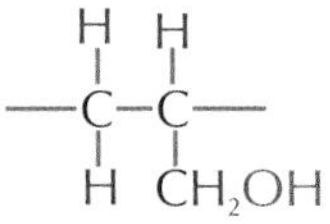

Q3

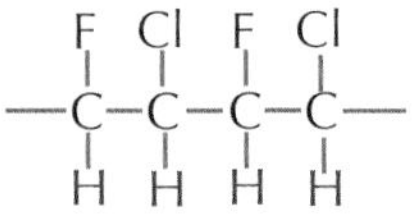

Q4 a) 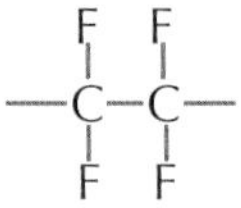   b)

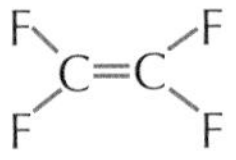

Page 48 — Fact Recall Questions

Q1   alkenes

Q2   addition polymerisation

Q3   A bit of molecule that repeats over and over again.

Q4   unreactive

2. Condensation Polymers

Page 52 — Application Questions

Q1   a) polyamide

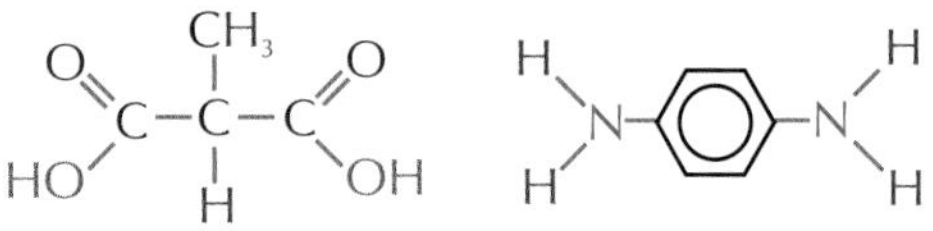

b) polyester 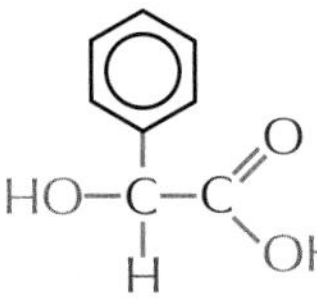   c) polyamide

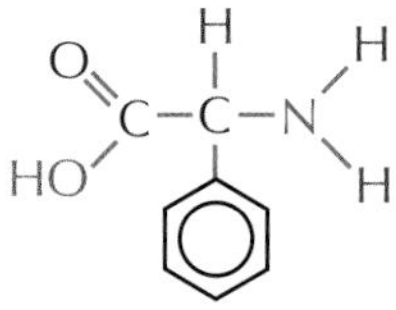

d) polyamide

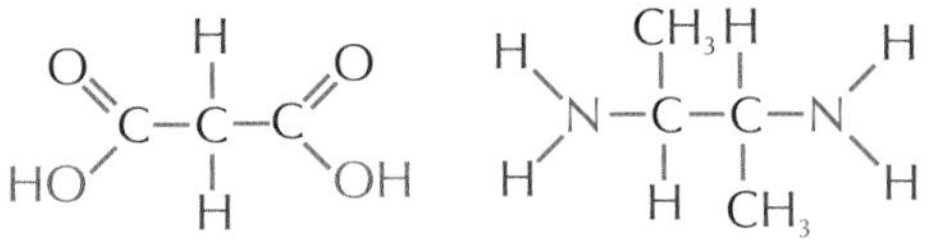

e) polyester

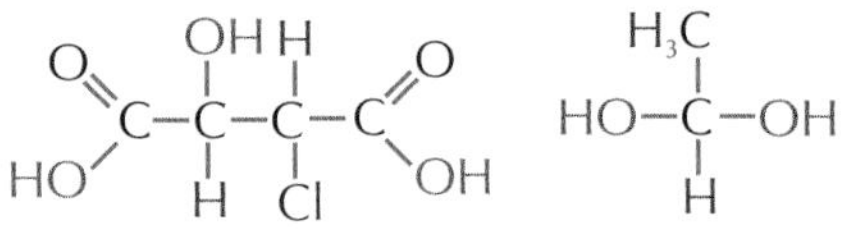

Q2   a)

b)

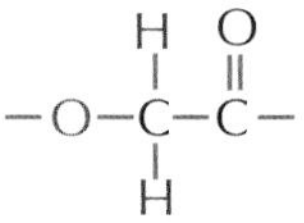

c)

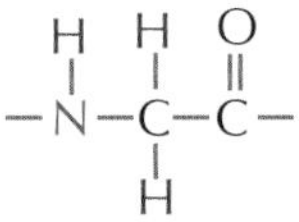

d)

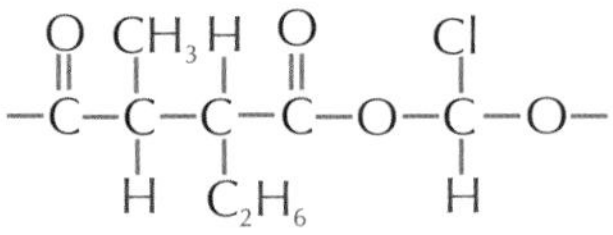

Page 52 — Fact Recall Questions

Q1   water

Q2   a) E.g. dicarboxylic acids and diamines.
     b) E.g. dicarboxylic acids and diols.

Q3   a) amide links
     b) ester links

Q4   E.g. in clothing.

3. Breaking Down Polymers

Page 54 — Application Questions

Q1   a)

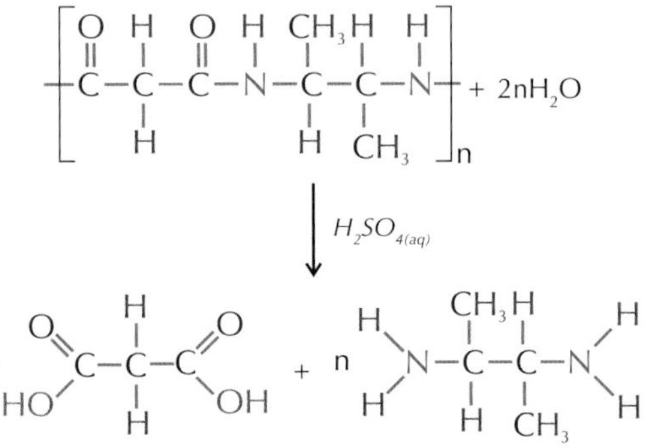

$+ 2nH_2O$

$H_2SO_{4(aq)}$

b)

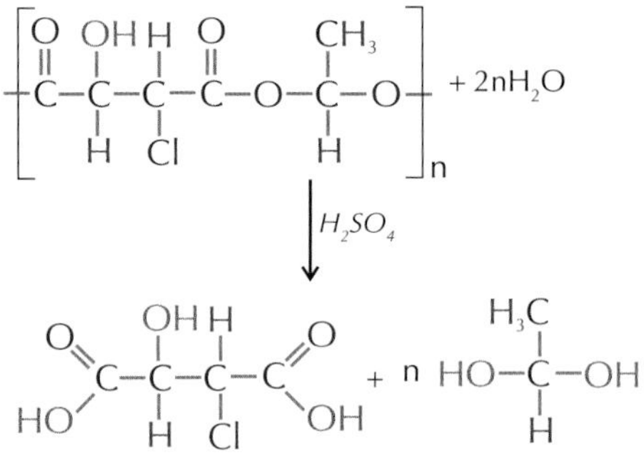

$+ 2nH_2O$

H_2SO_4

Q2   a)

$+ 2nNaOH$

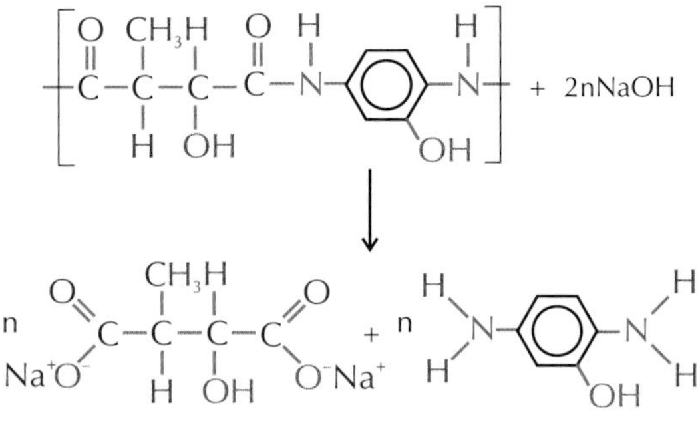

b)

[chemical structure: polyester + 2nNaOH]

↓

[chemical structure: sodium carboxylate products + n HO–CH₂–CH₂–OH]

Page 54 — Fact Recall Questions

Q1 Hydrolysis with just water is slow so an acid or an alkali is added to speed up the reaction.

Q2 an acid

Q3 E.g. a diol and a dicarboxylic acid salt.

Q4 PLA is a polyester. It's better for the environment because it is made from renewable resources so doesn't use up fossil fuels / it is biodegradable so won't stay around for a long time in landfill sites.

Q5 Photodegradable means a substance can be broken down by light.

4. Amino Acids and Proteins

Page 58 — Application Questions

Q1 a) E.g. they have different alkyl side-chains / different R groups.

  b) (i) [chemical structure] (ii) [chemical structure]

  (iii) [chemical structure]

  c) (i) base
   (ii) acid and base
   (iii) acid

  d) [chemical structure]

  or

  [chemical structure]

  There are two possible answers because the two amino acids can join together either way around.

Q2 a) [two chemical structures]

b)

[chemical structure: dipeptide + 2NaOH]

↓

[chemical structure: two sodium amino acid salts]

Page 58 — Fact Recall Questions

Q1 a) $RCH(NH_2)COOH$
  b) Carboxyl groups ($COOH$) and amino groups (NH_2).

Q2 Amino acids are amphoteric because they have a basic amino group and an acidic carboxyl group and so have both acidic and basic properties.

Q3 a) A zwitterion is a dipolar ion — it has both a positive and a negative charge in different parts of the molecule.
  b) At the isoelectric point — the pH where the average overall charge is zero for that amino acid.

Q4 a) condensation
  b) hydrolysis

Q5 carboxylate salts

5. Organic Synthesis

Page 61 — Application Questions

Q1 a) H_3PO_4 catalyst, steam, 300 °C, 60 atm
  b) Br_2, U.V. light
  c) ethanol, warm

Q2 a) step 1: $NaOH_{(aq)}$, reflux
   step 2: $K_2Cr_2O_7$, H_2SO_4, heat in distillation apparatus
   You have to do this reaction in distillation apparatus so that you don't form the carboxylic acid.
  b) step 1: HNO_2, HCl, <10 °C
   step 2: phenol, $NaOH_{(aq)}$, chill
  c) step 1: $K_2Cr_2O_7$, H_2SO_4, reflux
   step 2: methanol, conc. H_2SO_4, heat under reflux

Q3 X is nitrobenzene. Y is phenylamine.

Q4 step 1: $NaBH_4$ in water with methanol
  step 2: concentrated H_2SO_4 catalyst, reflux, 170 °C
  step 3: bromine water, 20 °C

Q5 step 1: HBr, 20 °C
  step 2: $NaOH_{(aq)}$, reflux
  step 3: $K_2Cr_2O_7$, H_2SO_4, reflux

6. Functional Groups

Page 64 — Application Questions

Q1 a) 3-amino-4-hydroxybutanal
  b) 3-amino-2-hydroxy-5-methylhexanoic acid

Q2 a) **A**   **B**

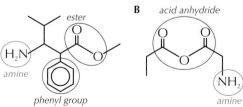

C

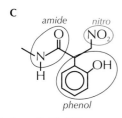

amide — O
nitro — NO₂
phenol

b) **A** — $C_{13}H_{19}NO_2$
   B — $C_5H_9NO_3$
   C — $C_{10}H_{12}N_2O_4$

c) Compound B
You know B will form esters with alcohols because it has an acid anhydride group.

d) Compound A
You know A will probably be sweet smelling because it has an ester group in it.

Page 64 — Fact Recall Questions

Q1 a)
$$-\overset{O}{\underset{}{C}}-O-$$

b) $-NO_2$

c) (benzene ring)

d) $C=C$

Q2 a) aldehydes
   b) acid anhydrides
   c) secondary amines
   d) ketones

Q3
$$\underset{\text{most important}}{-\overset{O}{\underset{}{C}}-OH} \longrightarrow \underset{}{-\overset{O}{\underset{}{C}}-N-} \longrightarrow -OH \longrightarrow \underset{\text{least important}}{-NH_2}$$

7. Stereoisomerism and Chirality

Page 68 — Application Questions

Q1 a) Z-isomer
   b) E-isomer

Q2 E-isomer:

$$\underset{(H_3C)_2HC}{\overset{H_3C}{>}}C=C\underset{CH_3}{\overset{Cl}{<}}$$

Z-isomer:

$$\underset{(H_3C)_2HC}{\overset{H_3C}{>}}C=C\underset{Cl}{\overset{CH_3}{<}}$$

Q3 a)
H   H   H
| | |
H—C—C—N—H
| |
H   Br

b)
H Cl CH₃ H
| | | |
H—C—C—C—C—H
| | | |
H   H CH₃ H

c)
H₃C H   H
| | |
H₃C—C—C—C—H
| | |
H   Br H

d)
H   H H   H Cl
| | | | \
H—C—C—C—C—C=C—H
| | | | /
H   F H CH₃ H

Q4 a)

$$\underset{H}{\overset{CH_3}{\underset{H_3C}{|}}}C\underset{}{CH_2OH} \quad \vdots \quad HOH_2C\overset{CH_3}{\underset{H}{|}}C_3H_7$$

b)

$$Cl_2HC\overset{H}{\underset{CH_3}{|}}C\underset{}{Br} \quad \vdots \quad Br\overset{H}{\underset{CH_3}{|}}C\underset{}{CHCl_2}$$

c)

$$HOH_2C\overset{H}{\underset{F}{|}}C\underset{}{OH} \quad \vdots \quad HO\overset{H}{\underset{F}{|}}C\underset{}{CH_2OH}$$

d)

$$H_3C\overset{H}{\underset{C_2H_5}{|}}C\underset{}{NH_2} \quad \vdots \quad H_2N\overset{H}{\underset{C_2H_5}{|}}C\underset{}{CH_3}$$

Q5

$$H_3CH_2C\overset{OH}{\underset{CN}{|}}C\underset{}{CH_3} \quad \vdots \quad H_3C\overset{OH}{\underset{CN}{|}}C\underset{}{CH_2CH_3}$$

Page 68 — Fact Recall Questions

Q1 A molecule that has the same structural formula as another molecule but its atoms are arranged differently in space.

Q2 You get E/Z-isomerism when a molecule has a carbon-carbon double bond and there are two different groups attached to the carbons either side of the double bond. The restricted rotation of the carbon-carbon double bond means that the atoms can be arranged differently in space.

Q3 Optical isomerism is a type of stereoisomerism. In optical isomers four groups are arranged in two different ways around a central carbon atom so that two different molecules are made — these molecules are non-superimposable mirror images of each other and are called enantiomers or optical isomers.

Q4 A chiral carbon atom is one that has four different groups attached to it.

Q5 Optically active molecules will rotate plane-polarised light.

8. Chirality and Drug Development

Page 70 — Fact Recall Questions

Q1 A racemic mixture is a mixture containing equal quantities of each enantiomer of an optically active compound.

Q2 When two molecules react there's an equal chance of forming each of the enantiomers, so you end up with equal amounts of each enantiomer and this is a racemic mixture.

Q3 Drugs containing both enantiomers may have harmful side effects because, whilst one enantiomer will work as you want it to, the other enantiomer could fit into a different active site.

Q4 There's no need to separate out the enantiomeric products, which reduces the difficulty and cost of producing the drug.

Q5 Chemical chiral synthesis is a technique which can be used to produce single enantiomer drugs. It involves using carefully chosen reagents and conditions which will ensure only one isomer is produced. Chemical chiral synthesis methods usually rely on chemically modifying the reagent molecule in a way that physically blocks most approaches to it, so that it can only be 'attacked' from one side.

Q6 E.g. using natural enzymes or bacteria which tend to produce only one isomer / using naturally occurring single optical isomer compounds as starting materials / using chiral catalysts.

Exam-style Questions — pages 72-74

1 a) (i) Stereoisomers are molecules with the same structural formula but different arrangements of atoms in space *(1 mark)*. 2-methyl-2-buten-1-ol shows E/Z isomerism *(1 mark)*.
   (ii) The C=C double bond *(1 mark)*.
   b)

(1 mark)

You only need to include square brackets if you're drawing the displayed formula of a polymer and have 'n' after it. If you're just drawing the repeat unit you don't really need them. Don't worry though— if you do put them in you shouldn't lose a mark.

   c) (i) Step 1: HBr, 20° C *(1 mark)*.
      Step 2: NaOH$_{(aq)}$, reflux *(1 mark)*.
   (ii) Yes. It has chiral carbon atoms *(1 mark)* so it exhibits optical isomerism *(1 mark)*.
   d) (i)

(1 mark)

It doesn't matter how you draw the molecule — whether you use a skeletal formula like this, or a displayed formula. As long as it's correct, you'll get the marks.

   (ii) polyester *(1 mark)*
   (iii) Photodegradation means being broken down by light *(1 mark)*. This polymer is photodegradable because it contains C=O groups *(1 mark)*, which absorb UV radiation causing the bonds either side of it to break *(1 mark)*.

2 a) (i) A and C are α-amino acids *(1 mark)*, because they have their carboxyl group and amino group attached to the same carbon *(1 mark)*.
   (ii) RCH(NH$_2$)COOH *(1 mark)*
   b) (i) 2-amino-3-methylbutanoic acid *(1 mark)*
   (ii)

(1 mark for each correctly drawn isomer).

   (iii)

(1 mark).

   c) (i) At a pH below its isoelectric point:

(1 mark)

At its isoelectric point:

(1 mark)

At a pH above its isoelectric point:

(1 mark)

   (ii) At a pH below its isoelectric point *(1 mark)*.
   d) (i) condensation polymerisation *(1 mark)*
   (ii)

(1 mark for correct structure, 1 mark for circling peptide link correctly).

You could also have drawn a displayed formula here. As long as you show the structure correctly, any type of drawing will do.

   (iii)

(1 mark)

3 a) (i)

(1 mark)

   (ii)

(1 mark)

   b) (i) Any three from: e.g. using natural enzymes or bacteria which tend to produce only one isomer / using naturally occurring single optical isomer compounds as starting materials / using chemical chiral synthesis / using chiral catalysts which produce only one isomer *(1 mark for each, maximum 3 marks)*.
   (ii) Any two from: e.g. they are less likely to cause harmful side-effects / half the dose is needed / the drug company is less likely to be sued over side-effects *(1 mark for each, maximum 2 marks)*.
   (iii) Any one from: e.g. they are expensive / they are difficult to produce *(1 mark)*.

4 a) Step 1: conc. HNO$_3$, conc H$_2$SO$_4$, warm *(1 mark)*.
   Product of step 1:

(1 mark)

You can also have this mark if you identified the product by saying that it is 1,3-dinitrobenzene.

   Step 2: concentrated HCl, Sn (tin), reflux, NaOH$_{(aq)}$ *(1 mark)*.

b)

HO⌁⌁OH

(1 mark)

reagents and conditions: acidified potassium dichromate ($K_2Cr_2O_7/H_2SO_4$), reflux *(1 mark)*.

c)

(1 mark)

polyamide *(1 mark)*

Module 3 — Analysis

1. Chromatography

Page 76 — Application Question

Q1 a) R_f value $= \dfrac{\text{distance travelled by spot}}{\text{distance travelled by solvent}}$

Spot P: R_f value $= 2.1 \div 8.0 = \mathbf{0.26}$
Spot Q: R_f value $= 3.7 \div 8.0 = \mathbf{0.46}$
Spot R: R_f value $= 5.9 \div 8.0 = \mathbf{0.74}$

  b) Spot P contains glycine, spot Q contains tyrosine and spot R contains leucine.

Page 76 — Fact Recall Questions

Q1 Chromatography is used to separate out the components of a mixture.

Q2 How far each part of the mixture travels up the plate depends on how strongly it's adsorbed to the stationary phase. A substance that's strongly adsorbed to the stationary phase spends more time stuck to the plate and less time dissolved in the solvent, so it moves slowly and doesn't travel as far as a weakly adsorbed substance. So the mixture separates out.
Remember, adsorption is the important idea here — as long as you're talking about differences in the strength of adsorption of the different components, you're on the right track.

Q3 R_f value $= \dfrac{\text{distance travelled by spot}}{\text{distance travelled by solvent}}$

2. Gas Chromatography

Page 79 — Application Questions

Q1 Components that are more soluble in the stationary phase take longer to travel through the tube, so the pure product will reach the detector after the impurities.

Q2 a) peak A
  b) component B
  c) component C

Q3 Total peak area $= 32 + 16 = 48$ cm^2
% of mixture that is Chemical 2 $= (16 \div 48) \times 100 = 33\%$
Peak 1 has twice the area of Peak 2. So the mixture must be two-thirds Chemical 1 and one-third Chemical 2.

Page 79 — Fact Recall Questions

Q1 E.g. helium gas/nitrogen gas.

Q2 Some of the components in a mixture will be more soluble in the stationary phase than others. This means that the components will spend different amounts of time dissolved in the stationary phase and travelling with the mobile phase. So they will take different amounts of time to pass through the tube and will be separated out.

Q3 The time taken from the injection of a sample to the detection of a substance.

Q4 The area under each peak tells you the relative amount of each component that's present in the mixture.

Q5 Similar compounds often have similar retention times, so they're difficult to identify accurately.
You can only use gas chromatography to identify substances that you already have reliable reference retention times for.

3. Mass Spectrometry

Page 82 — Application Questions

Q1 $CH_3CH_2CO^+$

Q2

This molecule is propanal.
This table shows all the m/z peaks from the mass spectrum and some of the fragment ions they can be assigned to:

m/z	fragment ion
15	CH_3^+
28	$C{=}O^+$
29	$CH_3CH_2^+ / CHO^+$
42	CH_2CO^+
57	$C_3H_5O^+$
58	$M\ (C_3H_6O^+)$

Don't forget that you don't have to assign all of these peaks — just as long as you've done enough to be able to prove that it's propanal...

Q3 Any two from: e.g. $CHO^+ / CH_2CHO^+ / CH_3CH_2CH_2^+ / CH_2CH_2CHO^+$.

Page 82 — Fact Recall Questions

Q1 Find the peak with the highest mass/charge ratio on the mass spectrum. Its m/z ratio will be the same as the M_r of the compound.

Q2 e.g. $CH_3CH_2^+$

4. Combining Chromatography with Mass Spectrometry

Page 84 — Application Question

Q1 a) The gas chromatograph (GC) separates out the chemicals in the water sample.
  b) E.g. the GC-MS machine will produce a mass spectrum for each individual chemical in the water sample. The scientist can compare these mass spectra to the mass spectrum of glyphosate looking for a match / examine the mass spectra, looking for one which shows the correct fragmentation pattern for glyphosate / use a computer to match up the mass spectra for each component of the mixture against a database.

Page 84 — Fact Recall Questions

Q1 The sample is separated out into its components using gas chromatography (GC). The separated components are fed into a mass spectrometer. This produces a mass spectrum for each component, which can be used to identify each one. Computers can be used to match up the mass spectrum for each component of the mixture against a database.

Q2 The components separated out by the GC can be positively identified by the MS. Identifying the components using GC alone can be impossible, because similar compounds often have similar retention times.

Q3 In HPLC, the stationary phase is a solid that is packed into a glass column. The mobile phase/a solvent and the sample are pushed through the column under high pressure. The sample separates as it moves through the column.

Q4 a) GC-MS can be used to look for specific substances like explosives or illegal drugs.
   b) Any two from: e.g. forensics/identifying substances found at crime scenes/fire investigation / in space probes / environmental analysis/monitoring pollutant/pesticide levels.

5. NMR Spectroscopy
Page 86 — Application Question
Q1 a) 4
   b) 3
   c) 2
   The molecules in parts b) and c) are symmetrical, so they have fewer carbon environments than carbon atoms in the molecule.

Page 86 — Fact Recall Questions
Q1 low-energy radio waves
Q2 parts per million/ppm
Q3 tetramethylsilane/TMS
Q4 An MRI scanner is used to study the internal structures of the body/produce images of the different tissues inside the body. This information can be used to diagnose and monitor tumours, examine bones and joints for signs of injury, and to study the brain and cardiovascular system.

6. ^{13}C NMR Spectroscopy
Page 89 — Application Questions
Q1 a) 4
   The number of peaks on the ^{13}C NMR spectrum is the same as the number of carbon environments in the molecule...
   b) 3
   c) 2
   This one's a bit tricky. If you draw the molecule, you should see that three of the carbons are CH_3 groups joined to the central carbon atom. These carbons are all in the same environment.
   d) 4
Q2 There are four peaks on the spectrum, so the molecule must have four carbon environments. All the peaks lie between $\delta = 10$ ppm and $\delta = 40$ ppm. Since the molecule only contains carbon and hydrogen, these must all represent carbon atoms in C–C bonds. The formula of the molecule is C_5H_{12}, so it must be an isomer of pentane with four carbon environments. The only molecule that fits this description is 2-methylbutane:

   Carbon 1 and the methyl group carbon are in the same environment. Carbons 2, 3 and 4 are all in different environments.
Q3 a) A carbon in a C–O environment.
   b) There are three peaks on the spectrum, so the molecule must have three carbon environments. The peaks at $\delta = 8$ ppm and $\delta = 25$ ppm must represent carbons in C–C bonds. The peak at $\delta = 65$ ppm must represent a carbon in a C–O bond. The formula of the molecule is $C_4H_{10}O$ and it must have three carbon environments. The only molecule that fits this description is 2-methylpropan-1-ol:

Page 89 — Fact Recall Questions
Q1 The number of carbon environments in the molecule.
Q2 The δ scale on a carbon-13 NMR spectrum increases from right to left.

7. ^{1}H NMR Spectroscopy
Page 92 — Application Questions
Q1 a) 2
   That's one environment for the two hydrogens on carbon 1 and one environment for the three hydrogens on carbon 3.
   b) 2
Q2 E.g.

   This is propane. You could also have had other things like butane or 2-methylpropane, but not ethane — that's only got one hydrogen environment.
Q3 a) 2
   b) 1 : 3
   c) 2 in environment A and 6 in environment B.
   You need to divide up the eight hydrogens between the two environments so that they end up in the ratio 1 : 3.
Q4 a) hydrogen atoms in an R–CH group
   b) hydrogen atoms in an HC=C– group
   You'd get the mark here for anything that showed clearly that you were talking about the right group (e.g. 'an H attached to a C=C group' or 'an H in an alkene group' would do for part b).
Q5 a) 2
   b) 1 : 1
   c) There will be one peak at $\delta = 2.0$-2.9 ppm and another at $\delta = 3.3$-4.2 ppm.

Page 92 — Fact Recall Questions
Q1 The number of hydrogen environments in the molecule.
Q2 The relative number of H atoms in each environment.
Q3 The relative areas under the peaks (and so the relative number of H atoms in each environment in the molecule).

8. More ^{1}H NMR Spectroscopy
Page 94 — Application Questions
Q1 2
   Think about the n + 1 rule — if the carbon next door has two hydrogens on it the peak will split into 2 + 1 = 3.
Q2 Environment 1: peak is a singlet / not split.
   Environment 2: peak split into four / quartet.
   Environment 3: peak split into two / doublet.

Page 96 — Application Questions
Q1 There are three peaks, so there must be three hydrogen environments in molecule **X**.
   The peak at $\delta = 2.5$ ppm is likely to be formed by hydrogens in a –COCH– environment. From the area ratio this peak has been caused by two protons (a $COCH_2$ group).
   It can't be an R –NH, an HC–N or a methylbenzene environment because none of those would fit with the molecular formula. And it can't be an R-OH group because the peak isn't a singlet.
   The peak at $\delta = 2.1$ ppm is also likely to be formed by hydrogens in a –COCH– environment. From the area ratio this peak has been caused by three protons (a $COCH_3$ group).
   This isn't likely to be an R-OH group because the area ratio tells you that the environment contains more than one hydrogen.
   The peak at $\delta = 1$ ppm is likely to be formed by hydrogens in an R–CH environment. From the area ratio this peak has been caused by three protons (a CH_3 group).
   It can't be an R –NH group because that wouldn't fit with the formula, and it isn't an R-OH group because it isn't a singlet.
   So the groups contained in molecule **X** are $COCH_2$, $COCH_3$ and CH_3. We know that the molecular formula is C_4H_8O and that the CH_3 group must be next to the $COCH_2$ (because their peaks are split into a triplet and a quartet).

So, the molecule must be butan-2-one:

Q2 There are three peaks, so there must be three hydrogen environments.

The peak at $\delta = 1.1$ ppm is likely to be formed by hydrogens in an R–CH environment. From the area ratio this peak has been caused by three protons (a –CH_3 group).

It can't be an R–OH group or an R–NH group because you don't find either of those groups in esters.

The peak at $\delta = 2.3$ ppm is likely to be formed by hydrogens in a –COCH– environment. From the area ratio this peak has been caused by two protons (a –$COCH_2$– group).

Again, it can't be any of the other groups that cause peaks at that chemical shift because none of them appear in an ester.

The peak at $\delta = 3.7$ ppm is likely to be formed by hydrogens in a HC–O– environment. From the area ratio this peak has been caused by three protons (an –O–CH_3 group).

And again — an ester doesn't contain any of the other groups that could be causing a peak at this chemical shift.

The peak at $\delta = 1.1$ ppm is a triplet, suggesting that it is adjacent to a carbon with two hydrogens. The peak at $\delta = 2.3$ ppm is a quartet, suggesting that it is adjacent to a carbon with three hydrogens. So these two groups must be next door to each other, giving CH_3–CH_2CO–.

The peak at $\delta = 3.7$ ppm is a singlet, so the –O–CH_3 group is not adjacent to any other hydrogens.

So the molecule is an ester containing the groups CH_3–CH_2CO– and –O–CH_3. It must be methyl propanoate:

Page 96 — Fact Recall Questions

Q1 The rule that states that, in ^{1}H NMR spectroscopy, peaks always split into the number of hydrogens on the neighbouring carbons, plus one.

Q2 a quartet

Q3 e.g. $CDCl_3$

Remember — the important thing here is that solvents for ^{1}H NMR can't contain any H atoms.

Q4 Run a ^{1}H NMR spectrum for the sample molecule just as normal. Then run another one with a little deuterium oxide/ D_2O, added. If an OH proton is present it'll swap with deuterium (to become an OD group). So the peak that was caused by the OH group on the first spectrum will be absent from the second spectrum.

9. Infrared Spectroscopy

Page 98 — Application Questions

Q1 The peak at ~1680 cm^{-1} could be due to the amide carbonyl group and the peak at 3350 cm^{-1} could be due to the amide N–H bond.

Q2 The strong, sharp peak at 1680 cm^{-1} probably represents a C=O bond in an aldehyde, ketone, carboxylic acid or ester. The broad peak at 2800 cm^{-1} could be due to a carboxylic acid OH bond. The medium peak at 3300 cm^{-1} is caused by a primary amine bond. So the compound must contain an NH_2 group and a COOH group. Since the molecular formula is $C_3H_7NO_2$, it must also contain two other carbon atoms and four other hydrogen atoms. Putting all those groups together the compound could either be:

or

10. More on Spectra

Page 102 — Application Questions

Q1 The mass spectrum shows that the M_r of the molecule is 58. It has a peak at m/z = 15, so it may contain a CH_3 group. It has a peak at 43, so it may contain a CH_3CO group or a $CH_3CH_2CH_2$ group.

The IR spectrum has a peak at 1700 cm^{-1}, so the molecule contains a carbonyl (C=O) group. As there are no peaks between 2500 cm^{-1} and 3300 cm^{-1} it can't contain any O–H or N–H bonds. So it isn't a carboxylic acid or an amide.

The ^{13}C NMR spectrum has two peaks, so the molecule has two carbon environments. The peak at $\delta = 205$ ppm is a carbon in a ketone or aldehyde group. The peak at $\delta = 29$ ppm is a carbon in a C–C group.

The ^{1}H NMR spectrum has one singlet peak, so the molecule has one hydrogen environment and there are no hydrogen atoms on adjacent carbons. This singlet peak at $\delta = 2.3$ ppm must be caused by hydrogens in a –$CHCO$– environment.

All the other groups that cause peaks at this chemical shift have been ruled out by the mass spectrum and IR spectrum. Since the peak is a singlet, there are no hydrogen atoms on adjacent carbons.

The molecule must be a ketone or aldehyde with an M_r of 58 — so it must be propanone (CH_3COCH_3) or propanal (CH_3CH_2CHO). Propanone has two carbon environments and one hydrogen environment. Propanal has three carbon environments and three hydrogen environments. So the molecule must be propanone:

It doesn't matter if you haven't answered this in exactly the same way as long as you've got most of the info down...

Q2 The IR spectrum has a strong peak at 1700 cm^{-1} and a broad peak at 3000 cm^{-1}, so it must contain a C=O bond and an O–H bond. Therefore it must be a carboxylic acid.

The ^{13}C NMR spectrum has three peaks, so the molecule must have three carbon environments.

There are only two carboxylic acids with the formula $C_4H_8O_2$ — butanoic acid ($CH_3CH_2CH_2COOH$) and 2-methylpropanoic acid ($C(CH_3)_2HCOOH$). Butanoic acid has four carbon environments, but 2-methylpropanoic acid has three. So the molecule must be 2-methylpropanoic acid:

Exam-style Questions — pages 104-106

1 **a)** The sample is separated using gas chromatography *(1 mark)*. The separated components are fed straight into a mass spectrometer, which is used to identify the individual components (by comparing the fragmentation pattern to a database of spectra) *(1 mark)*.

b) Gas chromatography uses retention times to identify the components of a mixture *(1 mark)*. Similar compounds have similar retention times, so can't be identified accurately *(1 mark)*.

c) (i) $CH_2CH_2CH_3^+$ *(1 mark)*
Remember you've been asked to identify the fragment ion, so don't forget to include the positive charge.
  (ii) 5 *(1 mark)*
If you had trouble with this, have a look back at the bit of the ^{13}C NMR topic about aromatic compounds and symmetry.

2 a) The spectrum has a strong peak at about 1200 cm^{-1}, suggesting a C–O bond in an alcohol, carboxylic acid or ester, and a broad peak at about 3500 cm^{-1}, suggesting an O–H bond in an alcohol or phenol *(1 mark)*. So the molecule must be an alcohol *(1 mark)*.
   b) (i) E.g. $CDCl_3$ *(1 mark)*.
Any deuterated solvent would get the mark here.
   (ii) The molecule is propan-2-ol:

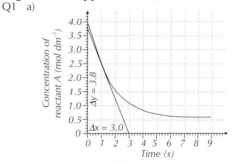

(1 mark for correctly identifying the molecule)
Plus any five from: There are three peaks, so the molecule must have three hydrogen environments *(1 mark)*. The peak at δ = 0.9 ppm must be due to hydrogens in an R–CH environment *(1 mark)*. This peak is a doublet, so there must be one hydrogen on adjacent carbons *(1 mark)*. The singlet peak at δ = 2.2 ppm must be due to a hydrogen in the alcohol group / an R–OH environment *(1 mark)*. The peak at δ = 4.0 ppm must be due to a hydrogen in an HC–O environment *(1 mark)*. It is a heptet, so there must be six hydrogens on adjacent carbons *(1 mark)*.
   (iii) The (singlet) peak at δ = 2.2 ppm would be missing *(1 mark)*.

3 a) Some components of the mixture will be more strongly adsorbed to the stationary phase than others *(1 mark)*. So the components will spend different amounts of time adsorbed to the stationary phase and will travel different distances in the same time *(1 mark)*.
   b) R_f value = $\dfrac{\text{distance travelled by spot}}{\text{distance travelled by solvent}}$
      = 2.2 cm ÷ 9.2 cm = **0.24** *(1 mark)*
   c) The peaks will be: a singlet caused by the hydrogens attached to carbon e *(1 mark)*, a heptet / seven-part peak caused by the hydrogen attached to carbon b *(1 mark)* and a doublet caused by the hydrogens attached to carbons a and c *(1 mark)*.

4 a) The compound has two hydrogen environments *(1 mark)*. The peak at δ = 1.8 ppm must represent hydrogens in R–CH environments *(1 mark)*. The peak at δ = 3.8 ppm must come from hydrogens in an HC–Cl environment *(1 mark)*. The peak at δ = 1.8 ppm is a quintet, so there must be four hydrogens on adjacent carbons *(1 mark)*. The peak at δ = 1.8 ppm is a triplet, so there must be two hydrogens on adjacent carbons *(1 mark)*. The only molecule with the formula $C_3H_6Cl_2$ that would fit this pattern of environments is 1,3-dichloropropane:

Cl–C–C–C–Cl (with H H H above and H H H below) *(1 mark)*
(Either quintet or triplet must be spelled correctly at least once to get full marks.)

b) The molecule is methylpropanal:

H–C–C–C–H (with CH$_3$, O double bond, and H's)

(1 mark for correctly identifying the molecule)
Plus any four from: the molecular ion peak on the mass spectrum is at m/z = 72, so the molecular mass of the molecule must be 72 *(1 mark)*. The mass spectrum has a peak at m/z = 15, so the molecule probably contains a CH_3 group *(1 mark for any peak on the mass spectrum matched to a correct fragment of the molecule)*. The ^{13}C NMR spectrum has three peaks, so the molecule must have three carbon environments *(1 mark)*. There is a peak at δ = 15 ppm and another at δ = 35 ppm, so the molecule must contain at least two carbons in C–C environments *(1 mark)*. There is a peak at δ = 205 ppm, so the molecule must contain at least one carbon in an aldehyde or ketone C=O environment *(1 mark)*. There are only three isomers that are aldehydes or ketones with an M$_r$ of 72 — butanone, butanal and methylpropanal. *(1 mark for any representation of the three possible isomers)*. Methylpropanal is the only possible isomer that has three carbon environments *(1 mark)*.
There are usually more things to say than there are marks for this type of question, so you don't need to say all of this to get full marks. Just make sure you've made it clear to the examiner how you got to your answer.

Unit 5

Module 1 — Rates, Equilibrium and pH

1. Reaction Rates
Page 109 — Application Question
Q1 a)

Rate = $\dfrac{\Delta y}{\Delta x}$ = $\dfrac{-3.8}{3.0}$ = –1.3 mol dm^{-3} s^{-1}

Drawing tangents accurately is tricky so there may be some variation between the answer you got and the 'official' answer. Don't worry though — in the exam, you'll usually be allowed a range of answers if you're asked to calculate a gradient. So for part a) allow yourself anything from –0.9 to –1.7.

b)

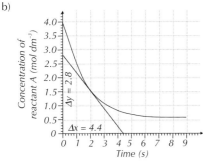

$$\text{Rate} = \frac{\Delta y}{\Delta x} = \frac{-2.8}{4.4} = -0.64 \text{ mol dm}^{-3} \text{ s}^{-1}$$

For part b) anything from −0.44 to −0.84 is OK.

c)

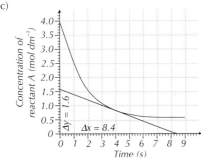

$$\text{Rate} = \frac{\Delta y}{\Delta x} = \frac{-1.6}{8.4} = -0.19 \text{ mol dm}^{-3} \text{ s}^{-1}$$

For part c) anything from −0.13 to −0.25 will do.

Page 109 — Fact Recall Questions

Q1 A reaction rate is the change in the amount of reactants or products per unit time.

Q2 The units of reaction rate are normally mol dm⁻³ s⁻¹.

Q3 E.g. by measuring the volume of gas produced / by measuring a colour change using a colorimeter / by measuring electrical conductivity.

Q4 a) Measure the concentration of a reactant at regular time points as a reaction progresses. Plot concentration against time to produce a concentration-time graph.

    b) Measure the gradient of the graph at that particular time. The gradient is the rate of reaction.

2. Rate Equations

Pages 112-113 — Application Questions

Q1 a) Rate = $k[Na_2S_2O_3]$

    b) If the concentration of $Na_2S_2O_3$ were doubled the rate of the reaction would also double.

Q2 a) Rate = $k[NO]^2[Cl_2]$

    b) $5.85 \times 10^{-6} = k(0.4)^2(0.4)$ so

$$k = \frac{5.85 \times 10^{-6}}{[0.4]^2[0.4]} = 9.14 \times 10^{-5}$$

Now find the units for k:

$$k = \frac{\text{mol dm}^{-3} \text{ s}^{-1}}{(\text{mol dm}^{-3})^2(\text{mol dm}^{-3})} = \text{mol}^{-2} \text{ dm}^6 \text{ s}^{-1}$$

$$k = \mathbf{9.14 \times 10^{-5} \text{ mol}^{-2} \text{ dm}^6 \text{ s}^{-1}}$$

    c) If the temperature was increased the value of k would increase.

d) Rate = $k[NO]^2[Cl_2]$
    Rate = $(9.14 \times 10^{-5}) \times (0.5)^2 \times 0.2$
    $= \mathbf{4.57 \times 10^{-6} \text{ mol dm}^{-3} \text{ s}^{-1}}$

These answers are all rounded to 3 significant figures. In your exam, round your answer to the same number of significant figures as is given in the question. If in doubt, go for 3.

Q3 a) Rate = $k[H_2][NO]^2$
    $0.0100 = k(5.00 \times 10^{-3})(5.00 \times 10^{-3})^2$ so

$$k = \frac{0.0100}{[5.00 \times 10^{-3}][5.00 \times 10^{-3}]^2} = 8.00 \times 10^4$$

$$k = \frac{\text{mol dm}^{-3} \text{ s}^{-1}}{(\text{mol dm}^{-3})(\text{mol dm}^{-3})^2} = \text{mol}^{-2} \text{ dm}^6 \text{ s}^{-1}$$

$$k = \mathbf{8.00 \times 10^4 \text{ mol}^{-2} \text{ dm}^6 \text{ s}^{-1}}$$

    b) Rate = $k[H_2][NO]^2$
    Rate = $(8.0 \times 10^4) \times (3.6 \times 10^{-3}) \times (6.4 \times 10^{-3})^2$
    $= \mathbf{0.012 \text{ mol dm}^{-3} \text{ s}^{-1}}$

    c) Temperature Y must be lower than temperature X. The value of k at temperature Y is lower than the value of k at temperature X, so the rate of reaction at temperature Y must be slower.

Page 113 — Fact Recall Questions

Q1 The rate equation tells you how the rate of a reaction is affected by the concentration of the reactants.

Q2 a) The rate constant.

    b) The concentration of reactant A.

    c) The order of the reaction with respect to A.

Q3 Rate = $k[A]^m[B]^n[C]^x$

Q4 The reaction order with respect to a particular reactant tells you how the reactant's concentration affects the rate of reaction.

Q5 The units of k vary.

Q6 The higher the temperature the higher the rate constant.

3. Reaction Orders and Half-Life

Pages 115-116 — Application Questions

Q1 a) A = first order
    B = zero order
    C = second order

    b) (i) If [A] was halved the rate of reaction would also halve.

    (ii) If [B] was tripled the rate of reaction would stay the same.

    (iii) If [C] was doubled, the reaction rate would increase by a factor of four (quadruple).

Q2 a)

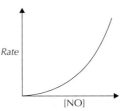

If you're asked to draw or sketch a graph in your exam, make sure you label the axes — if you don't your graph could be showing anything and you won't get the marks.

    b) If the concentration of O_2 was doubled the reaction rate would also double.

Q3 a) E.g.

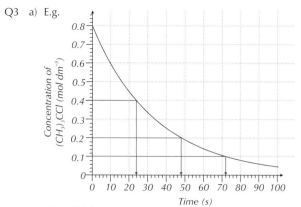

The half-life is 24 seconds.

b) The reaction is first order. The half-life is independent of the concentration (it's 24 seconds each time).

Page 116 — Fact Recall Questions

Q1 a) Find the gradient at various points along the concentration-time graph. Plot rate of reaction against concentration to produce a rate-concentration graph.

b) The shape of the rate-concentration graph indicates the order of reaction (horizontal line = zero order, straight line through the origin = first order, curve = second order).

Q2 The half-life of a reaction is the amount of time it takes for half of the reactant to be used up.

Q3 If the half-life is independent of concentration (i.e. the half-life stays constant during the reaction), the reaction is first order.

4. Initial Rates

Page 119 — Application Questions

Q1 Looking at experiments 1 and 2: doubling $[O_3]$ doubles the rate so the reaction is order 1 with respect to O_3.
Looking at experiments 2 and 3: tripling $[C_2H_4]$ triples the rate so the reaction is order 1 with respect to C_2H_4.

Q2 Looking at experiments 1 and 2: doubling [B] quadruples the rate so the reaction is order 2 with respect to B.
Looking at experiments 2 and 3: tripling [C] triples the rate so the reaction is order 1 with respect to C.
Look at experiments 2 and 4: the reaction is first order with respect to C so [C] double will double the rate of reaction to 2.00 mol dm^{-3} s^{-1}. So halving [A] must have halved the reaction rate back down to 1.00 mol dm^{-3} s^{-1}. This means that the reaction is first order with respect to A.
You could also work out the order with respect to A from experiments 3 and 4. Decreasing [C] by a third decreases the rate from 3.00 mol dm^{-3} s^{-1} to 2.00 mol dm^{-3} s^{-1}. Halving [A] decreases the rate from 2.00 mol dm^{-3} s^{-1} to 1.00 mol dm^{-3} s^{-1}, so the reaction must be first order with respect to A.

Page 119 — Fact Recall Questions

Q1 Draw a tangent to the curve at time zero and find the gradient of the tangent. The gradient is the initial rate.

Q2 a) The initial rate of a reaction.
b) E.g. the iodine clock reaction.

5. The Rate-Determining Step

Page 123 — Application Questions

Q1 Rate = $k[A]^2[B]$
Don't forget to include the rate constant in your answer. If you've just written rate = $[A]^2[B]$, your answer's not right, even though you've done all the hard work working out the reaction orders.

Q2 Rate = $k[Br_2][NO]$

Q3 a) Step 1. The rate equation shows that the rate-determining step involves two molecules of NO_2, and there are two NO_2 molecules in step 1.
Don't forget — if it's in the rate equation it must be involved in the rate-determining step.

b) If the reaction had a one-step mechanism, that step would have to involve CO. CO is not in the rate equation so can't be involved in the rate-determining step. So a one-step mechanism isn't possible.

Q4 E.g. $O_{3\,(g)} \rightarrow O_{2\,(g)} + O\bullet_{(g)}$
$O\bullet_{(g)} + O_{3\,(g)} \rightarrow 2O_{2\,(g)}$
If you didn't get this answer don't worry. As long at the equations add up to the overall equation, the first step (the rate determining step) only involves one molecule of O_3 and your equations are balanced you can have the mark.

Q5 E.g. $H_2O_{2\,(aq)} + I^-_{(aq)} \rightarrow H_2O_{(l)} + IO^-_{(aq)}$
$H_2O_{2\,(aq)} + IO^-_{(aq)} \rightarrow H_2O_{(l)} + O_{2\,(g)} + I^-_{(aq)}$
Don't forget — if you're given a reaction involving a catalyst, make sure the catalyst is regenerated at the end. If the catalyst hasn't been regenerated you must have gone wrong somewhere.

Page 123 — Fact Recall Questions

Q1 The rate-determining step is the slowest step in a reaction mechanism, so it's the step which determines the overall rate of the reaction.

Q2 2

Q3 1

6. The Equilibrium Constant

Page 127 — Application Questions

Q1 a) $K_c = \dfrac{[C_2H_5OH]}{[C_2H_4][H_2O]}$

b) The equation tells you that if 1 mole of C_2H_5OH decomposes, 1 mole of C_2H_4 and 1 mole of H_2O are formed. So if 1.85 moles of C_2H_4 are produced at equilibrium, there will also be **1.85** moles of H_2O. 1.85 moles of C_2H_5OH has decomposed so there must be 5 – 1.85 = **3.15** moles of C_2H_5OH remaining.

c) The volume of the reaction is 15 dm^3. So the molar concentrations are:
For H_2O and C_2H_4: 1.85 ÷ 15 = **0.123 mol dm^{-3}**.
For C_2H_5OH: 3.15 ÷ 15 = **0.210 mol dm^{-3}**.

d) $K_c = \dfrac{[C_2H_5OH]}{[C_2H_4][H_2O]} = \dfrac{0.210}{(0.123)(0.123)} = 13.9$

$K_c = \dfrac{(\text{mol dm}^{-3})}{(\text{mol dm}^{-3})(\text{mol dm}^{-3})} = \dfrac{1}{(\text{mol dm}^{-3})}$

$K_c = \textbf{13.9 mol}^{-1}\textbf{ dm}^3$

Setting your answer out like this makes it clear to the examiner what you've done and means you're more likely to pick up some method marks.

e) $K_c = \dfrac{[C_2H_5OH]}{[C_2H_4][H_2O]}$ so $3.8 = \dfrac{0.8}{[C_2H_4][H_2O]}$

$[C_2H_4][H_2O] = 0.8 \div 3.8 = 0.21$
$[C_2H_4]$ and $[H_2O] = \sqrt{0.21} = \textbf{0.46 mol dm}^{-3}$

Q2 a) $K_c = \dfrac{[SO_3]^2}{[SO_2]^2[O_2]}$

b) $K_c = \dfrac{[SO_3]^2}{[SO_2]^2[O_2]} = \dfrac{0.36^2}{(0.25)^2(0.18)} = 11.5$

$K_c = \dfrac{(mol\ dm^{-3})^2}{(mol\ dm^{-3})^2(mol\ dm^{-3})} = \dfrac{1}{(mol\ dm^{-3})}$

$K_c = \textbf{11.5 mol}^{-1}\textbf{ dm}^3$

c) $[SO_2]^2 = \dfrac{[SO_3]^2}{K_c \times [O_2]} = \dfrac{0.36^2}{15 \times 0.18} = 0.048$

$[SO_2] = \sqrt{0.048} = \textbf{0.22 mol dm}^{-3}$

Page 127 — Fact Recall Questions

Q1 A dynamic equilibrium occurs when the reaction is still happening but the forward and backward reaction are going at exactly the same rate so there is no net change in the concentrations of the reagents.

Q2 For a dynamic equilibrium to be established it must be a closed system and the temperature must be constant.

Q3 $K_c = \dfrac{[D]^d[E]^e}{[A]^a[B]^b}$

Q4 The units of K_c change depending on the concentration terms in the reaction.

7. Changing the Equilibrium

Page 130 — Application Questions

Q1 a) No effect — if the concentration of C_2F_4 increases the equilibrium will shift to counteract the change and K_c will stay the same.

b) The reaction is endothermic in the forward direction so increasing the temperature will shift the equilibrium to the right. As a result more product will be produced, so K_c will increase.

c) No effect — catalysts only affect the time taken to reach equilibrium and not the position of the equilibrium itself.
It's only changing temperature that changes the value of K_c.

Q2 a) Exothermic. If decreasing the temperature increases K_c then it must increase the amount of product formed. The equilibrium must have shifted to the right, so the forward reaction must be exothermic.

b) (i) The equilibrium would shift to the left.
(ii) The value of K_c would not change.

Q3 a) Increase the temperature.

b) E.g. decrease the pressure / increase the concentration of the reactants.

Page 130 — Fact Recall Questions

Q1 If there's a change in concentration, pressure or temperature then an equilibrium will move to help counteract the change.

Q2 a) It will increase K_c.

b) It will decrease K_c.

Q3 If the concentration of a reagent is changed the equilibrium will shift and the concentrations of other reagents will also change. So K_c will stay the same.

Q4 Increasing the pressure has no affect on the value of K_c.

Q5 Adding a catalyst doesn't change the position of the equilibrium or K_c, but it decreases the time taken to reach equilibrium.

8. Acids and Bases

Page 134 — Application Questions

Q1 a) Full: $2HCl_{(aq)} + 2Na_{(s)} \rightarrow 2NaCl_{(aq)} + H_{2(g)}$
Ionic: $2H^+_{(aq)} + 2Na_{(s)} \rightarrow 2Na^+_{(aq)} + H_{2(g)}$
Make sure you always include the H^+ ions in your ionic equations.

b) Full: $H_2SO_{4(aq)} + CaCO_{3(s)} \rightarrow CaSO_{4(aq)} + H_2O_{(l)} + CO_{2(g)}$
Ionic: $2H^+_{(aq)} + CO_3{}^{2-}_{(s)} \rightarrow H_2O_{(l)} + CO_{2(g)}$

c) Full: $HNO_{3(aq)} + KOH_{(aq)} \rightarrow KNO_{3(aq)} + H_2O_{(l)}$
Ionic: $H^+_{(aq)} + OH^-_{(aq)} \rightarrow H_2O_{(l)}$

d) Full: $2HCN_{(aq)} + Na_2O_{(aq)} \rightarrow 2NaCN_{(aq)} + H_2O_{(l)}$
Ionic: $2H^+_{(aq)} + O^{2-}_{(aq)} \rightarrow H_2O_{(l)}$

Q2 a) $H_2CO_{3(aq)} + H_2O_{(l)} \rightleftharpoons H_3O^+_{(aq)} + HCO_3{}^-_{(aq)}$
        acid 1   base 2   acid 2   base 1

b) $CH_3NH_{2(aq)} + H_2O_{(l)} \rightleftharpoons CH_3NH_3{}^+ + OH^-$
        base 1   acid 2   acid 1   base 2

c) $CH_3COO^-_{(aq)} + NH_4{}^+_{(aq)} \rightleftharpoons CH_3COOH_{(aq)} + NH_{3(aq)}$
        base 1   acid 2   acid 1   base 2

d) $HCl_{(aq)} + OH^-_{(aq)} \rightleftharpoons Cl^-_{(aq)} + H_2O_{(l)}$
    acid 1   base 2   base 1   acid 2

Page 134 — Fact Recall Questions

Q1 a) A Brønsted-Lowry acid is a proton donor.
b) A Brønsted-Lowry base is a proton acceptor.

Q2 a) hydrogen gas and a salt
b) carbon dioxide, water and a salt
c) water and a salt

Q3 a) A strong acid.
b) A weak base.

Q4 A conjugate pair is a set of two species that can be transformed into each other by gaining or losing a proton.

9. pH Calculations

Page 135 — Application Questions

Q1 $pH = -log[H^+] = -log[0.05] = \textbf{1.30}$

Q2 $[H^+] = 10^{-pH} = 10^{-2.86} = \textbf{1.38} \times \textbf{10}^{-3}\textbf{ mol dm}^{-3}$

Q3 $pH = -log[H^+] = -log[0.02] = \textbf{1.70}$

Page 136 — Application Questions

Q1 HCl is monobasic so $[H^+] = [HCl] = 0.080$ mol dm^{-3}
$pH = -log[H^+] = -log[0.08] = \textbf{1.10}$

Q2 HNO_3 is monobasic so $[H^+] = [HNO_3] = 0.12$ mol dm^{-3}
$pH = -log[H^+] = -log[0.12] = \textbf{0.92}$

Q3 $[H^+] = 10^{-pH} = 10^{-0.96} = 0.11$ mol dm^{-3}
HCl is monobasic so $[HCl] = [H^+] = \textbf{0.11 mol dm}^{-3}$

Q4 $[H^+] = 10^{-pH} = 10^{-1.28} = 0.0525$ mol dm^{-3}
HNO_3 is monobasic so $[HNO_3] = [H^+] = \textbf{0.0525 mol dm}^{-3}$

Page 136 — Fact Recall Questions

Q1 $pH = -log[H^+]$

Q2 $[H^+] = 10^{-pH}$

Q3 Monobasic means that each molecule of acid releases one proton.

Q4 For strong monobasic acids the concentration of H^+ ions is the same as the concentration of the acid.

10. The Ionic Product of Water

Page 138 — Application Questions

Q1 KOH is a strong base so $[OH^-] = [KOH] = 0.200$ mol dm^{-3}
$K_w = [H^+][OH^-]$ so $[H^+] = K_w \div [OH^-]$
$= (5.48 \times 10^{-14}) \div 0.200 = 2.74 \times 10^{-13}$
$pH = -log[H^+] = -log(2.74 \times 10^{-13}) = \textbf{12.6}$

Q2 NaOH is a strong base so $[OH^-] = [KOH] = 0.155$ mol dm^{-3}
$K_w = [H^+][OH^-]$ so $[H^+] = K_w \div [OH^-]$
$= (6.8 \times 10^{-15}) \div 0.155 = 4.39 \times 10^{-14}$
$pH = -log[H^+] = -log(4.39 \times 10^{-14}) = \textbf{13.4}$

Q3 KOH is a strong base so $[OH^-] = [KOH] = 0.084$ mol dm^{-3}
$K_w = [H^+][OH^-]$ so $[H^+] = K_w \div [OH^-]$
$= (2.9 \times 10^{-15}) \div 0.084 = 3.45 \times 10^{-14}$
$pH = -log[H^+] = -log(3.45 \times 10^{-14}) = \textbf{13.5}$

Page 139 — Application Questions

Q1 $[H^+] = 10^{-pH} = 10^{-12.40} = 3.98 \times 10^{-13}$ mol dm^{-3}
$K_w = [H^+][OH^-]$ so $[OH^-] = K_w \div [H^+]$
$= (6.8 \times 10^{-15}) \div (3.98 \times 10^{-13}) = 0.0171$ mol dm^{-3}
KOH is a strong base so $[KOH] = [OH^-] = \textbf{0.0171 mol dm}^{-3}$

Q2 $[H^+] = 10^{-pH} = 10^{-13.98} = 1.05 \times 10^{-14}$ mol dm^{-3}
$K_w = [H^+][OH^-]$ so $[OH^-] = K_w \div [H^+]$
$= (2.92 \times 10^{-14}) \div (1.05 \times 10^{-14}) = 2.78$ mol dm^{-3}
NaOH is a strong base so $[NaOH] = [OH^-] = \mathbf{2.78\ mol\ dm^{-3}}$

Q3 $[H^+] = 10^{-pH} = 10^{-13.25} = 5.62 \times 10^{-14}$ mol dm^{-3}
$K_w = [H^+][OH^-]$ so $[OH^-] = K_w \div [H^+]$
$= (1.47 \times 10^{-14}) \div (5.62 \times 10^{-14}) = 0.262$ mol dm^{-3}
KOH is a strong base so $[KOH] = [OH^-] = \mathbf{0.262\ mol\ dm^{-3}}$

Q4   For pure water $[H^+] = [OH^-]$ so $K_w = [H^+]^2$.
$[H^+] = \sqrt{K_w} = \sqrt{1.47 \times 10^{-14}} = 1.21 \times 10^{-7}$
pH $= -\log[H^+] = -\log(1.21 \times 10^{-7}) = \mathbf{6.92}$

Q5   For pure water $[H^+] = [OH^-]$ so $K_w = [H^+]^2$.
$[H^+] = \sqrt{K_w} = \sqrt{2.92 \times 10^{-14}} = 1.71 \times 10^{-7}$
pH $= -\log[H^+] = -\log(1.71 \times 10^{-7}) = \mathbf{6.77}$

Q6   For pure water $[H^+] = [OH^-]$ so $K_w = [H^+]^2$.
$[H^+] = \sqrt{K_w} = \sqrt{5.13 \times 10^{-13}} = 7.16 \times 10^{-7}$
pH $= -\log[H^+] = -\log(7.16 \times 10^{-7}) = \mathbf{6.15}$

Page 139 — Fact Recall Questions

Q1 $K_w = [H^+][OH^-]$
For this question you can't put $K_w = [H^+]^2$ because this only applies to pure water.

Q2   mol^2 dm^{-6}

Q3   In pure water, $[H^+] = [OH^-]$ so $K_w = [H^+]^2$.

11. The Acid Dissociation Constant

Page 143 — Application Questions

Q1   a) $K_a = [H^+][CN^-] \div [HCN]$ or $K_a = [H^+]^2 \div [HCN]$
b) $K_a = [H^+]^2 \div [HCN]$ so $[H^+]^2 = K_a \times [HCN]$
$= (4.9 \times 10^{-10}) \times 2.0 = 9.8 \times 10^{-10}$
$[H^+] = \sqrt{9.8 \times 10^{-10}} = 3.13 \times 10^{-5}$ mol dm^{-3}
pH $= -\log[H^+] = -\log[3.13 \times 10^{-5}] = \mathbf{4.50}$

Q2 $[H^+] = 10^{-pH} = 10^{-3.8} = 1.58 \times 10^{-4}$ mol dm^{-3}
$K_a = [H^+]^2 \div [HNO_2]$ so $[HNO_2] = [H^+]^2 \div K_a$
$= (1.58 \times 10^{-4})^2 \div 4.0 \times 10^{-4} = \mathbf{6.24 \times 10^{-5}\ mol\ dm^{-3}}$

Q3 $K_a = [H^+]^2 \div [HA]$ so $[H^+]^2 = K_a \times [HA]$
$= (1.38 \times 10^{-4}) \times 0.480 = 6.62 \times 10^{-5}$
$[H^+] = \sqrt{6.62 \times 10^{-5}} = 8.14 \times 10^{-3}$ mol dm^{-3}
pH $= -\log[8.14 \times 10^{-3}] = \mathbf{2.09}$

Q4 $[H^+] = 10^{-pH} = 10^{-4.11} = 7.76 \times 10^{-5}$ mol dm^{-3}
$K_a = [H^+]^2 \div [HA] = (7.76 \times 10^{-5})^2 \div 0.280$
$= \mathbf{2.15 \times 10^{-8}\ mol\ dm^{-3}}$

Q5 $[H^+] = 10^{-pH} = 10^{-3.67} = 2.14 \times 10^{-4}$ mol dm^{-3}
$K_a = [H^+]^2 \div [HCOOH]$ so $[HCOOH] = [H^+]^2 \div K_a$
$= (2.14 \times 10^{-4})^2 \div (1.8 \times 10^{-4}) = \mathbf{2.54 \times 10^{-4}\ mol\ dm^{-3}}$

Q6   a) $K_a = 10^{-pKa} = 10^{-4.78} = \mathbf{1.66 \times 10^{-5}\ mol\ dm^{-3}}$
b) $K_a = [H^+]^2 \div [CH_3COOH]$ so
$[H^+]^2 = K_a \times [CH_3COOH] = (1.66 \times 10^{-5}) \times 0.250$
$= 4.15 \times 10^{-6}$ mol^2 dm^{-6}
$[H^+] = \sqrt{4.15 \times 10^{-6}} = 2.04 \times 10^{-3}$ mol dm^{-3}
% dissociation $= ([H^+] \div [HA]) \times 100$
$= ((2.04 \times 10^{-3}) \div 0.250) \times 100 = \mathbf{0.82\%}$

Q7 $[H^+] = 10^{-pH} = 10^{-4.5} = 3.16 \times 10^{-5}$ mol dm^{-3}
$K_a = [H^+]^2 \div [HA] = (3.16 \times 10^{-5})^2 \div 0.154$
$= 6.49 \times 10^{-9}$ mol dm^{-3}
$pK_a = -\log(K_a) = -\log(6.49 \times 10^{-9}) = \mathbf{8.19}$

Q8 $K_a = 10^{-pKa} = 10^{-3.14} = 7.24 \times 10^{-4}$ mol dm^{-3}
$[H^+] = 10^{-pH} = 10^{-3.2} = 6.31 \times 10^{-4}$ mol dm^{-3}
$K_a = [H^+]^2 \div [HF]$ so $[HF] = [H^+]^2 \div K_a$
$= (6.31 \times 10^{-4})^2 \div 7.24 \times 10^{-4} = \mathbf{5.50 \times 10^{-4}\ mol\ dm^{-3}}$

Q9 $K_a = 10^{-pKa} = 10^{-4.5} = 3.16 \times 10^{-5}$ mol dm^{-3}
$K_a = [H^+]^2 \div [HX]$ so $[H^+]^2 = K_a \times [HX]$
$= (3.16 \times 10^{-5}) \times 0.60 = 1.90 \times 10^{-5}$ mol^2 dm^{-6}
so $[H^+] = \sqrt{1.9 \times 10^{-5}} = 4.36 \times 10^{-3}$ mol dm^{-3}
pH $= -\log[H^+] = -\log[4.36 \times 10^{-3}] = \mathbf{2.36}$

Page 143 — Fact Recall Questions

Q1   mol dm^{-3}

Q2   a) $K_a = [H^+][A^-] \div [HA]$ or $K_a = [H^+]^2 \div [HA]$
b) $[HA] = [H^+][A^-] \div K_a$ or $[HA] = [H^+]^2 \div K_a$

Q3   E.g. Calculating the pH of a weak acid and calculating the concentration of a weak acid.

Q4   a) $pK_a = -\log_{10}(K_a)$
b) $K_a = 10^{-pKa}$

12. Buffer Action

Page 145 — Fact Recall Questions

Q1   A buffer is a solution that resists changes in pH when small amounts of acid or alkali are added.

Q2   a)   When acid is added $[H^+]$ increases. Most of the extra H$^+$ ions combine with A$^-$ ions to form HA. This shifts the equilibrium to the left so $[H^+]$ is reduced to almost its original value and so the pH doesn't change much.
b)   When a base is added $[OH^-]$ increases. Most of the extra OH$^-$ ions react with H$^+$ ions to form water. This removes H$^+$ ions from the solution so the equilibrium shifts to the right and the HA dissociates to compensate. More H$^+$ ions are formed and so the pH doesn't change much.

Q3   By mixing a solution of a weak acid with a solution of one of its salts or by reacting an excess of a weak acid with an alkali.
When describing how to prepare a buffer from an acid and a base, make sure you say that the acid is in excess — you might lose a mark if you don't.

Q4   Carbonic acid is used to buffer the pH of blood and keep it at 7.4.

Q5   Because bacteria and fungi can cause changes in pH which cause food to deteriorate.

13. Calculating the pH of Buffers

Page 148 — Application Questions

Q1   a) $CH_3CH_2COOH \rightleftharpoons H^+ + CH_3CH_2COO^-$ so
$$K_a = \frac{[H^+][CH_3CH_2COO^-]}{[CH_3CH_2COOH]}$$
b) $K_a = [H^+][CH_3CH_2COO^-] \div [CH_3CH_2COOH]$ so
$[H^+] = (K_a \times [CH_3CH_2COOH]) \div [CH_3CH_2COO^-]$
$= ((1.35 \times 10^{-5}) \times 0.2) \div 0.35 = \mathbf{7.7 \times 10^{-6}\ mol\ dm^{-3}}$
c)   pH $= -\log[H^+] = -\log(7.7 \times 10^{-6}) = \mathbf{5.11}$

Q2 $CH_3COOH \rightleftharpoons H^+ + CH_3COO^-$ so
$K_a = [H^+][CH_3COO^-] \div [CH_3COOH]$ so
$[H^+] = (K_a \times [CH_3COOH]) \div [CH_3COO^-]$
$= ((1.74 \times 10^{-5}) \times 0.15) \div 0.25 = 1.04 \times 10^{-5}$ mol dm^{-3}
pH $= -\log[H^+] = -\log(1.04 \times 10^{-5}) = \mathbf{4.98}$

Q3   a) $CH_3CH_2COOH + KOH \rightarrow CH_3CH_2COO^-K^+ + H_2O$
b)   initial moles CH_3CH_2COOH = (conc. × vol.) ÷ 1000
$= (0.5 \times 30) \div 1000 = \mathbf{0.015\ moles.}$
initial moles KOH = (conc. × vol.) ÷ 1000
$= (0.25 \times 20) \div 1000 = \mathbf{5 \times 10^{-3}\ moles.}$
c)   From the equation: moles salt = moles base = 5×10^{-3} moles.
Also, 1 mole of base neutralises 1 mole of acid so 5×10^{-3} moles of base neutralises 5×10^{-3} moles of acid.
So $0.015 - (5 \times 10^{-3}) = 0.01$ moles of acid remain.
Total volume = 30 + 20 = 50 cm^3
conc. acid in buffer = (moles × 1000) ÷ vol.
$= (0.01 \times 1000) \div 50 = \mathbf{0.2\ mol\ dm^{-3}}$
conc. salt in buffer = (moles × 1000) ÷ vol.
$= ((5 \times 10^{-3}) \times 1000) \div 50 = \mathbf{0.1\ mol\ dm^{-3}}$

d) $K_a = [H^+][CH_3CH_2COO^-] \div [CH_3CH_2COOH]$ so
$[H^+] = (K_a \times [CH_3CH_2COOH]) \div [CH_3CH_2COO^-]$
$= ((1.35 \times 10^{-5}) \times 0.2) \div 0.1$
$= \textbf{2.7} \times \textbf{10}^{-5} \textbf{ mol dm}^{-3}$

e) $pH = -\log[H^+] = -\log(2.7 \times 10^{-5}) = \textbf{4.57}$

Q4 initial moles HCOOH = (conc. × vol.) ÷ 1000
$= (0.2 \times 25) \div 1000 = 5 \times 10^{-3}$ moles.
initial moles NaOH = (conc. × vol.) ÷ 1000
$= (0.1 \times 15) \div 1000 = 1.5 \times 10^{-3}$ moles.
$HCOOH + NaOH \rightarrow HCOO^-Na^+ + H_2O$ so moles salt
= moles base = 1.5×10^{-3} moles. Also, 1 mole of base
neutralises 1 mole of acid and 1.5×10^{-3} moles of base
neutralises 1.5×10^{-3} moles of acid.
So $(5 \times 10^{-3}) - (1.5 \times 10^{-3}) = 3.5 \times 10^{-3}$ moles of acid remain.
Total volume = 15 + 25 = 40 cm³
final conc. acid = (moles × 1000) ÷ vol.
$= ((3.5 \times 10^{-3}) \times 1000) \div 40 = 0.0875$ mol dm⁻³
final conc. salt = (moles × 1000) ÷ vol.
$= ((1.5 \times 10^{-3}) \times 1000) \div 40 = 0.0375$ mol dm⁻³
$K_a = [H^+][HCOO^-] \div [HCOOH]$ so
$[H^+] = (K_a \times [HCOOH]) \div [HCOO^-]$
$= ((1.60 \times 10^{-4}) \times 0.0875) \div 0.0375$
$= 3.73 \times 10^{-4}$ mol dm⁻³
$pH = -\log[H^+] = -\log(3.73 \times 10^{-4}) = \textbf{3.43}$

14. Titrations and pH Curves

Page 152 — Application Questions
Q1 a) Strong base/weak acid, phenolphthalein/cresol purple
b) Strong acid/weak base, methyl orange
c) Strong acid/strong base, phenolphthalein/cresol purple/
litmus
d) Weak base/strong acid, methyl orange

Q2 Any curve where the vertical section covers pH 6.8 to pH 8.0.
E.g.

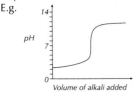

You could also have drawn a curve showing an acid being added
to an alkali.

Page 152 — Fact Recall Questions
Q1 a)

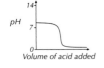

b)

c)

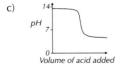

If the question says that a strong acid neutralises a strong
base, the base is being neutralised so it's the acid that's added.

Q2 a) At the end point of a titration a tiny amount of acid/base
causes a sudden big change in pH and the base/acid is
just neutralised.
b) The pH indicator changes colour/the pH meter shows a
sudden big change.
c) The pH curve becomes close to vertical.

Q3 For an indicator to be suitable it must change colour over a
narrow pH range that lies entirely within the vertical part of
the pH curve for the titration.

15. Titration Calculations

Page 154 — Application Questions
Q1 Moles HCl = (conc. × volume) ÷ 1000 =
$(1.5 \times 13.8) \div 1000 = 0.0207$ moles.
$HCl + NaOH \rightarrow NaCl + H_2O$ so 1 mole of HCl neutralises
1 mole of NaOH and 0.0207 moles of HCl must neutralise
0.0207 moles of NaOH.
Conc. NaOH = (moles × 1000) ÷ volume
$= (0.0207 \times 1000) \div 20 = \textbf{1.04 mol dm}^{-3}$

Q2 Moles NaOH = (conc. × volume) ÷ 1000 =
$(0.25 \times 30) \div 1000 = 7.5 \times 10^{-3}$ moles.
$HNO_3 + NaOH \rightarrow NaNO_3 + H_2O$ so 1 mole of NaOH
neutralises 1 mole of HNO_3 and 7.5×10^{-3} moles of NaOH
must neutralise 7.5×10^{-3} moles of HNO_3.
Conc. HNO_3 = (moles × 1000) ÷ volume
$= (7.5 \times 10^{-3} \times 1000) \div 17.8 = \textbf{0.42 mol dm}^{-3}$

Q3 From the graph, the volume of HCl required to neutralise the
NaOH solution was 27.5 cm³
This is the volume of HCl at the equivalence point.
Moles HCl = (conc. × volume) ÷ 1000 =
$(0.85 \times 27.5) \div 1000 = 0.0234$ moles.
$HCl + NaOH \rightarrow NaCl + H_2O$ so 1 mole of HCl neutralises
1 mole of NaOH and 0.0234 moles of HCl must neutralise
0.0234 moles of NaOH.
Conc. NaOH = (moles × 1000) ÷ volume
$= (0.0234 \times 1000) \div 30 = \textbf{0.78 mol dm}^{-3}$

Q4 Moles HCl = (conc. × volume) ÷ 1000 =
$(0.4 \times 18) \div 1000 = 7.2 \times 10^{-3}$ moles.
$HCl + NaOH \rightarrow NaCl + H_2O$ so 1 mole of HCl neutralises
1 mole of NaOH and 7.2×10^{-3} moles of HCl must
neutralise 7.2×10^{-3} moles of NaOH.
Conc. NaOH = (moles × 1000) ÷ volume
$= ((7.2 \times 10^{-3}) \times 1000) \div 32 = \textbf{0.225 mol dm}^{-3}$

Exam-style Questions — pages 156-158
1 (a) The reaction is first order with respect to H_2 *(1 mark)*
and second order with respect to NO *(1 mark)*.
*Finding the reaction order with respect to NO is tricky. You
know the reaction is first order with respect to H_2 from
experiments 1 and 2, so if only [H_2] changed from experiment
2 to 3 you would expect the rate of reaction to halve. But
the rate of reaction is four times greater than this, so the
reaction must be second order with respect to NO.*
(b) rate = $k[H_2][NO]^2$ *(1 mark)*
(c) rate = $k[H_2][NO]^2$ so k = rate ÷ $[H_2][NO]^2$
E.g. Using experiment 1:
$k = (4.5 \times 10^{-3}) \div (6 \times 10^{-3})(3 \times 10^{-3})^2 = 8.3 \times 10^4$
k = mol dm⁻³ s⁻¹ ÷ (mol dm⁻³)(mol dm⁻³)² = mol⁻² dm⁶ s⁻¹
$k = \textbf{8.3} \times \textbf{10}^4 \textbf{ mol}^{-2} \textbf{ dm}^6 \textbf{ s}^{-1}$
*(3 marks for correct answer, otherwise 1 mark
for correct method and 1 mark for correct units.)*
(d) rate = $k[H_2][NO]^2$
$= (8.3 \times 10^4) \times (2.5 \times 10^{-3}) \times (4.5 \times 10^{-3})^2$
$= \textbf{4.2} \times \textbf{10}^{-3} \textbf{ mol dm}^{-3} \textbf{ s}^{-1}$
*(1 mark for correct value, 1 mark for correct units —
full marks if the method is correct but error carried
forward from (c).)*
*If you used 6.5×10^5 as your value for k, an answer of
rate = 0.0329 mol dm⁻³ s⁻¹ will get you full marks.*
(e) (i) The rate equation shows that the rate-determining
step involves 2 molecules of NO and 1 molecule
of H_2 *(1 mark)*. There are 2 molecules of H_2 in
the overall equation so there must be another step
involving another molecule of H_2 *(1 mark)*.

(ii) A possible mechanism for this reaction would be:
Step 1: $2NO + H_2 \rightarrow N_2O + H_2O$
Step 2: $N_2O + H_2 \rightarrow H_2O + N_2$
***(1 mark for the left hand side of step 1,
1 mark for rest of step 1 and step 2)***

Other mechanisms are possible and will gain credit as long as:
- *The reactants in the first equation are 2NO and H_2.*
- *The steps add together to give the overall reaction.*
- *Both equations are balanced.*

2 (a) (i) $K_c = \dfrac{[CO_2][H_2]^4}{[CH_4][H_2O]^2}$ ***(1 mark)***.

(ii) $K_c = (0.2 \times (0.28)^4) \div (0.08 \times (0.32)^2) = 0.150$
$K_c = (\text{mol dm}^{-3} \times (\text{mol dm}^{-3})^4) \div (\text{mol dm}^{-3} \times (\text{mol dm}^{-3})^2) = \text{mol}^2 \text{ dm}^{-6}$ so $K_c =$ **0.150 mol^2 dm^{-6}**
(3 marks for correct answer, otherwise 1 mark for correct method and 1 mark for correct units.)

(b) (i) $[CH_4] = \dfrac{[CO_2][H_2]^4}{K_c \times [H_2O]^2}$
$= (0.42 \times 0.48^4) \div (0.0800 \times 0.56^2) =$ **0.889 mol dm^{-3}**
(2 marks for correct answer, otherwise 1 mark for correct equation.)

(ii) Lower ***(1 mark)***. K_c is lower at temperature Z than at temperature Y. This means temperature Z has caused the equilibrium to shift to the left ***(1 mark)***. As the reaction is endothermic in the forward direction, the temperature must be lowered to make it shift in the exothermic direction ***(1 mark)***.

(c) The value of K_c would not change ***(1 mark)***. Catalysts do not affect the position of the equilibrium, only the time taken to reach equilibrium ***(1 mark)***.

3 (a) (i) $K_w = [H^+][OH^-]$ ***(1 mark)***
(ii) $pH = -\log[H^+]$ ***(1 mark)***

(b) NaOH is a strong base so
$[OH^-] = [NaOH] = 0.150$ mol dm^{-3}
$K_w = [H^+][OH^-]$ so $[H^+] = K_w \div [OH^-]$
$= (1.00 \times 10^{-14}) \div 0.150 = 6.67 \times 10^{-14}$ mol dm^{-3}
$pH = -\log[H^+] = -\log[6.67 \times 10^{-14}] =$ **13.18**
(3 marks for correct answer, otherwise 1 mark for [OH⁻] = 0.150 and 1 mark for [H⁺] = 6.67 × 10⁻¹⁴.)

(c) (i) B ***(1 mark)***
This titration was a strong acid against a strong base so the curve should start at around pH 14 and fall to around pH 1.

(ii) Moles NaOH = (conc. × volume) ÷ 1000
$= (0.150 \times 25.0) \div 1000 = 3.75 \times 10^{-3}$ moles.
$HCl + NaOH \rightarrow NaCl + H_2O$
1 mole of NaOH neutralises 1 mole of HCl so 3.75×10^{-3} moles of NaOH must neutralise 3.75×10^{-3} moles of HCl.
Conc. HCl = (moles × 1000) ÷ volume
$= ((3.75 \times 10^{-3}) \times 1000) \div 18.5 =$ **0.20 mol dm^{-3}**
(3 marks for correct answer, otherwise 1 mark for moles NaOH = 3.75 × 10⁻³ and 1 mark for moles HCl = 3.75 × 10⁻³.)

(iii) HCl is a strong acid and fully dissociates so
$[H^+] = [HCl] = 0.20$ mol dm^{-3}
$pH = -\log[H^+] = -\log(0.2) =$ **0.70**
(2 marks for correct answer, otherwise 1 mark for [H⁺] = 0.20 mol dm⁻³.)

(d) (i) Any weak acid (e.g. methanoic acid/ethanoic acid/ hydrogen cyanide) ***(1 mark)***. Any strong base (e.g. potassium hydroxide/sodium hydroxide) ***(1 mark)***.
(ii) Phenolphthalein ***(1 mark)***

4 (a) (i) $HCOOH \rightleftharpoons H^+ + HCOO^-$ ***(1 mark)***
(ii) $K_a = [H^+][HCOO^-] \div [HCOOH]$ or
$K_a = [H^+]^2 \div [HCOOH]$ ***(1 mark)***

(iii) $[H^+] = 10^{-pH} = 10^{-2.2} = 6.31 \times 10^{-3}$
$K_a = [H^+]^2 \div [HCOOH] = (6.31 \times 10^{-3})^2 \div 0.240$
$= 1.66 \times 10^{-4}$ mol dm^{-3}
$pK_a = -\log(K_a) = -\log(1.66 \times 10^{-4}) =$ **3.78**
(3 marks for correct answer, otherwise 1 mark for [H⁺] = 6.31 × 10⁻³ and 1 mark for Kₐ = 1.66 × 10⁻⁴.)

(b) (i) $K_a = [H^+][HCOO^-] \div [HCOOH]$ so
$[H^+] = (K_a \times [HCOOH]) \div [HCOO^-]$
$= ((1.66 \times 10^{-4}) \times 0.084) \div (0.06)$
$= 2.32 \times 10^{-4}$ mol dm^{-3} ***(1 mark)***
$pH = -\log[H^+] = -\log(2.32 \times 10^{-4}) =$ **3.63**
(1 mark).
You calculated K_a for this acid in a previous part of the question. If you got it wrong then, you could still get full marks for this part of the question if everything else you did was right.

(ii) $HCOOH + NH_3 \rightarrow HCOO^- + NH_4^+$ ***(1 mark)***.
   acid 1   base 2   base 1   acid 2
(1 mark for correctly identifying acids and bases, 1 mark for correct pairings).

(iii) $HCOOH \rightleftharpoons H^+ + HCOO^-$. Adding an acid increases $[H^+]$ ***(1 mark)***. The excess H^+ combines with $HCOO^-$ to form $HCOOH$ ***(1 mark)***, so the equilibrium shifts to the left reducing the H^+ concentration to close to its original value and maintaining the pH ***(1 mark)***.

Module 2 — Energy

1. Neutralisation and Enthalpy
Pages 161-162 — Application Questions
Q1 $25.0 + 25.0 = 50.0$ so $m = 50.0$ g
$q = mc\Delta T = 50.0 \times 4.18 \times 3.45 = 721$ J $= 0.721$ kJ
$HCl + NaOH \rightarrow NaCl + H_2O$
moles of acid = conc. × vol
$= 0.500 \times (25.0 \div 1000) = 0.0125$ moles.
1 mole of acid produces 1 mole of water. So 0.0125 moles of acid will produce 0.0125 moles of water.
$q \div n = 0.721 \div 0.0125 = 57.7$
$\Delta H^{\circ}_{neutralisation} =$ **−57.7 kJ mol^{-1}**

Q2 $250 + 150 = 400$ so $m = 400$ g
$q = mc\Delta T = 400 \times 4.18 \times 1.26 = 2107$ J $= 2.11$ kJ
$HNO_3 + KOH \rightarrow KNO_3 + H_2O$
moles of acid = conc. × vol
$= 0.150 \times (250 \div 1000) = 0.0375$ moles.
1 mole of acid produces 1 mole of water. So 0.0375 moles of acid will produce 0.0375 moles of water.
$q \div n = 2.11 \div 0.0375 = 56.3$
$\Delta H^{\circ}_{neutralisation} =$ **−56.3 kJ mol^{-1}**

Q3 $32.0 + 28.0 = 60.0$ so $m = 60$ g
$q = mc\Delta T = 60 \times 4.18 \times 3.65 = 915$ J $= 0.915$ kJ
$HCl + LiOH \rightarrow LiCl + H_2O$
moles of acid = conc. × vol
$= 0.500 \times (32.0 \div 1000) = 0.0160$ moles.
1 mole of acid produces 1 mole of water. So 0.0160 moles of acid will produce 0.0160 moles of water.
$q \div n = 0.915 \div 0.0160 = 57.2$
$\Delta H^{\circ}_{neutralisation} =$ **−57.2 kJ mol^{-1}**

Q4 $125 + 75 = 200$ so $m = 200$ g
$q = mc\Delta T = 200 \times 4.18 \times 2.07 = 1731$ J $= 1.73$ kJ
$HBr + NaOH \rightarrow NaBr + H_2O$
moles of acid = conc. × vol
$= 0.240 \times (125 \div 1000) = 0.0300$ moles.
1 mole of acid produces 1 mole of water. So 0.0300 moles of acid will produce 0.300 moles of water.
$q \div n = 1.73 \div 0.0300 = 57.7$
$\Delta H^{\circ}_{neutralisation} =$ **−57.7 kJ mol^{-1}**

Page 162 — Fact Recall Questions

Q1 Enthalpy change is the heat energy transferred in a reaction at constant pressure.

Q2 ΔH

Q3 a) The enthalpy change of neutralisation, $\Delta H^{\ominus}_{neutralisation}$, is the enthalpy change when 1 mole of water is formed by the reaction between an acid and a base under standard conditions.

   b) Mix together known volumes of an acid and a base. Measure the temperature change of the reaction. Find the energy released by the reaction using $q = mc\Delta T$. Divide q by the number of moles of water produced to find $\Delta H^{\ominus}_{neutralisation}$, remembering to change the sign if the reaction is exothermic.

Q4 a) Enthalpy change of formation is the enthalpy change when 1 mole of a compound is formed from its elements in their standard states under standard conditions.

   b) Second electron affinity is the enthalpy change when 1 mole of gaseous 2– ions is made from 1 mole of gaseous 1– ions.

   c) The enthalpy change of solution is the enthalpy change when 1 mole of solute is dissolved in sufficient solvent that no further enthalpy change occurs on further dilution.

Q5 a) Enthalpy change of atomisation of an element.

   b) The first ionisation enthalpy.

Q6 a) $\Delta H^{\ominus}_{hyd}$

   b) $\Delta H^{\ominus}_{ie2}$

2. Lattice Enthalpy

Page 164 — Application Questions

Q1 a) Smaller ions attract more strongly because their charge density is higher. So the smaller the ionic radii of the ions involved the more exothermic the lattice enthalpy. The ionic radii increase from Cl^- to I^- so the lattice enthalpy becomes less exothermic from $NaCl$ to NaI.

   b) $NaCl$ contains the strongest ionic bonds.

Q2 The lattice enthalpy of MgO would be more negative than the lattice enthalpy of Na_2O. This is because MgO contains 2+ ions while Na_2O contains 1+ ions. The higher the charge on the ions, the more energy is released when the ionic lattice forms and the more negative the lattice enthalpy will be.

Page 164 — Fact Recall Questions

Q1 a) The standard lattice enthalpy, is the enthalpy change when 1 mole of a solid ionic compound is formed from its gaseous ions under standard conditions.

   b) $\Delta H^{\ominus}_{latt}$

Q2 The more negative the lattice enthalpy the stronger the ionic bonding in the lattice.

Q3 Ionic charge and ionic radius.

3. Calculating Lattice Enthalpies

Page 168 — Application Questions

Q1 $\Delta H6 = -\Delta H5 - \Delta H4 - \Delta H3 - \Delta H2 + \Delta H1$
   $= -(-349) - (+520) - (+159) - (+122) + (-409)$
   $= \textbf{-861 kJ mol}^{-1}$

Q2

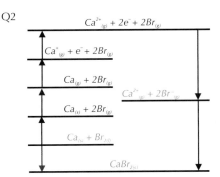

Q3 a)

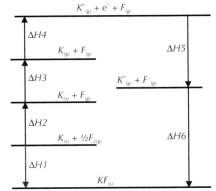

   b) $\Delta H6 = -\Delta H5 - \Delta H4 - \Delta H3 - \Delta H2 + \Delta H1$
   $= -(-328) - (+419) - (+89) - (+79) + (-563)$
   $= \textbf{-822 kJ mol}^{-1}$

Page 168 — Fact Recall Questions

Q1 The enthalpy change of atomisation ($\Delta H^{\ominus}_{at}$)
   The ionisation enthalpy ($\Delta H^{\ominus}_{ie}$)
   The electron affinity ($\Delta H^{\ominus}_{ea}$)
   The enthalpy change of formation ($\Delta H^{\ominus}_{f}$)

Q2 The total enthalpy change of a reaction is always the same, no matter which route is taken.

4. Enthalpies of Solution

Page 172 — Application Questions

Q1 $\Delta H3 = \Delta H1 + \Delta H2 = -(-826) + (-520 + -364) = \textbf{-58 kJ mol}^{-1}$

Q2 a)

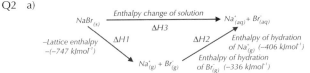

   b) $\Delta H3 = \Delta H1 + \Delta H2 = -(-747) + (-406 + -336)$
   $= \textbf{+5 kJ mol}^{-1}$

Q3 a) $\Delta H3 = \Delta H1 + \Delta H2 = -(-807) + (-520 + -336)$
   $= \textbf{-49 kJ mol}^{-1}$

   b) $\Delta H3 = \Delta H1 + \Delta H2 = -(-701) + (-322 + -364)$
   $= \textbf{+15 kJ mol}^{-1}$

   c) $\Delta H3 = \Delta H1 + \Delta H2 = -(-2440) + (-1921 + (-336 \times 2))$
   $= \textbf{-153 kJ mol}^{-1}$

Q4 Magnesium ions (Mg^{2+}) are smaller and have a higher charge than potassium ions (K^+). The higher charge and smaller size create a higher charge density. This creates a stronger attraction for the water molecules and gives magnesium ions a much more negative enthalpy of hydration than potassium ions.

Page 172 — Fact Recall Questions

Q1 a) The bonds between the ions break, and bonds between the ions and water are made.

b) Bonds breaking is endothermic and bonds being made is exothermic.

Q2 The lattice enthalpy and enthalpy change of hydration.

Q3 The endothermic nature of the reaction is compensated for by an increase in entropy.

Q4 Ionic charge and ionic radius.

5. Entropy

Page 175 — Application Questions

Q1 The entropy will increase when the solid sodium hydroxide dissolves in the aqueous hydrogen chloride. The entropy of the water will increase when it turns to a gas and the entropy of the sodium chloride will decrease when it turns to a solid.

Q2 a) $\Delta S_{system} = S_{products} - S_{reactants}$
$= (214 + (2 \times 69.9)) - (186 + (2 \times 205))$
$= \textbf{−242 J K}^{-1} \textbf{mol}^{-1}$

b) $\Delta H^{\ominus} = -730$ kJ mol^{-1} $= -730 \times 10^3$ J mol^{-1}
$\Delta S_{surroundings} = -\Delta H \div T = -(-730 \times 10^3) \div 298$
$= \textbf{−2450 J K}^{-1} \textbf{mol}^{-1}$

c) $\Delta S^{\ominus}_{total} = \Delta S^{\ominus}_{system} + \Delta S^{\ominus}_{surroundings}$
$= -242 + (-2450) = \textbf{−2692 J K}^{-1} \textbf{mol}^{-1}$

d) The reaction won't happen spontaneously because $\Delta S^{\ominus}_{total}$ is negative.

Q3 $\Delta S_{system} = S_{products} - S_{reactants}$
$= ((3 \times 31.6) + (2 \times 69.9)) - (248 + (2 \times 206))$
$= -425$ J K^{-1} mol^{-1}
$\Delta H^{\ominus} = -235$ kJ mol^{-1} $= -235 \times 10^3$ J mol^{-1}
$\Delta S_{surroundings} = -\Delta H \div T = -(-235 \times 10^3) \div 298$
$= +789$ J K^{-1} mol^{-1}
$\Delta S^{\ominus}_{total} = \Delta S^{\ominus}_{system} + \Delta S^{\ominus}_{surroundings}$
$= -425.4 + (+789) = \textbf{+364 J K}^{-1} \textbf{mol}^{-1}$

Page 175 — Fact Recall Questions

Q1 a) A measure of the amount of disorder in a system (e.g. the number of ways that particles can be arranged and the number of ways that the energy can be shared out between the particles).

b) ΔS

Q2 a) The entropy increases because particles move around more in gases than in liquids and their arrangement is more random.

b) The entropy increases because particles move around more in liquids than in solids and their arrangement is more random.

c) The entropy increases because the more particles you've got, the more ways they can be arranged.

Q3 Enthalpy is not the only factor to affect entropy. Things like changing states and changing the number of molecules can also affect entropy. If the increase in entropy due to other factors is greater than the decrease in entropy due to the reaction being endothermic, then the overall entropy change will be positive and the reaction will happen spontaneously.

Q4 a) $\Delta S_{total} = \Delta S_{system} + \Delta S_{surroundings}$

b) $\Delta S_{system} = S_{products} - S_{reactants}$

c) $\Delta S_{surroundings} = -\Delta H \div T$

6. Free-Energy Change

Page 177 — Application Questions

Q1 a) $\Delta S_{system} = S_{products} - S_{reactants}$
$= ((2 \times 28.3) + (3 \times 27.0)) - (51.0 + (3 \times 32.5))$
$= \textbf{−10.9 J K}^{-1} \textbf{mol}^{-1}$

b) $\Delta H^{\ominus} = -130$ kJ mol^{-1} $= -130 \times 10^3$ J mol^{-1}
$\Delta G = \Delta H - T\Delta S_{system}$
$= -130 \times 10^3 - (298 \times -10.9)$
$= \textbf{−126 752 J mol}^{-1}$

c) The reaction is feasible at 298 K because ΔG is negative.

Q2 a) (i) $\Delta H^{\ominus} = 71$ kJ mol^{-1} $= 71 \times 10^3$ J mol^{-1}
$\Delta G = \Delta H - T\Delta S_{system}$
$= 71 \times 10^3 - (298 \times 176)$
$= \textbf{18 552 J mol}^{-1}$
The reaction is not feasible at 298 K because ΔG is positive.

(ii) $\Delta H^{\ominus} = 71$ kJ mol^{-1} $= 71 \times 10^3$ J mol^{-1}
$\Delta G = \Delta H - T\Delta S_{system}$
$= (71 \times 10^3) - (600 \times 176)$
$= \textbf{−34 600 J mol}^{-1}$
The reaction is feasible at 600 K because ΔG is negative.

b) $\Delta H^{\ominus} = 71$ kJ mol^{-1} $= (71 \times 10^3)$ J mol^{-1}
$T = \Delta H \div \Delta S_{system} = (71 \times 10^3) \div 176 = \textbf{403 K}$

Q3 $\Delta H^{\ominus} = 178$ kJ mol^{-1} $= 178 \times 10^3$ J mol^{-1}
$T = \Delta H \div \Delta S_{system} = (178 \times 10^3) \div 165 = \textbf{1079 K}$

Page 177 — Fact Recall Questions

Q1 a) Free energy change is a measure used to predict whether a reaction is feasible.

b) ΔG

Q2 $\Delta G = \Delta H - T\Delta S_{system}$

Q3 no

Q4 $T = \Delta H \div \Delta S_{system}$

7. Redox Equations

Page 180 — Application Questions

Q1 a) +1
b) +6
c) −1

Q2 $Cu_{(s)} + 2Ag^{+}_{(aq)} \rightarrow Cu^{2+}_{(aq)} + 2Ag_{(s)}$

Q3 $Cl_{2(g)} + 2e^{-} \rightarrow 2Cl^{-}_{(aq)}$

Q4 a) $Zn \rightarrow Zn^{2+} + 2e^{-}$
$Cr_2O_7^{2-} + 14H^{+} + 6e^{-} \rightarrow 2Cr^{3+} + 7H_2O$

b) $Cr_2O_7^{2-} + 14H^{+} + 3Zn \rightarrow 2Cr^{3+} + 3Zn^{2+} + 7H_2O$

Don't forget to double-check that the charges on each side of the equation balance, as well as the atoms.

Page 180 — Fact Recall Questions

Q1 a) The loss of electrons.
b) Something that accepts electrons and gets reduced.

Q2 a) 0
b) +1

Q3 It decreases by one.

8. Electrode Potentials

Page 184 — Application Questions

Q1 a)

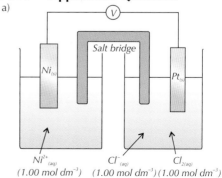

$Ni^{2+}_{(aq)}$ $\quad$ $Cl^{-}_{(aq)}$ $\quad$ $Cl_{2(aq)}$
(1.00 mol dm^{-3}) (1.00 mol dm^{-3})(1.00 mol dm^{-3})

b) The Ni/Ni²⁺ reaction goes in the direction of oxidation (Ni is oxidised and Cl_2 is reduced).
You know that Ni is oxidised because the Ni/Ni²⁺ half-reaction has the more negative electrode potential.

Q2 a)

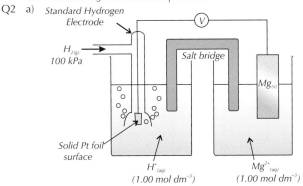

H⁺₍ₐq₎ (1.00 mol dm⁻³) Mg²⁺₍ₐq₎ (1.00 mol dm⁻³)

b)

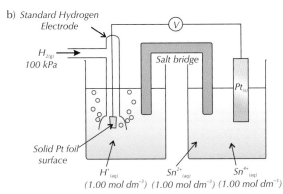

H⁺₍ₐq₎ (1.00 mol dm⁻³) Sn²⁺₍ₐq₎ (1.00 mol dm⁻³) Sn⁴⁺₍ₐq₎ (1.00 mol dm⁻³)

c)

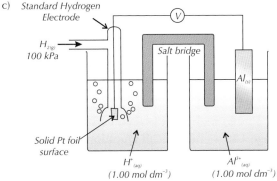

H⁺₍ₐq₎ (1.00 mol dm⁻³) Al³⁺₍ₐq₎ (1.00 mol dm⁻³)

Page 184 — Fact Recall Questions

Q1 a) A platinum electrode.
   b) Platinum is inert, so it won't react with the solution. It is also a solid that conducts electricity so will complete the circuit.
Q2 reduction
Q3 The voltage measured under standard conditions when the half-cell is connected to a standard hydrogen electrode.
Q4 Hydrogen gas is bubbled into a solution of aqueous H⁺ ions. The electrode is made of platinum. The standard conditions used are a temperature of 298 K (25 °C), a pressure of 100 kPa and all ion solutions having a concentration of 1.00 mol dm⁻³.

9. Electrochemical Series

Page 188 — Application Questions

Q1 a)

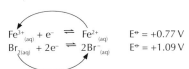

$Mg^{2+}_{(aq)} + 2e^- \rightleftharpoons Mg_{(s)}$ $E^\ominus = -2.37$ V
$Ni^{2+}_{(aq)} + 2e^- \rightleftharpoons Ni_{(s)}$ $E^\ominus = -0.25$ V

Yes, the reaction will occur.

b)

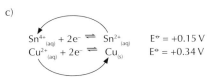

$Fe^{3+}_{(aq)} + e^- \rightleftharpoons Fe^{2+}_{(aq)}$ $E^\ominus = +0.77$ V
$Br_{2(aq)} + 2e^- \rightleftharpoons 2Br^-_{(aq)}$ $E^\ominus = +1.09$ V

No, the reaction will not occur.

c)

$Sn^{4+}_{(aq)} + 2e^- \rightleftharpoons Sn^{2+}_{(aq)}$ $E^\ominus = +0.15$ V
$Cu^{2+}_{(aq)} + 2e^- \rightleftharpoons Cu_{(s)}$ $E^\ominus = +0.34$ V

Yes, the reaction will occur.

Q2 a) $E^\ominus_{cell} = E^\ominus_{reduced} - E^\ominus_{oxidised} = 0.80 - (-1.66) = $ **+2.46 V**
   b) $E^\ominus_{cell} = E^\ominus_{reduced} - E^\ominus_{oxidised} = 1.36 - 0.34 = $ **+1.02 V**
   c) $E^\ominus_{cell} = E^\ominus_{reduced} - E^\ominus_{oxidised} = 0.77 - 0.15 = $ **+0.62 V**
   Your values for the e.m.f. should always be positive. If you get a negative answer, go back and check your calculation because you must have gone wrong somewhere.

Page 188 — Fact Recall Questions

Q1 A list of electrode potentials for different electrochemical half-cells, written in order from the most negative to the most positive.
Q2 In the direction of reduction.
Q3 Reduction.
Q4 E.g. the conditions are not standard / the reaction kinetics are not favourable / the activation energy may be too high / the rate of reaction may be too slow.

10. Energy Storage Cells

Page 190 — Application Questions

Q1 a) $E^\ominus_{cell} = E^\ominus_{reduced} - E^\ominus_{oxidised} = 0.52 - (-0.88) = +1.40$ V
   b) $2NiO(OH)_{(s)} + Cd_{(s)} + 2H_2O_{(l)} \rightarrow 2Ni(OH)_{2(s)} + Cd(OH)_{2(s)}$
   c) $2Ni(OH)_{2(s)} + Cd(OH)_{2(s)} \rightarrow 2NiO(OH)_{(s)} + Cd_{(s)} + 2H_2O_{(l)}$
Q2 a) $E^\ominus_{cell} = E^\ominus_{reduced} - E^\ominus_{oxidised} = 0.75 - (-0.76) = +1.51$ V
   b) $2MnO_{2(s)} + 2NH_4^+_{(aq)} + Zn_{(s)} \rightarrow Mn_2O_{3(s)} + 2NH_{3(aq)} + H_2O_{(l)} + Zn^{2+}_{(aq)}$
   c) The reactions that occur within this cell are not reversible so the cell cannot be recharged.
Q3 a) $E^\ominus_{cell} = E^\ominus_{reduced} - E^\ominus_{oxidised} = 1.69 - (-0.36) = +2.05$ V
   b) $PbO_{2(s)} + 2SO_4^{2-}_{(aq)} + 4H^+_{(aq)} + Pb_{(s)} \rightleftharpoons 2PbSO_{4(s)} + 2H_2O_{(l)}$
   c) $PbSO_{4(s)} + 2e^- \rightleftharpoons Pb_{(s)} + SO_4^{2-}_{(aq)}$
      $PbSO_{4(s)} + 2H_2O_{(l)} \rightleftharpoons PbO_{2(s)} + SO_4^{2-}_{(aq)} + 4H^+_{(aq)} + 2e^-$

Page 190 — Fact Recall Questions

Q1 battery
Q2 $E^\ominus_{cell} = E^\ominus_{reduced} - E^\ominus_{oxidised}$
Q3 Some energy storage cells can be recharged because the reactions that occur within them can be reversed if a current is supplied to force the electrons to flow in the opposite direction around the circuit.

11. Fuel Cells
Page 193 — Fact Recall Questions

Q1 Fuel cells produce electricity by reacting a fuel, usually hydrogen, with an oxidant, which is most likely to be oxygen.

Q2 At the anode the platinum catalyst splits the H_2 into protons and electrons. The polymer electrolyte membrane (PEM) only allows the H^+ across and this forces the e^- to travel around the circuit to get to the cathode. An electric current is created in the circuit, which is used to power something like a car or a bike. At the cathode, O_2 combines with the H^+ from the anode and the e^- from the circuit to make H_2O. This is the only waste product.

Q3 a) FCVs are fuel cell vehicles — electric vehicles which are powered by fuel cells as opposed to petrol or diesel.
 b) E.g. they produce a lot less pollution because the only waste product is water and the fuel cell is twice as efficient at converting fuel to power vs a petrol engine.

Q4 a) Any three from: e.g. as a gas / as a liquid / adsorbed to the surface of a solid like charcoal / absorbed into a material like palladium.
 b) E.g. if you store it as a gas it is very explosive / if you store it as a liquid you need really expensive fridges because it has such a low boiling point / materials like charcoal/palladium can be very expensive and often have a limited life span.

Q5 Any three from: e.g. they are expensive to make / their production involves toxic chemicals which need to be disposed of afterwards / they have a limited life span / disposing of them is expensive / storing and transporting the hydrogen needed is difficult / producing hydrogen takes energy.

Q6 a) The term hydrogen economy means an economy where all the energy needs of cars, buildings and electronics will be powered by hydrogen fuel cells.
 b) E.g. many people have concerns about the safety and reliability of hydrogen as a fuel / the infrastructure for hydrogen fuel supplies would be difficult to set up / hydrogen is only an energy carrier — it needs energy to make it.

Exam-style Questions — pages 194-196

1 a) It is the enthalpy change when 1 mole *(1 mark)* of a solid ionic compound is formed from its gaseous ions *(1 mark)* under standard conditions *(1 mark)*.
 b)

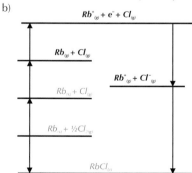

(1 mark for each correct label).

 c) $\Delta H_{latt} = -\Delta H_{ea(Cl)} - \Delta H_{ie(Rb)} - \Delta H_{at(Rb)} - \Delta H_{at(Cl)} + \Delta H_{f(RbCl)}$
   $= -(-349) - (+403) - (+81) - (+122) + (-435)$
   $= \mathbf{-692\ kJ\ mol^{-1}}$
   (3 marks for correct answer, otherwise 1 mark for correct equation, 1 mark for correct substitution)

 d) Sodium has a smaller ionic radius than rubidium *(1 mark)*. Smaller ions have a higher charge density and attract more strongly *(1 mark)*. So more energy is released when sodium chloride forms than when rubidium chloride forms *(1 mark)*.
 e)

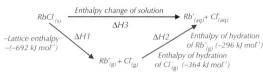

$\Delta H3 = \Delta H1 + \Delta H2 = -(-692) + (-296 + -364)$ *(1 mark)*
  $= \mathbf{+32\ kJ\ mol^{-1}}$ *(1 mark)*

If you used the value of $-300\ kJ\ mol^{-1}$ for the standard lattice enthalpy of rubidium chloride you'll get an answer of $-360\ kJ\ mol^{-1}$. If you got this answer, give yourself full marks.

2 a) (i) Increase. 2 solids are reacting to produce a solid and a gas *(1 mark)*. Gases have higher entropy than solids because they are more disordered *(1 mark)*.

You generally don't get marks for 50:50 guesses at A2 — so you won't get any marks just for saying it increases. The marks come for the explanation.

   (ii) $\Delta S_{system} = S_{products} - S_{reactants}$
    $= (32 + 214) - (53 + 5.7)$
    $= +187.3\ J\ K^{-1}\ mol^{-1}$ *(1 mark)*.
    $\Delta H^{\oplus} = +127\ kJ\ mol^{-1} = +127 \times 10^3\ J\ mol^{-1}$
    $\Delta G = \Delta H - T\Delta S_{system}$ *(1 mark)*.
    $= (+127 \times 10^3) - (1473 \times +187.3)$ *(1 mark)*.
    $= \mathbf{-148893\ J\ mol^{-1}}$ *(1 mark)*.

   (ii) If the free energy change is negative or equal to zero the reaction is feasible *(1 mark)*. If the free energy change is positive, the reaction is not feasible *(1 mark)*.
 b) (i) $T = \Delta H \div \Delta S_{system}$ *(1 mark)*.
   (ii) $T = (+127 \times 10^3) \div 187.3$
    $= \mathbf{678\ K}$
    (2 marks for correct answer, otherwise 1 mark for correct substitution).

Don't forget, reactions become feasible when ΔG is less than or equal to 0.

3 a) (i) $E^{\oplus}$ for Sn^{4+}/Sn^{2+} is more negative than $E^{\oplus}$ for VO_2^+/VO^{2+}, so Sn^{2+} ions will react with VO_2^+ ions *(1 mark)*.
    $2VO_2^+{}_{(aq)} + Sn^{2+}{}_{(aq)} + 4H^+{}_{(aq)} \rightarrow 2VO^{2+}{}_{(aq)} + Sn^{4+}{}_{(aq)} + 2H_2O_{(l)}$ *(1 mark)*.
    $E^{\oplus}$ for Sn^{4+}/Sn^{2+} is more negative than $E^{\oplus}$ for VO^{2+}/V^{3+}, so Sn^{2+} ions will react with VO^{2+} ions created in the previous reaction *(1 mark)*.
    $2VO^{2+}{}_{(aq)} + Sn^{2+}{}_{(aq)} + 4H^+{}_{(aq)} \rightarrow 2V^{3+} + Sn^{4+} + 2H_2O$ *(1 mark)*.

The V^{3+} ions made in this reaction don't react with the Sn^{2+} ions because the electrode potential for V^{3+}/V^{2+} is more negative than that for Sn^{4+}/Sn^{2+}.

   (ii) Any two from: e.g. the conditions may be non-standard / the reaction kinetics may not be favourable / the activation energy may be too high / the rate of reaction may be too slow *(1 mark for each, maximum 2 marks)*.

b) (i)

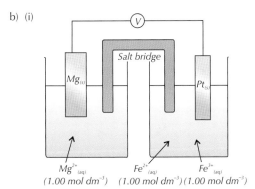

Mg²⁺(aq)   *Fe²⁺(aq)*   *Fe³⁺(aq)*
(1.00 mol dm⁻³) (1.00 mol dm⁻³)(1.00 mol dm⁻³)

(1 mark for complete circuit with voltmeter and salt bridge, 1 mark for Mg/Mg²⁺ half-cell correct, 1 mark for Fe²⁺/Fe³⁺ half-cell correct).

Don't forget to include the platinum electrode for the Fe²⁺/Fe³⁺ half-cell and label all the solutions as 1.00 mol dm⁻³. If you forget, you might lose out on some valuable marks.

  (ii) $E_{cell} = E_{reduced} - E_{oxidised} = 0.77 - (-2.38) = $ **3.15 V**
(1 mark).

  (iii) $Mg_{(s)} + 2Fe^{3+} \rightarrow Mg^{2+}_{(aq)} + 2Fe^{2+}$ **(1 mark for correct reactants and products, 1 mark for balancing).**

c) (i) A temperature of 298 K **(1 mark)**. A pressure of 100 kPa **(1 mark)**. Any solutions of ions have a concentration of 1.00 mol dm⁻³ **(1 mark)**.

  (ii) E.g. platinum is inert / platinum is a solid that conducts electricity **(1 mark)**.

d) (i) +0.80 V **(1 mark)**.

  (ii) Silver is less reactive than vanadium **(1 mark)** because it has a less negative electrode potential **(1 mark)**.

4 a) (i) $2NiOOH_{(s)} + Zn_{(s)} + 2H_2O \rightarrow 2Ni(OH)_{2(s)} + Zn(OH)_{2(s)}$ **(1 mark for correct reactants and products, 1 mark for balancing)**.

  (ii) $E_{cell} = E_{reduced} - E_{oxidised}$ so $E_{reduced} = E_{cell} + E_{oxidised}$
= 1.73 + (-1.25) = **+0.48 V**
(3 marks for correct answer, otherwise 1 mark for rearranging equation, 1 mark for correct substitution).

You know you're looking for $E_{reduced}$ because in the half-equations $Zn_{(s)}$ is being oxidised, so $NiOOH_{(s)}$ must be being reduced.

b) Oxidation: $H_2 \rightarrow 2H^+ + 2e^-$ **(1 mark)**.
Reduction: $\frac{1}{2}O_2 + 2H^+ + 2e^- \rightarrow H_2O$ **(1 mark)**.
Advantages: e.g. they produce less pollution / they are more efficient at converting fuel to power **(1 mark for each, maximum 2 marks)**.
Disadvantages: e.g. they are expensive to make / their production involves toxic chemicals which need to be disposed of afterwards / they have a limited life span / disposing of them is expensive / storing and transporting the hydrogen needed is difficult / producing hydrogen takes energy **(1 mark for each, maximum 2 marks)**.

Module 3 — Transition Elements

1. Transition Elements

Page 199 — Application Questions

Q1 a) [Ar]3d³4s²
  b) [Ar]3d⁷4s²
  c) [Ar]3d¹⁰4s¹
  d) [Ar]3d⁸4s²

For these questions you don't have to write [Ar]. Writing out the whole electron configuration starting from 1s² is fine too — but in the exam it'll save time if you can use the shorthand.

Q2 a) [Ar]3d²
  b) [Ar]3d⁷
  c) [Ar]3d⁹
  d) [Ar]3d⁸
Don't forget, the s electrons are always removed first, then the d electrons.
  e) [Ar]3d⁴
  f) [Ar]3d¹
  g) [Ar]

Q3 Zinc has the electron configuration 1s²2s²2p⁶3s²3p⁶3d¹⁰4s². It can only form Zn²⁺ ions which have an electron configuration of 1s²2s²2p⁶3s²3p⁶3d¹⁰. This ion has a full d-subshell, so zinc cannot form a stable ion with a partially filled d-subshell and it therefore can't be a transition metal.

Page 199 — Fact Recall Questions

Q1 In the d-block.
Q2 A transition metal is a metal that can form one or more stable ions with an incomplete d-subshell.
Q3 10
Q4 Electrons fill up the lowest energy subshells first and electrons fill orbitals singly before they start sharing.
Q5 a) Chromium prefers to have one electron in each orbital of the 3d subshell and just one in the 4s subshell because this gives it more stability.
  b) Copper prefers to have a full 3d subshell and one electron in the 4s subshell because it's more stable that way.

2. Transition Element Properties

Page 202 — Fact Recall Questions

Q1 Any two from: e.g. they can form complex ions / they form coloured ions / they make good catalysts.
Q2 Vanadium(V) oxide / V_2O_5
Q3 E.g. to harden margarine.
Q4 A — 3   B — 4
   C — 2   D — 1
Q5 $Co^{2+}_{(aq)} + 2OH^-_{(aq)} \rightarrow Co(OH)_{2(s)}$
Q6 An orange precipitate would form in the yellow solution. The precipitate would darken on standing.
Q7 E.g. the scientist could add sodium hydroxide to the solution. If a green precipitate forms iron(II) ions are present. If an orange precipitate forms iron(III) ions are present.
Q8 Their incomplete d-subshell.

3. Complex Ions

Page 205 — Application Questions

Q1 a) Octahedral:

When you're drawing the shapes of ions and molecules make sure you include the dashed arrows and the wedged arrows to show that it's 3D.

  b) Octahedral:

You could also draw this structure with the two ⁻OH ligands next to each other. See page 207 for more on this.

c) Octahedral:

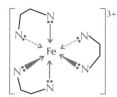

Q2 a) 6
   b) 6
   c) 6
Q3 a)

   b) $[Cr(C_2O_4)_3]^{3-}$

Oxygen atoms are small so six of them will fit around a central metal ion and form coordinate bonds with it. This means that three molecules of $C_2O_4^{2-}$ will each form two coordinate bonds with the ion.

Q4 a) Square planar
   b)

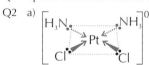

Page 205 — Fact Recall Questions
Q1 a) An atom, ion or molecule that donates a pair of electrons to a central metal ion.
   b) A covalent bond where both of the electrons in the shared pair come from the same atom, ion or molecule.
   c) A metal ion surrounded by coordinately bonded ligands.
Q2 A ligand that can donate two lone pairs of electrons to a central metal ion to form two coordinate bonds.
Q3 E.g. $[Fe(H_2O)_6]^{2+}$ / $[Co(NH_3)_6]^{3+}$ / $[Cu(NH_3)_4(H_2O)_2]^{2+}$.

4. Isomerism in Complex Ions
Page 207 — Application Questions
Q1 a) cis-trans isomerism
   b) optical isomerism
   c) cis-trans isomerism
Q2 cis: trans:

Remember, you don't have to draw square planar structures like these in 3D if you don't want to — hurrah.

Page 207 — Fact Recall Questions
Q1 optical isomerism and cis-trans isomerism
Q2 a)

   b) Cisplatin can bind to the DNA molecules in cancer cells and prevent them from dividing.

5. Ligand Substitution
Page 211 — Fact Recall Questions
Q1 a) There will be no change in coordination number or shape but the colour may change.
   b) There will be a change in coordination number and shape and the colour may change.
Q2 a) octahedral
   b) tetrahedral
Q3 a) $[Cu(H_2O)_6]^{2+}_{(aq)} + 4Cl^-_{(aq)} \rightleftharpoons [CuCl_4]^{2-}_{(aq)} + 6H_2O_{(l)}$
   b) pale blue to yellow-green
Q4 a) $[Cu(H_2O)_6]^{2+}_{(aq)} + 4NH_{3(aq)} \rightarrow [Cu(NH_3)_4(H_2O)_2]^{2+}_{(aq)} + 4H_2O_{(l)}$
   b) (elongated) octahedral
Q5 a) It helps transport oxygen around the body.
   b) Four come from nitrogen atoms in the porphyrin ring, one comes from a nitrogen atom in a globin protein and one comes from either water or oxygen.
Q6 a) In the lungs, the concentration of oxygen is high. So water ligands that were bound to the haemoglobin are substituted for oxygen ligands, forming oxyhaemoglobin.
   b) At sites where oxygen is needed the concentration of oxygen is low. So oxygen ligands that were bound to haemoglobin are substituted for water ligands, forming deoxyhaemoglobin.
Q7 Carbon monoxide is a very strong ligand for haemoglobin. When it is inhaled, it binds to haemoglobin and prevents it from binding to oxygen. As a result, oxygen can no longer be transported around the body.

6. Stability Constants
Page 213 — Application Questions
Q1 $K_{stab} = \dfrac{[[Cr(OH)_6]^{3-}]}{[Cr^{3+}][OH^-]^6}$

Q2 $K_{stab} = \dfrac{[[Al(H_2O)_3(OH)_3]]}{[Al^{3+}][OH^-]^3}$

Q3 a) $K_{stab} = \dfrac{[[Co(NH_3)_6]^{2+}]}{[Co(H_2O)_6]^{2+}[NH_3]^6}$

   b) $[Ni(NH_3)_6]^{2+}$ is more stable than $[Co(NH_3)_6]^{2+}$ because it has a higher stability constant.
   Watch out for powers of 10. At a first glance 2.45×10^4 may look bigger than 1.02×10^8, but it's not.

Page 213 — Fact Recall Questions
Q1 The stability constant, K_{stab}, of a complex ion is the equilibrium constant for the formation of the complex ion from its constituent ions in solution.
Q2 Since all the ions are in solution, there's so much water around that the few extra molecules produced don't alter its concentration much — it's practically constant.
Q3 How stable a new complex ion is and how likely it is to form.

7. Redox Reactions
Page 217 — Application Questions
Q1 a) $MnO_4^-_{(aq)} + 8H^+_{(aq)} + 5Fe^{2+}_{(aq)} \rightarrow Mn^{2+}_{(aq)} + 4H_2O_{(l)} + 5Fe^{3+}_{(aq)}$
   b) Moles Fe^{2+} = (conc. × volume) ÷ 1000
      = $(0.0500 \times 28.3) \div 1000$ = **1.42×10^{-3} moles**
   c) From the balanced ion equation 5 moles of Fe^{2+} reacts with 1 mole of MnO_4^- and so 1.42×10^{-3} moles of Fe^{2+} must react with $(1.42 \times 10^{-3}) \div 5$
      = 2.84×10^{-4} moles of MnO_4^-.
      Conc. MnO_4^- = (moles × 1000) ÷ volume
      = $((2.84 \times 10^{-4}) \times 1000) \div 30.0$ = **9.47×10^{-3} mol dm^{-3}**

Q2 Moles Fe^{2+} = (conc. × volume) ÷ 1000
= (0.600 × 28.0) ÷ 1000 = 0.0168 moles.
$MnO_4^-{}_{(aq)} + 8H^+{}_{(aq)} + 5Fe^{2+}{}_{(aq)} \rightarrow Mn^{2+}{}_{(aq)} + 4H_2O_{(l)} + 5Fe^{3+}{}_{(aq)}$
so 5 moles of Fe^{2+} reacts with 1 mole of MnO_4^- and
0.0168 moles of Fe^{2+} must react with (0.0168) ÷ 5
= 3.36×10^{-3} moles of MnO_4^-.
Volume MnO_4^- = (moles × 1000) ÷ conc.
= ((3.36 × 10⁻³) × 1000) ÷ 0.0750 = **44.8 cm³**

Q3 a) $Cr_2O_7^{2-}{}_{(aq)} + 14H^+{}_{(aq)} + 6Fe^{2+}{}_{(aq)} \rightarrow 2Cr^{3+}{}_{(aq)} + 7H_2O_{(l)} + 6Fe^{3+}{}_{(aq)}$
b) Moles $Cr_2O_7^{2-}$ = (conc. × volume) ÷ 1000
= (0.150 × 22.5) ÷ 1000 = **3.38 ×10⁻³ moles**
c) Using the balanced equation, 1 mole of $Cr_2O_7^{2-}$ reacts
with 6 moles of Fe^{2+} and so 3.38 ×10⁻³ moles of $Cr_2O_7^{2-}$
must react with (3.38 × 10⁻³) × 6 = 0.0203 moles of Fe^{2+}.
Conc. Fe^{2+} = (moles × 1000) ÷ volume
= (0.0203 × 1000) ÷ 20.0 = **1.02 mol dm⁻³**

Q4 Moles $Cr_2O_7^{2-}$ = (conc. × volume) ÷ 1000
= (0.0550 × 24.0) ÷ 1000 = 1.32 ×10⁻³ moles.
$Cr_2O_7^{2-}{}_{(aq)} + 14H^+{}_{(aq)} + 6Fe^{2+}{}_{(aq)} \rightarrow 2Cr^{3+}{}_{(aq)} + 7H_2O_{(l)} + 6Fe^{3+}{}_{(aq)}$
1 mole of $Cr_2O_7^{2-}$ reacts with 6 moles of Fe^{2+},
so 1.32 × 10⁻³ moles of $Cr_2O_7^{2-}$ must react with
(1.32 × 10⁻³) × 6 = 7.92 × 10⁻³ moles of Fe^{2+}.
Volume Fe^{2+} = (moles × 1000) ÷ conc.
= ((7.92 × 10⁻³) × 1000) ÷ 0.450 = **17.6 cm³**

Q5 a) $Cr_2O_7^{2-}{}_{(aq)} + 14H^+{}_{(aq)} + 3Zn_{(s)} \rightarrow 2Cr^{3+}{}_{(aq)} + 7H_2O_{(l)} + 3Zn^{2+}{}_{(aq)}$
b) Moles $Cr_2O_7^{2-}$ = (conc. × volume) ÷ 1000
= (0.230 × 30.0) ÷ 1000 = **6.90 × 10⁻³ moles**
c) Using the balanced equation, 1 mole of $Cr_2O_7^{2-}$ reacts
with 3 moles of Zn, so 6.90 × 10⁻³ moles of $Cr_2O_7^{2-}$ must
react with (6.90 × 10⁻³ moles) × 3 = 0.0207 moles of Zn.
mass Zn = moles × M_r
= 0.0207 × 65.4 = **1.35 g**

Page 217 — Fact Recall Questions

Q1 E.g. Acidified potassium manganate(VII) solution/$KMnO_{4(aq)}$ /
Acidified potassium dichromate(VI) solution/$K_2Cr_2O_{7(aq)}$.

Q2 Acid is added to make sure there are plenty of H^+ ions to
allow all the oxidising agent to be reduced.

Q3 E.g. the end point is when the mixture in the flask just
becomes tainted with the colour of the oxidising agent.

8. More Titrations

Page 220 — Application Questions

Q1 a) Moles $Na_2S_2O_3$ = (conc. × volume) ÷ 1000
= (0.200 × 41.1) ÷ 1000 = **0.00822 moles**.
b) Using the balanced equation given in the question 1
mole of I_2 reacts with 2 moles of $Na_2S_2O_3$ and so
0.00822 moles of $Na_2S_2O_3$ must react with 0.00822 ÷ 2
= **0.00411 moles** of I_2.
c) Using the balanced equation:
$IO_3^-{}_{(aq)} + 5I^-{}_{(aq)} + 6H^+{}_{(aq)} \rightarrow 3I_{2(aq)} + 3H_2O$, 1 mole of
IO_3^- will react to give 3 moles of I_2. So, 0.00411 moles
of I_2 will be produced from 0.00411 ÷ 3
= **0.00137 moles** of IO_3^-.
d) Concentration of IO_3^- = (moles × 1000) ÷ volume
= (0.00137 × 1000) ÷ 13.2 = **0.104 mol dm⁻³**

Q2 a) Moles $Na_2S_2O_3$ = (conc. × volume) ÷ 1000
= (0.750 × 4.00) ÷ 1000 = **0.00300 moles**.
b) Using the balanced equation given in the question
2 moles of $Na_2S_2O_3$ react with 1 mole of I_2, and so
0.00300 moles of $Na_2S_2O_3$ must react with
0.00300 ÷ 2 = 0.00150 moles of I_2.
The total volume of the solution formed by adding the
potassium manganate(VII) solution to the acidified
potassium iodide solution was 100 cm³, but only
25.0 cm³ of the solution was used in the titration.

So the total number of moles of I_2 formed in the
oxidation reaction was 0.00150 × 4 = **0.00600 moles**.
c) Using the balanced equation given in the question,
5 moles of I_2 will be produced from 2 moles of MnO_4^-.
So, 0.00600 moles of I_2 will be produced from
(0.00600 ÷ 5) × 2 = 0.00240 moles of MnO_4^-.
Concentration of MnO_4^- = (moles × 1000) ÷ volume
= (0.00240 × 1000) ÷ 39.0 = **0.0615 mol dm⁻³**

Q3 Moles $Na_2S_2O_3$ = (conc. × volume) ÷ 1000
= (0.0600 × 22.3) ÷ 1000 = 1.34 × 10⁻³ moles.
Using the balanced equation given in the question, 1 mole
of I_2 reacts with 2 moles of $Na_2S_2O_3$ and so 1.34 × 10⁻³
moles of $Na_2S_2O_3$ must react with 1.34 × 10⁻³ ÷ 2
= 6.70 × 10⁻⁴ moles of I_2.
Using the balanced equation given in the question, 1 mole
of $Cr_2O_7^{2-}$ will produce 3 moles of I_2. So, 6.70 × 10⁻⁴ moles
of I_2 will be produced from 6.70 × 10⁻⁴ ÷ 3 = 2.23 × 10⁻⁴
moles of $Cr_2O_7^{2-}$.
Concentration of $Cr_2O_7^{2-}$ = (moles × 1000) ÷ volume
= (2.23 × 10⁻⁴ × 1000) ÷ 15.0 = **1.49 × 10⁻² mol dm⁻³**

Page 220 — Fact Recall Questions

Q1 $IO_3^-{}_{(aq)} + 5I^-{}_{(aq)} + 6H^+{}_{(aq)} \rightarrow 3I_{2(aq)} + 3H_2O_{(l)}$

Q2 $I_{2(aq)} + 2S_2O_3^{2-}{}_{(aq)} \rightarrow 2I^-{}_{(aq)} + S_4O_6^{2-}{}_{(aq)}$

Q3 Put the flask containing the iodine solution under a burette.
From the burette, add sodium thiosulfate solution to the
flask drop by drop. When the iodine colour fades to a
pale yellow, add 2 cm³ of starch solution (to detect the
presence of iodine). The solution in the conical flask will
go dark blue, showing there's still some iodine there. Add
sodium thiosulfate one drop at a time until the blue colour
disappears. Jot down the volume of sodium thiosulfate
added to the solution.

Exam-style Questions — pages 222-224

Q1 a) (i) pale blue **(1 mark)**
(ii) Cu: 1s²2s²2p⁶3s²3p⁶3d¹⁰4s¹/[Ar]3d¹⁰4s¹ **(1 mark)**
Cu²⁺: 1s²2s²2p⁶3s²3p⁶3d⁹/[Ar]3d⁹ **(1 mark)**
(iii) Cu²⁺ has the characteristic chemical properties of
transition element ions because it has an incomplete
d-subshell **(1 mark)**.
b) (i) A ligand is a species that donates an electron pair
to form a coordinate bond with a central metal ion
(1 mark).
(ii)

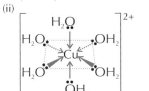

(1 mark)

*Don't forget to include the charge on the complex ion when
you're drawing its structure.*
The shape of $[Cu(H_2O)_6]^{2+}$ is octahedral **(1 mark)**.
(iii) 6 **(1 mark)**
c) (i) Place the flask containing the iodine solution
produced by the reaction underneath a burette
(1 mark). From the burette, add sodium thiosulfate
solution to the flask drop by drop **(1 mark)**. When
the iodine colour fades to a pale yellow, add starch
solution **(1 mark)**. The solution in the conical flask
will go dark blue, showing there's still some iodine
there **(1 mark)**. Add sodium thiosulfate one drop at
a time until the blue colour disappears — this is the
end point of the reaction **(1 mark)**.

(ii) Moles $Na_2S_2O_3$ = (conc. × volume) ÷ 1000
= (0.500 × 23.6) ÷ 1000 = 0.0118 moles *(1 mark)*.
Using the balanced equation given in the question,
1 mole of I_2 reacts with 2 moles of $Na_2S_2O_3$ and so
0.0118 moles of $Na_2S_2O_3$ must react with 0.0118 ÷ 2
= **0.0059 moles** of I_2 *(1 mark)*.
Using the balanced equation given in the question,
2 moles of Cu^{2+} will react to give 1 mole of I_2. So,
0.0059 moles of I_2 will be formed from 0.0059 × 2 =
0.0118 moles of Cu^{2+} *(1 mark)*.
(iii) mass = number of moles × M_r = 0.0118 × 63.5
= 0.749 g of copper present in the brass *(1 mark)*.
So, (0.749 ÷ 1) × 100 = 74.9%. The brass is **74.9%**
copper *(1 mark)*.

Q2 a) (i) square-planar *(1 mark)*
(ii) cis-trans isomerism/E-Z isomerism *(1 mark)*
(iii)

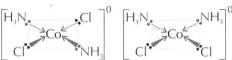

(1 mark for each correctly drawn isomer)

b) (i) optical isomerism *(1 mark)*
(ii) The oxygen atoms have lone pairs of electrons
(1 mark) which they can donate to the chromium(III)
ion to form coordinate bonds *(1 mark)*.

(iii)

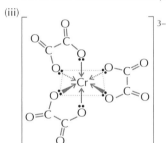

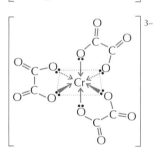

**(1 mark for each correctly drawn isomer.
The structures must be shown as 3D i.e. with
wedged and dotted bonds)**

These are fiendishly difficult isomers to draw so don't worry if
you've messed up your first few attempts — you can always
simplify the structure of the ligands to make the whole thing
a bit easier. Make sure you get lots of practice drawing them
before the exam and you'll be fine.

c) (i) Cisplatin easily loses its chlorine ligands and forms
coordinate bonds with nitrogen atoms in the DNA
molecule *(1 mark)*. This prevents the DNA from
unwinding and replicating so the cell can't divide
(1 mark).
(ii) E.g. cisplatin could bind to DNA in normal cells and
prevent them from dividing *(1 mark)*.

Q3 a) VO^{2+}: +4 *(1 mark)*
VO_2^+: +5 *(1 mark)*
b) (i) manganese/MnO_4^- *(1 mark)*
(ii) vanadium/VO^{2+} *(1 mark)*
c) Moles MnO_4^- = (conc. × volume) ÷ 1000
= (0.0500 × 14.2) ÷ 1000 = 7.1 × 10^{-4} moles *(1 mark)*.
From the equation given in the question, 5 moles of VO^{2+}
react with 1 mole of MnO_4^- and so, 7.10 × 10^{-4} moles of
MnO_4^- must react with (7.1 × 10^{-4}) × 5
= 3.55 × 10^{-3} moles of VO^{2+} *(1 mark)*.
Concentration VO^{2+} = (moles × 1000) ÷ volume
= ((3.55 × 10^{-3}) × 1000) ÷ 20.0 = **0.178 mol dm^{-3}**
(1 mark)

Q4 a) A transition element is an element that can form one or
more stable ions with an incomplete d-subshell *(1 mark)*.
b) (i) $Fe^{2+}_{(aq)}$ + $2OH^-_{(aq)}$ → $Fe(OH)_{2(s)}$ *(1 mark)*
(ii) green *(1 mark)*
c) (i) A transition metal ion surrounded by coordinately
bonded ligands *(1 mark)*.
(ii) $Fe^{2+}_{(aq)}$ + $4Cl^-_{(aq)}$ → $[FeCl_4]^{2-}_{(aq)}$
*(1 mark for correct product, 1 mark for correctly
balanced equation)*
(iii)

(1 mark)

You need to draw the structure in 3D, with wedged and dashed
bonds to get the mark here.

d) (i) $[Fe(H_2O)_6]^{2+}_{(aq)}$ + $6CN^-_{(aq)}$ → $[Fe(CN)_6]^{4-}_{(aq)}$ + $6H_2O_{(l)}$
(1 mark)
(ii) The coordination number doesn't change because
there are 6 ligands bonded to the Fe^{2+} before the
reaction and 6 ligands bonded afterwards *(1 mark)*.
The shape of the complex ion doesn't change
because the CN^- and H_2O ligands are similar sizes
(1 mark). The colour of the complex ion may change
as there has been a change in the type of ligand
bonded to the Fe^{2+} *(1 mark)*.
e) (i) In the lungs oxygen molecules bond to Fe^{2+}
to form oxyhaemoglobin *(1 mark)*. When the
oxyhaemoglobin gets to a place where oxygen is
needed, the oxygen molecules are replaced by water
molecules *(1 mark)*.
(ii) When carbon monoxide is inhaled, the haemoglobin
can substitute its water ligands for carbon monoxide
ligands *(1 mark)*. This is dangerous because carbon
monoxide forms a very strong bond with the Fe^{2+} ion
and doesn't readily exchange with oxygen or water
ligands, meaning the haemoglobin can't transport
oxygen any more *(1 mark)*.
f) (i)
$$K_{stab} = \frac{[[Fe(OH)(H_2O)_5]^+]}{[Fe(H_2O)_6]^{2+}[OH^-]}$$
*(1 mark for correct numerator, 1 mark for correct
denominator)*
(ii) Reaction B is more likely to occur because it has a
higher stability constant *(1 mark)*. This means that
$[Fe(EDTA)]^{2-}$ is very stable and is more likely to form
than $[Fe(OH)(H_2O)_5]^+$ *(1 mark)*.

Glossary

A

α-amino acid
An amino acid with the amino group and the carboxylic acid group attached to the same carbon.

Accurate result
A result that's really close to the true answer.

Acid anhydride
A molecule formed from two identical carboxylic acid molecules joined via an oxygen atom.

Acid dissociation constant, K_a
An equilibrium constant specific to weak acids that relates the acid concentration to the concentration of $[H^+]$ ions. $K_a = [H^+][A^-] \div [HA]$.

Acidic buffer
A buffer with a pH of less than 7 made by mixing a weak acid with one of its salts or by adding a small amount of alkali to a weak acid.

Addition polymer
A type of polymer formed by joining small alkenes (monomers) together.

Adsorption
The attraction between a substance and the surface of the solid stationary phase in thin-layer chromatography or gas chromatography.

Aldehyde
A substance with the general formula $C_nH_{2n}O$ which has a hydrogen and one alkyl group attached to the carbonyl carbon atom.

Aliphatic compound
An organic compound that does not contain a benzene ring.

Amide link
The -CONH- unit which is found between monomers in a polyamide.

Amine
A molecule where one or more of the hydrogen atoms in ammonia have been replaced with an alkyl group.

Amino acid
A molecule with an amino group (NH_2) and a carboxyl group (COOH).

Amphoteric
Having both acidic and basic properties.

Anomalous result
A result that doesn't fit with the pattern of the other results in a set of data.

Aromatic compound
A compound that contains a benzene ring.

Azo dye
Man-made dyes that contain the azo group, –N=N–.

B

Benzene
An organic compound with the formula C_6H_6. Its six carbon atoms are joined together in a ring. The ring is planar (flat) and the hydrogens all stick out in the same plane.

Bidentate ligand
A ligand that can form two coordinate bonds.

Biodegradable
A material that can be broken down by natural organisms or processes.

Biodiesel
A mixture of methyl and ethyl esters of fatty acids which can be used as a fuel.

Born-Haber cycle
An enthalpy cycle that allows you to calculate the standard lattice enthalpy for a system.

Brady's reagent
2,4-dinitrophenylhydrazine (2,4-DNPH) dissolved in methanol and concentrated sulfuric acid. Used to test for carbonyl compounds (aldehydes and ketones).

Brønsted-Lowry acid
A proton donor.

Brønsted-Lowry base
A proton acceptor.

Buffer
A solution that resists changes in pH when small amounts of acid or alkali are added.

C

Carbonyl compound
A compound that contains a carbon-oxygen double bond.

Carboxylic acid
A substance which has a COOH group attached to the end of a carbon chain.

Catalyst
A substance that increases the rate of a reaction by providing an alternative reaction pathway with a lower activation energy. The catalyst is chemically unchanged at the end of the reaction.

Categoric data
Data that can be sorted into categories.

Causal link
The relationship between two variables where a change in one variable causes a change in the other.

Cell potential
The voltage between two half-cells in an electrochemical cell.

Chemical shift
Nuclei in different environments absorb energy of different frequencies. NMR spectroscopy measures these differences relative to a standard substance — the difference is called the chemical shift (δ).

Chiral molecule
A molecule that contains a carbon atom with four different groups attached to it.

Chromatogram
A visual record (such as a pattern of spots or a graph) of the results of a chromatography experiment.

Chromatography
An analytical technique which uses a mobile phase and a stationary phase to separate out mixtures.

Clock reaction
A method used to find the initial rate of a reaction. In clock reactions you measure the time it takes for a given amount of product to form.

Closed system
A system where nothing can get in or out.

Complex ion
A metal ion surrounded by coordinately bonded ligands.

Condensation polymer
A type of polymer formed through a series of condensation reactions.

Condensation reaction
A chemical reaction in which two molecules are joined together and a small molecule is eliminated.

Conjugate pair
A set of two species that can be transformed into each other by gaining or losing a proton.

Continuous data
Data that can have any value on a scale.

Coordinate bond
A covalent bond in which both electrons in the shared pair come from the same atom (also called a dative covalent bond).

Coordination number
The number of coordinate bonds that are formed with the central metal ion in a complex ion.

Correlation
The relationship between two variables.

d-block
The block of elements in the middle of the periodic table.

d-subshell
A type of subshell. Each can hold ten electrons.

Dative covalent bond
A covalent bond in which both electrons in the shared pair come from the same atom (also called a coordinate bond).

Delocalisation
When an electron is no longer associated with a single atom or one covalent bond.

Dependent variable
The variable that you measure in an experiment.

Deuterated solvent
A solvent which has had all of its hydrogen atoms exchanged for deuterium atoms.

Deuterium
An isotope of hydrogen. It contains one neutron, one proton and one electron.

Diazonium compound
A compound which contains the $-\overset{+}{N}\equiv N-$ group.

Dipeptide
Two amino acids joined together via a peptide link.

Discrete data
Data that can only take certain values.

Dynamic equilibrium
When the forward and backward reactions of a reversible reaction are happening at exactly the same rate, so the concentration of reactants and products doesn't change.

E/Z isomerism
A type of stereoisomerism that is caused by the restricted rotation about a carbon-carbon double bond. Each of the carbon atoms must have two different groups attached.

Electrochemical cell
An electrical circuit made from two metal electrodes dipped in salt solutions and connected by a wire.

Electrochemical series
A list of electrode potentials written in order from most negative to most positive.

Electrode potential
The voltage measured when a half-cell is connected to a standard hydrogen electrode.

Electromotive force (e.m.f.)
Another name for cell potential.

Electronegativity
The ability to attract the bonding electrons in a covalent bond.

Electrophile
An electron deficient (and usually positively charged) species which is attracted to regions of high electron density.

Electrophilic substitution
A reaction mechanism where an electrophile substitutes for another atom (usually a hydrogen) in a molecule.

Enantiomer
A molecule that has the same structural formula as another molecule but with four groups arranged around a chiral carbon atom so that it is a non-superimposable mirror image of the other molecule.

End point
The point in a titration at which all the acid is just neutralised and the pH curve becomes vertical.

Endothermic reaction
A reaction that absorbs energy (ΔH is positive).

Energy carrier
Something which can be used as a store of energy — but requires energy to make it.

Enthalpy change of atomisation of a compound ($\Delta H^{\oplus}_{at}$)
The enthalpy change when 1 mole of a species in its standard state is converted to gaseous atoms.

Enthalpy change of atomisation of an element ($\Delta H^{\oplus}_{at}$)
The enthalpy change when 1 mole of gaseous atoms is formed from an element in its standard state.

Enthalpy change of formation ($\Delta H^{\oplus}_{f}$)
The enthalpy change when 1 mole of a compound is formed from its elements in their standard states under standard conditions.

Enthalpy change of hydration ($\Delta H^{\oplus}_{hyd}$)
The enthalpy change when 1 mole of aqueous ions is formed from gaseous ions.

Enthalpy change of neutralisation ($\Delta H^{\oplus}_{neutralisation}$)
The enthalpy change when 1 mole of water is formed by the reaction between an acid and a base under standard conditions.

Enthalpy change of solution ($\Delta H^{\oplus}_{solution}$)
The enthalpy change when 1 mole of solute is dissolved in sufficient solvent that no further enthalpy change occurs on further dilution.

Entropy (S)
A measure of the amount of disorder in a system (e.g. the number of ways that particles can be arranged and the number of ways that the energy can be shared out between the particles).

Equilibrium constant, K_c
A ratio worked out from the concentration of the products and reactants once a reversible reaction has reached equilibrium.

Ester
A molecule that contains the functional group RCOOR.

Ester link
The -COO- unit which is found between monomers in a polyester.

Esterification
Forming an ester by heating a carboxylic acid and an alcohol in the presence of a strong acid catalyst (or by reacting an acid anhydride with an alcohol).

Exothermic reaction
A reaction that gives out energy (ΔH is negative).

Fatty acid
A long chain carboxylic acid which can combine with glycerol to form a fat or an oil.

Feasible reaction
A reaction which has a free energy change that is less than or equal to zero and can happen spontaneously.

First electron affinity (ΔH°_{ea1})
The enthalpy change when 1 mole of gaseous 1– ions is made from 1 mole of gaseous atoms.

First ionisation enthalpy (ΔH°_{ie1})
The enthalpy change when 1 mole of gaseous 1+ ions is formed from 1 mole of gaseous atoms.

Free energy change (ΔG)
A measure which links enthalpy and entropy changes to predict whether a reaction is feasible.
$\Delta G = \Delta H - T\Delta S_{system}$

Fuel cell
A device that converts the energy of a fuel into electricity through an oxidation reaction.

Fuel cell vehicle (FCV)
An electric vehicle powered by a fuel cell.

Functional group
A group of atoms within a molecule that is responsible for its characteristic reactions (e.g. COOH for carboxylic acids, C=C for alkenes).

Gas chromatography (GC)
A type of chromatography where the stationary phase is a liquid or solid held on a solid support, and the mobile phase is an unreactive gas.

Haemoglobin
A protein found in blood that helps to transport oxygen around the body.

Half-cell
One half of an electrochemical cell.

Half-equation
An ionic equation that shows oxidation or reduction — one half of a full redox equation.

Half-life
The time it takes for half of the reactant to be used up during a reaction.

Halogen carrier
A molecule which can accept a halogen atom (e.g. $AlCl_3$). Used as a catalyst in the halogenation of benzene.

Hess's law
The total enthalpy change of a reaction is always the same, no matter which route is taken.

Hydrogen-rich fuel
A fuel such as methanol, natural gas or petrol that is rich in hydrogen and can be converted into hydrogen gas to be used in a fuel cell.

Hydrolysis
A reaction where a molecule is split apart by water.

Hypothesis
A specific testable statement, based on a theory, about what will happen in a test situation.

Independent variable
The variable that you change in an experiment.

Indicator
A substance that changes colour over a particular pH range.

Infrared (IR) spectroscopy
An analytical technique used to identify the functional groups present in a molecule by measuring the frequency of energy absorbed by its bonds.

Initial rates method
An experimental technique that can be used to work out the order of reaction with respect to each reactant.

Integration trace
A line on an ^{1}H NMR spectrum that has a change in height that is proportional to the area of the peak it's next to.

Ionic product of water, K_w
A constant generated by multiplying the K_c for the dissociation of water by $[H_2O]$. $K_w = [H^+][OH^-]$.

Isoelectric point
The pH at which the average overall charge on a molecule is zero.

K

Ketone
A substance with the general formula $C_nH_{2n}O$ which has two alkyl groups attached to the carbonyl carbon atom.

L

Le Chatelier's Principle
If there's a change in concentration, pressure or temperature, an equilibrium will move to help counteract the change.

Ligand
An atom, ion or molecule that donates a pair of electrons to a central metal ion in a complex ion.

Ligand substitution reaction
A reaction where one or more ligands are changed for one or more other ligands in a complex ion. (Also called a ligand exchange reaction.)

M

M peak
The peak on a mass spectrum caused by the molecular ion.

Magnetic resonance imaging (MRI)
A scanning technique based on NMR technology that's used to study the internal structures of the body and diagnose illnesses.

Mass spectrometry
An analytical technique used to find the structure of a molecule by looking at the pattern of ions it produces when it is bombarded with electrons.

Mass spectrum
A chart produced by a mass spectrometer giving information on the relative abundance of fragment ions formed from a molecule.

Methyl orange
A pH indicator that changes colour between pH 3.1 and 4.4.

Mobile phase
A liquid or a gas used in chromatography which contains molecules that can move freely.

Model
A simplified picture or representation of a real physical situation.

Monobasic acid
An acid that releases one H^+ ion per molecule. (Also known as a monoprotic acid.)

Monodentate ligand
A ligand that can only form one coordinate bond. (Also known as a unidentate ligand.)

Monomer
A small molecule which can join together with other monomers to form a polymer.

Multidentate ligand
A ligand that can form two or more coordinate bonds.

Multiplet
A split peak on a ^1H NMR spectrum. (General term for a doublet, triplet, quartet, quintet etc.)

N

n + 1 rule
Peaks on a ^1H NMR spectrum always split into the number of hydrogens on the neighbouring carbon, plus one.

Nitration
A reaction in which a nitro group ($-NO_2$) is added to a molecule.

Nuclear magnetic resonance (NMR) spectroscopy
An analytical technique which uses the absorption of low-energy radio waves to determine the relative environment of an atom within a compound.

Nucleophile
An electron-pair donor. Nucleophiles are electron rich, so they are attracted to areas of positive charge.

Nucleophilic addition
A reaction mechanism where a nucleophile adds on to the δ^+ carbon atom of a carbonyl group.

O

Optical isomer
A molecule that has the same structural formula as another molecule but with four groups arranged around a chiral carbon atom so that it is a non-superimposable mirror image of the other molecule.

Orbital
A region of a subshell that contains a maximum of two electrons.

Ordered (ordinal) data
Categoric data where the categories can be put in order.

Oxidation
Loss of electrons.

Oxidation number
The total number of electrons an element has donated or accepted. (Also called oxidation state.)

Oxidising agent
Something that accepts electrons and gets reduced.

P

Peer review
The evaluation of a scientific report by other scientists who are experts in the same area (peers). They go through it bit by bit, examining the methods and data, and checking it's all logical.

Peptide bond
The covalent bond between the C=O carbon and the N–H nitrogen in a peptide link.

Peptide link
The -CONH- unit which is found between monomers in a protein.

pH
A measure of the hydrogen ion concentration in a solution.
$pH = -\log_{10}[H^+]$

pH curve
A graph used to follow the progress of an acid-base titration. You make a pH curve by plotting the pH against the volume of acid (or alkali) added.

Phenol
An aromatic organic compound with the formula C_6H_5OH.

Phenolphthalein
A pH indicator that changes colour between pH 8.3 and 10.

Photodegradable
A substance that can be broken down by light.

Polar chemical
A chemical containing atoms with different electronegativities, so the electrons in the bond are pulled more towards one atom than the other and a dipole is created.

Polyamide
A polymer that has amide links between the monomers.

Polyester
A polymer that has ester links between the monomers.

Polymer
A long molecule formed from lots of repeating units (called monomers).

Polymerisation
The process of forming a polymer from monomers.

Polypeptide
A polymer formed from reactions between amino acids.

Precipitate
A solid that forms in a solution.

Precise result
A result taken using sensitive instruments that measure in small increments.

Protein
One or more polypeptides folded into a 3D shape which has a biological function.

Protocol
An accepted method to test a certain thing that all scientists can use.

R

Racemate (or racemic mixture)
A mixture that contains equal quantities of each enantiomer of an optically active compound.

Rate constant, k
A constant in the rate equation. The larger it is the faster the rate of reaction.

Rate-determining step
The slowest step in a reaction mechanism which determines the overall rate of a reaction.

Rate equation
An equation of the form rate = $k[A]^m[B]^n$ which tells you how the rate of a reaction is affected by the concentration of the reactants.

Reaction order
A number that tells you how the concentration of a particular reactant affects the reaction rate.

Reaction rate
The change in the amount of reactants or products per unit time.

Redox reaction
A reaction where reduction and oxidation happen simultaneously.

Redox titration
A titration that can be performed to determine how much reducing agent is needed to exactly react with a quantity of oxidising agent, or vice versa.

Reducing agent
Something that donates electrons and gets oxidised.

Reduction
Gain of electrons.

Reliable result
A result that can be consistently reproduced in independent experiments.

Retention time
The time taken from the injection of a sample to the moment when a substance is detected in gas chromatography.

R_f value
The ratio of the distance travelled by a spot to the distance travelled by the solvent in thin-layer chromatography.

S

Salt bridge
A connection between two half-cells that ions can flow through, used to complete the circuit. Usually a piece of filter paper soaked in a salt solution or a glass tube filled with a salt solution.

Saturated fatty acid
A fatty acid that contains no double bonds.

Second electron affinity ($\Delta H^{\ominus}_{ea2}$)
The enthalpy change when 1 mole of gaseous 2– ions is made from 1 mole of gaseous 1– ions.

Second ionisation enthalpy ($\Delta H^{\ominus}_{ie2}$)
The enthalpy change when 1 mole of gaseous 2+ ions is formed from 1 mole of gaseous 1+ ions.

Solvent front
The distance travelled by the solvent in thin-layer chromatography.

Splitting pattern
Peaks on ^{1}H NMR spectra may be split into further peaks. The resultant group of peaks is called a splitting pattern.

Spontaneous reaction
A reaction that occurs by itself.

Stability constant, K_{stab}
The equilibrium constant for the formation of a complex ion from its constituent ions in solution.

Standard conditions
A temperature of 298 K (25 °C), a pressure of 100 kPa and all ion solutions having a concentration of 1.00 mol dm^{-3}.

Standard electrode potential
The voltage measured under standard conditions when a half-cell is connected to a standard hydrogen electrode.

Standard hydrogen electrode
An electrode where hydrogen gas is bubbled through a solution of aqueous H^+ ions under standard conditions.

Standard lattice enthalpy ($\Delta H^{\ominus}_{latt}$)
The enthalpy change when 1 mole of a solid ionic compound is formed from its gaseous ions under standard conditions.

Stationary phase
A solid, or a liquid held on a solid support, used in chromatography. It contains molecules that can't move.

Stereoisomer
A molecule that has the same structural formula as another molecule but with the atoms arranged differently in space.

Strong acid/base
An acid or base that dissociates almost fully in water.

Subshell
A subdivision of an energy level (shell). Subshells may be s, p, d or f subshells.

Synthesis
A method detailing how to create a chemical.

Tangent
A line that just touches a curve and has the same gradient as the curve does at that point.

Theory
A possible explanation for something. (Usually something that has been observed.)

Thin-layer chromatography (TLC)
A type of chromatography where the stationary phase is a thin layer of solid on a glass or plastic plate and the mobile phase is a liquid solvent.

Titration
An analytical technique that allows you to calculate the concentration of a species in solution.

Tollens' reagent
A colourless solution of silver nitrate dissolved in aqueous ammonia which can be used to distinguish between aldehydes and ketones.

Trans fat
A triglyceride made from trans fatty acids.

Trans fatty acid
A fatty acid containing a carbon-carbon double bond in a trans configuration.

Transition element
A metal that can form one or more stable ions with a partially filled d-subshell.

Triglyceride
A triester formed by reacting glycerol (propane-1,2,3-triol) with three fatty acid molecules.

Unidentate ligand
A ligand that can only form one coordinate bond. (Also called a monodentate ligand.)

Unsaturated fatty acid
A fatty acid that contains double bonds.

Valid result
A result which answers the question it was intended to answer using reliable data.

Validation
The process of repeating an experiment done by someone else, using a theory to make new predictions and then testing them with new experiments, in order to provide evidence for or against the theory.

Variable
A quantity that has the potential to change.

Weak acid/base
An acid or base that only partially dissociates in water.

Zwitterion
A dipolar ion which has both a negative and a positive charge in different parts of the molecule.

Acknowledgements

Photograph acknowledgements
Cover Photo **Andrew Lambert Photography**/Science Photo Library, p 1 **Charles D. Winters**/Science Photo Library, p 2 Science Photo Library, p 3 **NASA**/Science Photo Library, p 4 (top) **Martyn F. Chillmaid**/Science Photo Library, p 4 (bottom) **Robert Brook**/ Science Photo Library, p 6 **Clive Freeman**, **The Royal Institution**/Science Photo Library, p 7 **Laguna Design**/Science Photo Library, p 11 **Ria Novosti**/Science Photo Library, p 14 **Martyn F. Chillmaid**/Science Photo Library, p 15 Science Photo Library, p 17 (top) **Andrew Lambert Photography**/Science Photo Library, p 17 (bottom) **Andrew Lambert Photography**/Science Photo Library, p 18 **Andrew Lambert Photography**/Science Photo Library, p 22 **Andrew Lambert Photography**/Science Photo Library, p 23 **Andrew Lambert Photography**/Science Photo Library, p 25 **Martyn F. Chillmaid**/Science Photo Library, p 29 Science Photo Library, p 30 **Cordelia Molloy**/Science Photo Library, p 32 (top) **Angel Fitor**/Science Photo Library, p 32 (bottom) **Cordelia Molloy**/ Science Photo Library, p 34 (top) **Laguna Design**/Science Photo Library, p 34 (bottom) **Ria Novosti**/Science Photo Library, p 35 **Martin Shields**/Science Photo Library, p 37 **Martyn F. Chillmaid**/Science Photo Library, p 39 Science Photo Library, p 40 **Bob Edwards**/Science Photo Library, p 47 **Martyn F. Chillmaid**/Science Photo Library, p 48 **Martyn F. Chillmaid**/Science Photo Library, p 50 (top) **Cordelia Molloy**/Science Photo Library, p 50 (middle) **Eye of Science**/Science Photo Library, p 50 (bottom) **Cordelia Molloy**/Science Photo Library, p 51 **GIPhotoStock**/Science Photo Library, p 54 (top) **Thierry Berrod, Mona Lisa Production**/Science Photo Library, p 54 (bottom) **Martyn F. Chillmaid**/Science Photo Library, p 55 **Laguna Design**/Science Photo Library, p 56 **Laguna Design**/Science Photo Library, p 57 **J.C. Revy**, **ISM**/Science Photo Library, p 61 **Martyn F. Chillmaid**/ Science Photo Library, p 65 (top) **Dr Tim Evans**/Science Photo Library, p 65 (bottom) **Dr Tim Evans**/Science Photo Library, p 66 **Klaus Guldbransen**/Science Photo Library, p 70 Science Photo Library, p 75 **Sinclair Stammers**/Science Photo Library, p 77 **Stephen Ausmus/US Department of Agriculture**/Science Photo Library, p 78 **Pasieka**/Science Photo Library, p 79 **Massimo Brega**, **The Lighthouse**/Science Photo Library, p 80 **Pascal Goetgheluck**/Science Photo Library, p 81 Science Photo Library, p 84 (top) **Chagnon**/Science Photo Library, p 84 bottom **Peggy Greb/US Department of Agriculture**/Science Photo Library, p 85 **Hank Morgan**/Science Photo Library, p 86 **Patrice Latron/Look at Sciences**/Science Photo Library, p 89 **Jerry Mason**/Science Photo Library, p 92 **Mark Sykes**/Science Photo Library, p 94 **Friedrich Saurer**/Science Photo Library, p 95 **Hank Morgan**/Science Photo Library, p 98 Science Photo Library, p 99 **Stephen Ausmus/US Department of Agriculture**/Science Photo Library, p 107 (top) **Andrew Lambert Photography**/Science Photo Library, p 107 (bottom) **Andrew Lambert Photography**/Science Photo Library, p 108 **Andrew Lambert Photography**/Science Photo Library, p 112 **Martyn F. Chillmaid**/Science Photo Library, p 115 **Andrew Lambert Photography**/Science Photo Library, p 118 **Andrew Lambert Photography**/Science Photo Library, p 123 **Charles D. Winters**/Science Photo Library, p 124 **Charles D. Winters**/Science Photo Library, p 128 Science Photo Library, p 129 (top) **Martyn F. Chillmaid**/Science Photo Library, p 129 (bottom) **Martyn F. Chillmaid**/Science Photo Library, p 131 **Martyn F. Chillmaid**/ Science Photo Library, p 132 **Andrew Lambert Photography**/Science Photo Library, p 133 **Martyn F. Chillmaid**/Science Photo Library, p 134 Science Photo Library, p 135 **Charles D. Winters**/Science Photo Library, p 136 **Richard J. Green**/Science Photo Library, p 137 **Martyn F. Chillmaid**/Science Photo Library, p 138 **Martyn F. Chillmaid**/Science Photo Library, p 139 **Martin Shields**/Science Photo Library, p 140 **Martyn F. Chillmaid**/Science Photo Library, p 141 **Andrew Lambert Photography**/Science Photo Library, p 144 **Charles D. Winters**/Science Photo Library, p 145 **Power and Syred**/Science Photo Library, p 149 **Martyn F. Chillmaid**/Science Photo Library, p 150 Science Photo Library, p 151 (top) **Andrew Lambert Photography**/Science Photo Library, p 151 (bottom) **Andrew Lambert Photography**/Science Photo Library, p 153 **Andrew Lambert Photography**/Science Photo Library, p 159 **Charles D. Winters**/Science Photo Library, p 160 **Martin Shields**/Science Photo Library, p 163 **David Taylor**/ Science Photo Library, p 165 Science Photo Library, p 166 **Emilio Segre Visual Archives/American Institute of Physics**/Science Photo Library, p 167 **Andrew Lambert Photography**/Science Photo Library, p 170 **Andrew Lambert Photography**/Science Photo Library, p 171 **Martyn F. Chillmaid**/Science Photo Library, p 173 **Adam Hart-Davis**/Science Photo Library, p 174 **Peter Menzel**/ Science Photo Library, p 176 Science Photo Library, p 180 **Martyn F. Chillmaid**/Science Photo Library, p 181 **Charles D. Winters**/ Science Photo Library, p 182 **Martyn F. Chillmaid**/Science Photo Library, p 183 **E.R.Degginger**/Science Photo Library, p 186 **Andrew Lambert Photography**/Science Photo Library, p 189 (top) **Martyn F. Chillmaid**/Science Photo Library, p 189 (bottom) **Cordelia Molloy**/Science Photo Library, p 190 **rocksolidlunchkids**/iStockphoto, p 192 (top) **Friedrich Saurer**/Science Photo Library, p 192 (middle) **Charles D. Winters**/Science Photo Library, p 192 (bottom) **Martin Bond**/Science Photo Library, p 197 **Klaus Guldbransen**/Science Photo Library, p 199 **Astrid & Hanns-Frieder Michler**/Science Photo Library, p 200 **Andrew Lambert Photography**/Science Photo Library, p 201 (top left) **Andrew Lambert Photography**/Science Photo Library, p 201 (top right) **Martyn F. Chillmaid**/Science Photo Library, p 201 (bottom left) **Charles D. Winters**/Science Photo Library, p 201 (bottom right) **Andrew Lambert Photography**/Science Photo Library, p 204 **Dr Mark J. Winter**/Science Photo Library, p 205 **Andrew Lambert Photography**/Science Photo Library, p 209 **Martyn F. Chillmaid**/Science Photo Library, p 210 **Power and Syred**/Science Photo Library, p 211 **Andrew Lambert Photography**/Science Photo Library, p 214 (top) **Andrew Lambert Photography**/Science Photo Library, p 214 (bottom) **Andrew Lambert Photography**/Science Photo Library, p 215 **Martyn F. Chillmaid**/Science Photo Library, p 216 **Andrew Lambert Photography**/Science Photo Library, p 219 **Andrew Lambert Photography**/Science Photo Library, p 225 **Charles D. Winters**/Science Photo Library, p 226 **Garry Watson**/Science Photo Library, p 229 **Monty Rakusen**/Science Photo Library, p 230 Science Photo Library, p 237 (top) **Charles D. Winters**/Science Photo Library, p 237 (bottom) **Martyn F. Chillmaid**/ Science Photo Library, p 238 **Photostock-Israel**/Science Photo Library.

Index

The Periodic Table

Relative Atomic Mass (A_r)

Atomic (proton) number

1.0
H
Hydrogen
1

Group 1	Group 2											Group 3	Group 4	Group 5	Group 6	Group 7	Group 0
																	4.0 **He** Helium 2
6.9 **Li** Lithium 3	9.0 **Be** Beryllium 4											10.8 **B** Boron 5	12.0 **C** Carbon 6	14.0 **N** Nitrogen 7	16.0 **O** Oxygen 8	19.0 **F** Fluorine 9	20.2 **Ne** Neon 10
23.0 **Na** Sodium 11	24.3 **Mg** Magnesium 12											27.0 **Al** Aluminium 13	28.1 **Si** Silicon 14	31.0 **P** Phosphorus 15	32.1 **S** Sulfur 16	35.5 **Cl** Chlorine 17	39.9 **Ar** Argon 18
39.1 **K** Potassium 19	40.1 **Ca** Calcium 20	45.0 **Sc** Scandium 21	47.9 **Ti** Titanium 22	50.9 **V** Vanadium 23	52.0 **Cr** Chromium 24	54.9 **Mn** Manganese 25	55.8 **Fe** Iron 26	58.9 **Co** Cobalt 27	58.7 **Ni** Nickel 28	63.5 **Cu** Copper 29	65.4 **Zn** Zinc 30	69.7 **Ga** Gallium 31	72.6 **Ge** Germanium 32	74.9 **As** Arsenic 33	79.0 **Se** Selenium 34	79.9 **Br** Bromine 35	83.8 **Kr** Krypton 36
85.5 **Rb** Rubidium 37	87.6 **Sr** Strontium 38	88.9 **Y** Yttrium 39	91.2 **Zr** Zirconium 40	92.9 **Nb** Niobium 41	95.9 **Mo** Molybdenum 42	98 **Tc** Technetium 43	101.1 **Ru** Ruthenium 44	102.9 **Rh** Rhodium 45	106.4 **Pd** Palladium 46	107.9 **Ag** Silver 47	112.4 **Cd** Cadmium 48	114.8 **In** Indium 49	118.7 **Sn** Tin 50	121.8 **Sb** Antimony 51	127.6 **Te** Tellurium 52	126.9 **I** Iodine 53	131.3 **Xe** Xenon 54
132.9 **Cs** Caesium 55	137.3 **Ba** Barium 56	138.9 **La** Lanthanum 57	178.5 **Hf** Hafnium 72	180.9 **Ta** Tantalum 73	183.8 **W** Tungsten 74	186.2 **Re** Rhenium 75	190.2 **Os** Osmium 76	192.2 **Ir** Iridium 77	195.1 **Pt** Platinum 78	197.0 **Au** Gold 79	200.6 **Hg** Mercury 80	204.4 **Tl** Thallium 81	207.2 **Pb** Lead 82	209.0 **Bi** Bismuth 83	209 **Po** Polonium 84	210 **At** Astatine 85	222 **Rn** Radon 86
223 **Fr** Francium 87	226 **Ra** Radium 88	227 **Ac** Actinium 89	261 **Rf** Rutherfordium 104	262 **Db** Dubnium 105	266 **Sg** Seaborgium 106	264 **Bh** Bohrium 107	277 **Hs** Hassium 108	268 **Mt** Meitnerium 109	271 **Ds** Darmstadtium 110	272 **Rg** Roentgenium 111							

The Lanthanides

140.1 **Ce** Cerium 58	140.9 **Pr** Praseodymium 59	144.2 **Nd** Neodymium 60	144.9 **Pm** Promethium 61	150.4 **Sm** Samarium 62	152.0 **Eu** Europium 63	157.2 **Gd** Gadolinium 64	158.9 **Tb** Terbium 65	162.5 **Dy** Dysprosium 66	164.9 **Ho** Holmium 67	167.3 **Er** Erbium 68	168.9 **Tm** Thulium 69	173.0 **Yb** Ytterbium 70	175.0 **Lu** Lutetium 71

The Actinides

232.0 **Th** Thorium 90	231.0 **Pa** Protactinium 91	238.1 **U** Uranium 92	237.0 **Np** Neptunium 93	242 **Pu** Plutonium 94	243 **Am** Americium 95	247 **Cm** Curium 96	245 **Bk** Berkelium 97	251 **Cf** Californium 98	254 **Es** Einsteinium 99	253 **Fm** Fermium 100	256 **Md** Mendelevium 101	254 **No** Nobelium 102	257 **Lr** Lawrencium 103

Periods 1 2 3 4 5 6 7